Shahryar
Shahrivar

Introduction to Design
and Analysis with Advanced
Composite Materials

Introduction to Design and Analysis with Advanced Composite Materials

STEPHEN R. SWANSON
Department of Mechanical Engineering
University of Utah
Salt Lake City, Utah

Prentice Hall, Upper Saddle River, New Jersey 07458

Library of Congress Cataloging-in-Publication Data

Swanson, S. R. (Stephen R.)
    Introduction to design and analysis with advanced composite
materials / Stephen R. Swanson
        p.   cm.
    Includes bibliographical references and index.
    ISBN 0-02-418554-X
        1. Composite materials—Congresses.   2. Structural analysis
(Engineering)—Congresses.   3. Composite construction—Congresses.
4. Structural design—Congresses.   I. Title.
TA418.9.C6S815   1997
620.1' 18—dc20   96-43585
                                                        CIP

Acquisitions editor: Bill Stenquist
Editor-in-chief: Marcia Horton
Production services: Thompson Steele Production Services
Copy editing: Thompson Steele Production Services
Editorial/production supervision: Irwin Zucker
Director of production and manufacturing: David W. Riccardi
Cover director: Jayne Conte
Managing editor: Bayani Mendoza de Leon
Manufacturing buyer: Julia Meehan
Editorial assistant: Meg Weist

 © 1997 by Prentice-Hall, Inc.
Simon & Schuster / A Viacom Company
Upper Saddle River, NJ 07458

The author and publisher of this book have used their best efforts in preparing this book. These
efforts include the development, research, and testing of the theories and programs to determine their
effectiveness. The author and publisher make no warranty of any kind, expressed or implied, with
regard to these programs or the documentation contained in this book. The author and publisher
shall not be liable in any event for incidental or consequential damages in connection with, or
arising out of, the furnishing, performance, or use of these programs.

Printed in the United States of America

10 9 8 7 6 5 4 3 2 1

ISBN 0-02-418554-X

Prentice-Hall International (UK) Limited, *London*
Prentice-Hall of Australia Pty. Limited, *Sydney*
Prentice-Hall Canada Inc., *Toronto*
Prentice-Hall Hispanoamericana, S.A., *Mexico*
Prentice-Hall of India Private Limited, *New Delhi*
Prentice-Hall of Japan, Inc., *Tokyo*
Simon & Schuster Asia Pte. Ltd., *Singapore*
Editora Prentice-Hall do Brasil, Ltda., *Rio de Janeiro*

This book is dedicated to my wife, Nancy, and son, Eric, with thanks for their constant support and encouragement in everything.

Brief Contents

Contents

2   Stress–Strain Relationships for an Orthotropic Lamina   29

3   Laminate Analysis   65

Preface

The development of advanced composite materials has constituted a revolution in materials applications in recent years. The high stiffness and strength to weight of fibers, along with other properties such as environmental resistance, make composite materials increasingly popular as potential candidates for materials substitution. Composite materials are being increasingly utilized in many fields including both military and commercial aerospace applications, sporting goods, and chemical industries. Resistance to chemical attack, along with the potential for relatively low-cost manufacturing, has made glass fiber a strong competitor in many fields such as for piping, tanks, and marine structures. During the last 25 years, a number of other fibers have become important. Early applications for carbon and boron fibers were in military aircraft, and although military aviation is at the forefront in usage of composites, other markets such as commercial aviation and sporting goods have grown significantly. Other fibers such as aramid and ultrahigh-molecular-weight polyethylene have a number of important applications. Although the high-volume applications use polymer matrix composites, more specialized material forms such as metal matrix and ceramix matrix composites are in use or under development, with increases in temperature resistance. On average, there have been significant reductions in the materials costs as production has increased. There are currently large potential markets in transportation and infrastructure applications such as reinforcement for concrete, and retrofitting of structures for earthquake resistance.

One of the interesting aspects of composite materials is the freedom to select the precise form of the material to suit the application. Along with this freedom is the responsibility of making design decisions about aspects of the material. For example, in using fiber composites, one has the ability to specify the type of fibers, their amount and orientation, and the matrix material. Although this freedom permits highly effective products, it also requires a certain knowledge on the part of the designer.

There has been a large and active research interest in the field, with an extensive literature. Perhaps because of this large literature base, it is often difficult for one without an extensive background in the field to grasp the fundamentals, and to realize what can be applied in practice. This text is an attempt to bring together those basic principles and results that will be useful for the engineer who is involved with design and analysis with composite materials. The text is intended to be useful to the senior undergraduate or first-year graduate student, and to the practicing engineer.

The material presented here should be suitable for a one-term course. The first three chapters introduce the basics of material forms and properties, manufacturing techniques, nonisotropic properties of fiber composites, and the basics of stiffness property characterization. Chapter 1 gives an overview of the material forms, general properties, and current applications for composite materials. Chapter 2 treats the subject of the directional properties of fiber composites, and how the composite properties are related to the properties of the constituents. Chapter 3 develops the basic principles of lamination theory, which form the underlying theory for understanding the stiffness, thermal properties, and stress and strain distributions in fiber composites. Thus, Chapters 2 and 3 should be covered thoroughly to give the reader a basic understanding of the mechanical and thermal response of composites, subjects that are essential for all design and analysis with composites. Chapter 4 treats the failure and strength properties of laminates, enabling the engineer to use the first four chapters to design for both stiffness and strength. Chapter 5 covers the topics of delamination, matrix cracking, and durability. The issues discussed in Chapters 4 and 5 will be increasingly important in design, as composite materials are called upon to withstand loads over their useful life. The issues of strength and durability are not completely reduced to practice, but the material presented gives the reader an introduction to these durability issues. Chapter 6 gives a brief introduction to the analysis of composite plates. This chapter is a compromise, in that it gives only an overview of analysis techniques. It will be useful to many, but others may find the material either too involved or not sufficiently detailed. Chapter 7 presents material on the analysis of fiber composite beams. This chapter will bring to the forefront the essential differences between analysis of structures composed of isotropic materials and those made of fiber composites, as well as the similarities. This chapter emphasizes beams because they are important engineering structures, and also because the material demonstrates how to combine the necessary aspects of lamination theory with traditional principles of mechanics of materials to achieve a design and analysis methodology. Finally, Chapter 8 gives examples of design with fiber composites, and indicates how the analysis procedures described in this text can be applied to real engineering design situations. This chapter provides a "capstone" for the student that will show how the principles involved in the text can be applied to practical design situations.

In using this book as a text, it will be seen that some of the material is more specialized, or requires more background on the part of the student, than the remainder of the book. These parts may be omitted at the preference of the instructor. Part of the section of Chapter 2 on micromechanics is in this category, as it requires some familiarity with elasticity theory to be fully appreciated. Although the basic results are important, the mathematical aspects may be either emphasized or not at the discretion of the instructor. Although intended to be self-contained, parts of Chapter 5 on delamination are perhaps more accessible to those familiar with the rudiments of fracture mechanics. Here again, the instructor may use this material to give the student an introduction to an important application of fracture mechanics in composites, or else deemphasize this material. It is possible to omit Chapter 6 entirely, as this chapter deals with the analysis of orthotropic plates and forms an independent subject area. Chapter 6 may be omitted without interrupting the continuity of the rest of the material.

Many of the mathematical operations involved in the analysis of composite materials involve matrix manipulations that previously have been tedious to do by hand. The widespread availability of general-purpose mathematical computer programs that are matrix-oriented has greatly eased this burden. It is now relatively straightforward for the user to carry out the matrix manipulations involved with analysis of composite material design and analysis problems. A useful set of programs is available on the web for use with this text. These are in the form of both MATLAB files and separate compiled programs (see the Appendix for information on accessing and downloading this software). These programs will be useful for those involved with design and analysis with composite materials, and certainly for carrying out the homework problems in the text.

The author wishes to acknowledge the contribution of M. Nabil Kallas, Charles E. Bakis, Donald M. Blackketter, Daniel Adams, and Michael D. Engelhardt, the reviewers of the text, and to personally thank them for their efforts. They carried out the review in an extremely competent and thorough manner, and the author believes that the text has been significantly improved because of their contribution.

Stephen R. Swanson

1

Advanced Composite Materials and Applications

1.1 INTRODUCTION

Composite materials are composed of two or more distinct constituents. Examples of engineering use of composites date back to the use of straw in clay as a construction material by the Egyptians. Modern composites using fiber-reinforced matrices of various types have created a revolution in high-performance structures in recent years. Advanced composite materials offer significant advantages in strength and stiffness coupled with light weight, relative to conventional metallic materials. Along with this structural performance comes the freedom to select the orientation of the fibers for optimum performance. Modern composites have been described as being revolutionary in the sense that the material can be designed as well as the structure.

The advantages of fiber composites relative to more conventional materials such as metals are often related to the high ratios of stiffness and strength to weight. These properties make materials such as the carbon-fiber composites attractive for applications in aerospace and sporting goods. In addition, composites often have superior resistance to environmental attack, and glass-fiber composites are used extensively in the chemical industries and in marine applications because of this advantage. Both glass- and carbon-fiber composites are being considered for infrastructure applications, such as for bridges and concrete reinforcement, because of this environmental resistance.

The cost competitiveness of composites depends on how important the weight reduction or environmental resistance provided by the composite is to the overall function of the particular application. Although glass fibers are typically lower in cost than aluminum on a weight basis, carbon fibers are still higher in material cost. Equally or more important than the material cost is the cost of manufacturing. In some cases, composite structures can achieve significant cost savings in manufacturing, often by reducing the number of parts

1

involved in a complex assembly. There is a large variability in cost and labor content be-tween the various methods of composite manufacture, and much attention is currently being given to reducing manufacturing costs.

Along with the freedom to design both the material and the structure comes additional responsibility for the designer as well. The use of composite materials poses new and chal-lenging problems in their efficient utilization. The fundamental purpose of this text is to help engineers to understand how to use these materials in a rational manner.

1.2 TYPICAL ADVANCED COMPOSITES

Modern composite materials typically utilize a reinforcement phase and a binder phase, in many cases with more rigid and higher-strength fibers in a more compliant matrix, although this is not universally the case. Modern applications started with glass fibers, followed by the more recent high-performance fibers such as carbon, aramid, boron, silicon carbide, and others. A typical example is carbon fiber, which is being widely introduced into aerospace and sporting goods applications. The tensile strength of carbon fiber varies with the specific type being considered, but a typical range of values is on the order of 3.1 to 5.5 GPa (450 to 800 ksi) for fiber tensile strength, and stiffness on the order of 240 GPa (35 Msi), combined with a specific gravity of 1.7. Thus, the fiber itself is stronger than 7075 T6 aluminum by a factor of 5 to 10, and stiffer by a factor of 3.5, at approximately 60% of the weight. The po-tential for advantages in mechanical design of high-performance structures is obvious. An illustration of the potential for composite materials is given in Figure 1.1, where the specific modulus (modulus divided by density) and specific strength (tensile strength divided by density) are shown for a number of fibers and other engineering materials.

On the other hand, current costs for carbon fibers are several times to an order of mag-nitude or more higher than aluminum, although lower-cost carbon fibers have appeared on the market recently. The cost differential indicates that composite materials will be utilized in demanding applications, where increases in performance justify the higher material cost. However, the material cost is only part of the story, as manufacturing costs must also be considered. In many instances, it has been possible to form parts of composites with a sig-nificantly fewer number of individual components compared to metallic structures, and thus leading to an overall lower-cost structure. On the other hand, fiber composite compo-nents may involve a significant amount of hand labor, and thus have high manufacturing costs.

It must be mentioned, without going into detail as yet, that the comparison of fiber properties with those of metals is somewhat misleading. It must be considered that the fiber will be utilized in conjunction with a matrix, which in many cases has quite different strength and stiffness properties. For example, with polymeric matrices, the matrix has al-most negligible strength and stiffness in comparison to the fiber. Because the volume of fiber in the total composite volume (the fiber-volume fraction) will be on the order of, say, 60%, the strength and stiffness will be diluted by a similar percentage, that is, a 40% loss of stiffness and strength will take place. Further, if the loads are not strictly in one direction, some fraction of the fibers will have to be aligned in other than the principal load direction. This further reduces the strength and stiffness in any one direction. However, experience

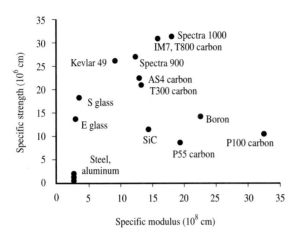

Figure 1.1   Specific modulus and specific strength for various engineering materials and fibers.

has shown that significant structural advantages can still be obtained. Currently, composite applications in aircraft often deliver about 30% weight reduction.

In very general terms, the characteristics of and differences between the various composite materials can be described as follows.

1.3 FIBERS

A list of selected fibers and their stiffness and strength properties is given in Table 1.1, taken from [1.1, 1.2]. The various types of fibers currently in use are discussed in what follows.

1.3.1 Glass Fiber

Glass fiber with polymeric matrices has been widely used in various commercial products such as piping, tanks, boats, and sporting goods. Glass is by far the most widely used fiber, because of the combination of low cost, corrosion resistance, and in many cases efficient manufacturing potential. It has relatively low stiffness, high elongation, and moderate strength and weight, and generally lower cost relative to other composites. It has been used extensively where corrosion resistance is important, such as in piping for the chemical industry and in marine applications. It is used as a continuous fiber in textile forms such as cloth and as a chopped fiber in less critical applications.

Glass fiber comes in several types, with E (electrical) being the cheaper fiber and S (high strength) having higher strength properties. Despite being widely used in marine applications, glass fiber is subject to strength loss under moisture and load.

1.3.2 Aramid Fiber

Aramid fibers (sold under the trade names Kevlar and Twaron) offer higher strength and stiffness relative to glass coupled with light weight, high tensile strength, but lower compressive strength. Both glass-fiber and aramid-fiber composites show good toughness in impact environments. Aramid tends to respond under impact in a ductile manner, as opposed to carbon fiber, which tends to fail in a more brittle manner. Aramid fiber is used as a higher-performance replacement for glass fiber in industrial applications and sporting goods, and in protective clothing.

1.3.3 Carbon Fiber

As mentioned before, carbon fibers are widely used in aerospace and some applications of sporting goods, taking advantage of the relatively high stiffness-to-weight and high strength-to-weight ratios of these fibers. The high stiffness and strength combined with low density and intermediate cost have made carbon fiber second only to glass fiber in use. Carbon fibers vary in strength and stiffness with the processing variables, so that different grades are available such as high modulus or intermediate modulus, with the trade-off being between high modulus and high strength. The intermediate-modulus and high-strength grades are almost universally made from a PAN (polyacrylonitrile) precursor, which is then heated and stretched to align the structure and remove noncarbon material. Higher-modulus fibers with much lower strength can be made from a petroleum pitch precursor, at lower cost.

A schematic of the processing sequence for PAN and pitch-based fibers is shown in Figure 1.2. The pitch-based fibers have a higher modulus, but lower strength than the PAN fibers. Even among various PAN-fiber grades, as mentioned before, there is a wide difference in modulus and strength, as well as large differences in the price of the fibers. Standard-modulus carbon fibers such as AS4, T300, T700, G30-500, and Panex 33 have a tensile modulus in the range of 207 to 240 GPa (30 to 35 Msi). Intermediate-modulus fibers such as IM6 and IM7 and T800 have a modulus in the range of 240 to 340 GPa (35 to 50 Msi), and high tensile strength. High-modulus carbon fibers have a tensile modulus in the range of 340 to 960 GPa (50 to 140 Msi). Recent developments have included fibers with tensile strengths approaching 6900 MPa (10^6 psi). Other recent developments have been the introduction of lower-cost fibers, available in increased fiber bundle size for both lower production cost and subsequent fabrication efficiency. Because of the range of properties

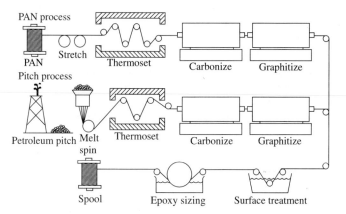

Figure 1.2   Processing polyacrylonitrile (PAN) and pitch-based carbon fibers. Highly oriented polymer chains are obtained in PAN by hot stretching. (*Source:* From [1.3].)

available in commercial carbon fibers, a specific grade of fiber must be identified, typically based on manufacturers' product specification sheets. However, there are popular ranges of properties, and these will be indicated in subsequent chapters. Carbon fibers typically have a diameter on the order of 5 to 8 microns, which is much smaller than a typical human hair. Because of this small size, the fibers are grouped into tows or yarns consisting of from 2 to 12 thousand (12k) individual fibers, with the new low-cost fibers having tow sizes up to 48k.

Typical mechanical properties of some commercially available carbon fibers are found in Table 1.1. Later chapters give more detail on these properties. It should be also noted that there have been consolidation and changes in the companies that are offering carbon-fiber products that is still ongoing. Thus, manufacturers' names have changed and are still changing.

1.3.4 Other Fibers

Boron fibers offer very high stiffness, but also at very high cost. Boron was one of the earliest fibers to be introduced into an aerospace application. However, whereas the prices of carbon fibers have dropped steadily since the introduction in the late 1960s, boron fibers have remained expensive. Boron fibers have a relatively large diameter, typically on the order of 200 microns, high stiffness-to-weight ratio, and good compressive strength. These fibers have been used in specialized applications both in aluminum and polymeric matrices.

A fiber that is being used in textile applications is oriented polyethylene, marketed under the trademark of Spectra fiber. This fiber offers high strength with extremely light weight. The fiber itself has a specific gravity of 0.97, meaning that it is lighter than water. It has a very low range of temperature usage, and the difficulty of obtaining adhesion to matrix materials has limited its application in structural composites. It is being used as a hybrid with carbon fiber in certain applications, in an attempt to combine the light weight and

Table 1.1   Mechanical Properties of Typical Fibers

Fiber	Fiber Diameter (μm)	Fiber Density (lb/in³)	(g/cc)	Tensile Strength (ksi)	(GPa)	Tensile Modulus (Msi)	(GPa)
E-glass	8–14	0.092	2.54	500	3.45	10.5	72.4
S-glass	8–14	0.090	2.49	665	4.58	12.5	86.2
Polyethylene	10–12	0.035	0.97	392	2.70	12.6	87.0
Aramid (Kevlar 49)	12	0.052	1.44	525	3.62	19.0	130.0
HS Carbon, T300	7	0.063	1.76	514	3.53	33.6	230
AS4 Carbon	7	0.065	1.80	580	4.00	33.0	228
IM7 Carbon	5	0.065	1.80	785	5.41	40.0	276
XUHM Carbon	—	0.068	1.88	550	3.79	62.0	428
GY80 Carbon	8.4	0.071	1.96	270	1.86	83.0	572
Boron	50–203	0.094	2.60	500	3.44	59.0	407
Silicon Carbide		0.115	3.19	220	1.52	70.0	483

Sources: From [1.1, 1.2] and product literature.

toughness of the Spectra fiber with the stiffness of carbon fiber. It is also used in cordage and in protective clothing.

A number of other fibers are under development for use with ceramic matrices to obtain very high-temperature applications such as for engine components. An example is silicon carbide fiber, used in whisker form. These fibers may prove to be important in high-temperature applications. Their present use is a very small fraction of the use of glass, carbon, and Kevlar fibers, however.

1.4 MATRICES

The majority of current applications utilize polymeric matrices. The matrix material plays an important role in the overall function of the composite and must satisfy a number of somewhat conflicting demands regarding strength, toughness, moisture and environmental resistance, elevated temperature properties, and cost. A number of alternatives have evolved for different applications.

The polymeric matrices can be classified into two general categories as thermosets and thermoplastics. The thermosets, including the epoxies, cure by chemical reaction, and the cure is a one-time irreversible process. The thermoplastics, on the other hand, can be formed repeatedly by heating to an elevated temperature at which softening occurs. The manufacturing process for the composite parts in general will be quite different for thermoplastic and thermoset matrices.

The thermoset polymers have been heavily utilized, and a large amount of characterization data are available for these materials. Lower-cost materials are polyester and vinyl ester with similar but somewhat improved mechanical properties and improved solvent resistance. Table 1.2 gives a further general overview and comparison of glass–fiber resin composites in various forms. It should be noted that fiber reinforcement dominates many of the properties listed, and thus the properties reflect both resin and fiber properties. It also can be seen by comparing the values listed in Tables 1.1 and 1.2 that the composite stiffness and strength properties are less than that of the fiber itself, because of the dilution by the weaker matrix and also because of the need to orient fibers in different directions. It also can be seen that the properties can depend on the form of the fiber reinforcement, with

Table 1.2   Typical Properties of Glass–Polyester Composites in Various Forms

Form	Density (g/cc)	Tensile Strength		Tensile Modulus	
		(ksi)	(MPa)	(Msi)	(GPa)
Unidirectional roving	2.0	100	690	6.0	40
Woven glass fabric	1.9	48	330	3.8	26
Chopped strand mat	1.7	42	290	2.4	16.7
Sheet molding compound R50	1.87	24	164	2.3	16

Sources: From [1.4, 1.5].

chopped-fiber composites having lower stiffness and strength relative to continuous-fiber composites.

The epoxy resins are widely used thermosets that offer superior performance, but are more costly relative to the polyesters. There is a wide range of epoxy resins available commercially, and manufacturer's literature must be consulted to select the proper range of properties needed and the cost required to achieve these objectives. Typical cure temperatures for the epoxies are in the range of 121 to 177°C (250 to 350°F), although some ambient temperature products are available. Variables to consider are the interlaminar shear strength, which is a laminate property related to the shear strength of the matrix, the brittleness or toughness of the matrix, moisture and environmental resistance, and the range of elevated temperature properties if that is part of the product requirement. Early aerospace epoxies used in prepregs (a material form discussed in what follows) emphasized resistance to hot, wet conditions, and while achieving these objectives tended to be brittle and subject to damage from accidental impact. More recent developments have been the high-toughness epoxies, available at higher cost.

Thermoplastic resins soften at elevated temperature, and thus can be formed and then cooled to manufacture the final item; they do not use a cure cycle. An advantage of this process is that in theory parts can be reformed and/or repaired. The manufacturing process is thus quite different than that used with a thermoset matrix. Thermoplastic resins range from the common engineering plastics to others specifically developed to be used in high-performance fiber composites. Materials such as polypropylene and nylon, for example, are commonly used with chopped glass fiber. The product is processed much as it would be without the fiber, say, by injection molding, for example; the process gives a finished material with higher mechanical properties than from the thermoplastic alone, but considerably lower than with the continuous-fiber composites. A process developed for continuous-fiber composites with thermoplastic resins would involve softening layers of combined fiber and resin at elevated temperature, and then placing them in a mold to be formed, similar to metal stamping. The higher-performance, higher-cost thermoplastics have excellent toughness properties. The use of thermoplastics in combination with continuous-fiber systems has been held back because of a general lack of experience, and in some cases high material costs. They are likely to increase in use because of the increased toughness that they may offer, as well as the potential for advanced manufacturing techniques.

Polymeric matrix materials are limited in the temperature range for practical use, with the epoxies typically limited to 150°C (300°F) or less, depending on the specific material. Higher-temperature polymers such as bismaleimides and polyimides are available, but typically display increased brittleness. They are being used in applications such as cowlings and ducts for jet engines.

Metal matrix composites are being utilized for higher-temperature use than that available with polymeric matrices. Aluminum has been utilized with boron and carbon fibers. A successful application is that of a metal matrix piston manufactured by Toyota in Japan, used for increased wear resistance and high thermal conductivity. Over one million of these have been manufactured. For still higher temperature ranges, ceramic matrix materials are under development. Here the fiber is not necessarily higher in strength and stiffness than the matrix, but is used primarily to add toughness to the ceramic matrix.

1.5 MATERIAL FORMS AND MANUFACTURING

Composite materials come in a wide variety of material forms. The fiber itself may be used in continuous form or as a chopped fiber. Chopped glass fibers are typically used to reinforce various polymers, with accordingly lower strength and stiffness relative to continuous-fiber composites. Chopped fibers with automated fabrication techniques have been utilized for automotive body parts with high production rates.

Continuous-fiber materials are available in a number of different forms, with the specific form utilized depending on the manufacturing process. Thus, it is useful to consider both the material and the manufacturing process at the same time. The fibers themselves are very small in diameter, with sizes of 5 to 7 microns (0.0002 to 0.0003 in) for the carbon fibers. A large number of fibers, typically, 2000 to 12,000 are gathered together in the manufacturing process to form a tow (also called a roving or yarn). The filament winding process utilizes these tows directly. The tows may be further processed by "prepregging," which is the process of coating the individual fibers with the matrix material. This process is widely used with thermoset polymeric resins. The resin is partially cured and the resulting "ply" placed on a paper backing. The prepregged material is available in continuous rolls of various widths of from 75 to 1000 mm (3 to 40 in) wide. These rolls must be kept refrigerated until they are assembled and placed in the curing process. Note that the ply consists of a number of fibers through the thickness, and that these fibers are aligned and continuous. Typical volume fractions of fiber are on the order of 60%. These popular material forms—dry fibers, prepregs, and fabrics—are shown in Figure 1.3. These material forms are then used with a variety of specific manufacturing techniques. Some of the more popular techniques are described in what follows.

1.5.1 Sheet Molding Compound

The sheet molding compound (SMC) is a manufacturing process for producing glass fiber with polyester resin. The process lends itself to high rates of production, and has been used for automobile body panels. As illustrated in Figure 1.4, the glass fiber is typically used in chopped-fiber form and added to a resin mixture that is carried on plastic carrier film. After partial cure, the carrier films are removed; the sheet molding material is cut into lengths and placed into matched metal dies under heat and pressure. Catalysts and other additives such as thermoplastics are mixed with the resin. Typical properties of sheet molding compound materials are shown in Table 1.2.

1.5.2 Filament Winding

As illustrated in Figures 1.5 and 1.6, the process consists of winding continuous-fiber tow around a mandrel to form the structure. Typically, the mandrel itself rotates while the fiber placement is controlled to move longitudinally in syncronization. The matrix may be added to the fiber by running the fiber tow through a matrix bath at the time of placement, in a process called wet winding, or else the tows may be prepregged prior to winding. Filament winding has been widely used for making glass-fiber pipe, for making rocket motor cases, and other similar products such as sailboard masts. The advantages are that it is a highly

(a)

(b)

(c)

Figure 1.3   Carbon-fiber forms: (a) dry fibers, (b) prepreg plies, and (c) cloth. (*Source:* Alliant Techsystems.)

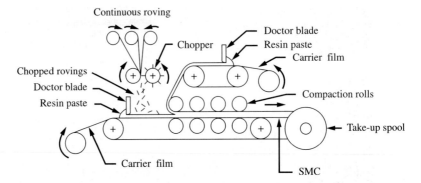

Figure 1.4   Process for producing sheet molding compound (SMC). (*Source:* From [1.6].)

automated process, with typically low manufacturing costs. Obviously, it lends itself most readily to convex axisymmetric articles, but a number of specialized techniques are being considered for more complicated shapes. Filament winding is typically a low-cost method because of the use of fibers and resins in their lowest-cost form, and because of the potential for high production rates. Mandrels must be constructed so that they can be removed from the finished article. The winding tension is typically sufficient to consolidate the part, and shrink tape can be wrapped over the outside to give additional consolidation pressure during cure. Thus, additional pressure during cure is usually not used.

1.5.3 Prepreg and Prepreg Layup

The word "prepreg" refers to a partially cured mixture of fiber and resin. The dry, spooled fiber is combined with the resin, as illustrated in Figure 1.7, by commercial firms called "prepreggers" that make the product available in the form of unidirectional prepreg tape, partially cured to a point that it can be handled and wound on spools with a removable paper backing, as illustrated in Figure 1.3. A further illustration of the various sizes available in

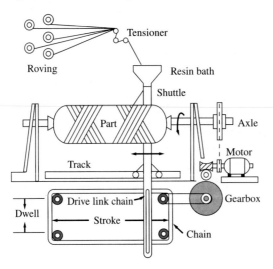

Figure 1.5   The wet-filament winding process.

Figure 1.6   Filament winding of a rocket motor case. (*Source:* Alliant Techsystems.)

carbon-fiber tape prepregs is shown in Figure 1.8. (Names and addresses of prepreg suppli-
ers are listed in [1.7].) Prepreg tape with thermosetting polymer resin matrices must be
stored under refrigeration to prevent further cure until final use. Prepreg has a limited shelf
life in the freezer and a further limited "out time" during assembly of the final product. Both
of these times are highly variable with the specific system. The prepreg tape is typically
available from the prepregger in rolls with widths from 25 to 1525 mm (1 to 60 in), and in
amounts varying from 5 to 225 kg (10 to 500 lb). The individual layers of unidirectional

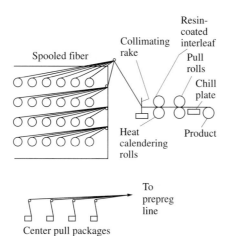

Figure 1.7   Process for producing prepreg
fiber and resin.

Figure 1.8   Carbon-fiber/epoxy prepreg tape. (*Source:* Alliant Techsystems.)

prepreg are often made in thicknesses from 0.08 to 0.25 mm (0.003 to 0.01 in), and a nominal value of 0.127 mm (0.005 in) is common.

The unidirectional prepreg can then be cut and stacked to form the final product. Because the individual fibers are relatively straight, the use of a unidirectional prepreg provides a method, along with filament winding, of achieving finished products with good mechanical properties.

The final manufacturing procedure involves removing the prepreg tape from the freezer, cutting the tape to the final shape, removing the paper backing and assembling (stacking) the individual layers together in the desired orientations, placing the assemblage in tooling to control the final shape, and then covering with appropriate materials for the cure process. The individual tape layers can be cut easily with scissors or a razor, or with laser tools and automated machinery. The individual layers can be placed in the desired orientation by the operator in a process called hand layup or large-scale and highly automated equipment can be employed, as illustrated in Figure 1.9. A small increase of temperature of the prepreg is often employed to make the prepreg more pliable and increase tackiness during assembly.

Appropriate tooling must be used to control the final part geometry. The tooling can be constructed of metal or a variety of other materials, including other composites, but must

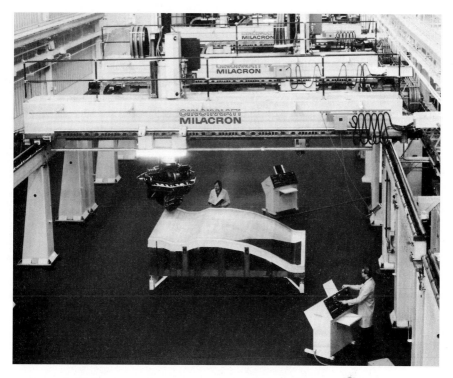

Figure 1.9   Automated tape-laying equipment. (*Source:* From [1.6].)

be capable of withstanding the temperatures used in the curing process. Separation of the part from the tooling requires release agents in either liquid or spray-on form, or a sheet of plastic, release ply material.

The prepreg material and often the tooling are then wrapped with several additional materials that are used in the curing process. A schematic of this is shown in Figure 1.10. The objective of the cure process is to remove volatiles and excess air to facilitate consoli-

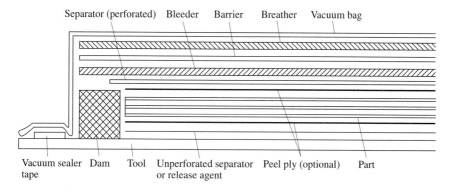

Figure 1.10   Prepreg layup process, ready for autoclave cure.

dation of the laminate, and to apply temperature and pressure to ensure good bonding during cure. To this end, the laminate is covered with a peel ply (for removal of the other curing materials), and a breather ply, which is often a fiberglass mat. A bleeder may be used optionally to absorb excess resin, although the net resin process omits this step. Finally, the assemblage is covered with a vacuum bag and sealed at the edges, usually with an adhesive sealant product called "tacky tape." A vacuum is drawn, and after inspection, the heat-up process is started. If an autoclave is used, pressure on the order of 0.1 to 0.7 MPa (20 to 100 psi) is then added to ensure the final consolidation. Autoclave processing ensures good lamination but requires a somewhat expensive piece of hardware. A typical temperature and pressure cure cycle, as recommended by the prepreg manufacturer, is shown in Figure 1.11. Although unidirectional plies have been described here, cloth layers also can be used. The bends in the individual fibers that occur with cloth bring about a performance penalty, but manufacturing considerations such as drapeability may make cloth desirable. The peel ply, fiberglass-mat breather material, and vacuum bag are consumable items that add to the final cost, but are required in the curing process. Removal of the cured part from the tooling may be easy in many cases, but if closed forms with internal mandrels are used, such as for tubular parts, it requires careful consideration.

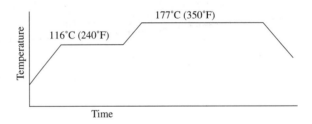

1. Place vacuum bagged layup in autoclave and close clave.

2. Apply minimum vacuum of 25 in of Hg.

3. Apply 85±5 psig.

4. At a rate of 3 to 5°F/min, raise the laminate temperature to 240±10°F, while holding 85±5 psig autoclave pressure and 20–29 in of Hg vacuum.

5. Hold at 240±10°F, 85±5° psig, and 20–29 in of Hg for 60 to 70 min.

6. Raise pressure to 100±5 psig and vent the vacuum bag to ambient atmospheric pressure.

7. Raise temperature at a rate of 3 to 5°F/min to 350±10°F. Hold for 120±10 min under 100± 5 psig autoclave pressure.

8. At a rate of 5±1°F/min, lower the laminate temperature to 200°F. Release autoclave pressure.

9. Remove from autoclave and unbag.

Figure 1.11   Typical pressure and temperature schedule for prepreg cure.

Parts of surprising complexity and good quality can be made by the hand layup process. However, the process is labor-intensive. Note that because the individual plies are relatively thin (on the order of 0.13 mm, 0.005 in), a large number of plies will be required with thicker parts. The history of many applications of fiber composites in both aerospace and sporting goods applications has been to fabricate parts using hand layup of prepreg tape, followed by a search for lower-cost production techniques.

Thermoplastic prepreg is also available. The individual sheets do not have to be stored under refrigeration. The layers tend to be stiff and "boardy" and are usually softened before assembly. The final manufacture could involve heating and forming in matched molds. An illustration of this is shown in Figure 1.12.

1.5.4 Textile Forms and RTM

The individual dry-fiber tows may be combined in a variety of textile processes such as braiding and weaving. The resulting material forms can be then used in a variety of final manufacturing processes. Glass-fiber cloth is a familiar product available in hardware stores. It is combined with the resin by hand in a wet layup process. It is difficult to control the relative fractions of fiber and resin in a wet layup, and although suitable for many products such as glass-fiber boats and canoes, it would not be particularly appropriate for more stringent requirements. However, cloth is also available in prepreg form, which gives better control of the resin content. Although the fiber bends involved in cloth will tend to lower stiffness and strength somewhat, it may be desirable because of its ability to conform to

Figure 1.12   Compression molding of a thermoplastic sheet. (*Source:* From [1.6].)

complex shapes and the efficiency of applying a layer with two perpendicular fiber directions in one operation.

A manufacturing technique with a number of potential advantages is to assemble a dry-fiber preform, usually with the fibers in one or more textile forms, and then place this preform in a closed mold. The resin is then introduced into the mold in a process often called resin transfer molding (RTM). This technique promises a significant degree of automation, with good control of the part geometry and the relative fiber and resin volume fractions. The fiber preforms can use stitched layers of cloth or mat, and other textile forms such as knits or braids. RTM is being considered for a number of automotive structural parts. An example of an automotive structural member is shown in Figure 1.13.

Braiding is a traditional textile process that has been adapted for use with advanced fibers such as glass, Kevlar, and carbon. A typical braiding machine is illustrated in Figure 1.14 and a typical product in Figure 1.15. Tubular goods can be braided on a mandrel, and then removed and placed in a mold. The tubular braided preform also can be cut and flattened for other than tubular products. The braid patterns can be more or less two-dimensional, or can be highly three-dimensional with fibers oriented in the through-the-thickness direction.

1.5.5 Pultrusion

Pultrusion is a process in which the fiber and matrix are pulled through a die. Pultrusion is similar in overall function to extrusion in metals and polymer materials, except that the fibers are pulled rather than pushed. The pultrusion apparatus provides the functions of as-

Figure 1.13   Front structure made by resin transfer molding. (*Source:* Ford Motor Co.)

sembling the fibers, impregnating the resin, shaping the product, and curing the resin. Glass-fiber and polyester or vinyl ester resin are widely used in the pultrusion process, as well as other material systems such as aramid (Kevlar and Twaron) or carbon fibers with epoxy resin. Pultruded products include solid and hollow shapes in standard sizes, as well as custom shapes for a variety of specific applications. Fishing rods and electrical insulator rods manufactured by pultrusion are popular examples. The pultrusion process is illustrated in Figure 1.16.

1.5.6 Tube Rolling

Tubular products such as fishing rods and golf club shafts are often made by a wrapping or rolling process, as an alternative to other processes such as filament winding. Prepreg tape is typically used, and the tube may be either wrapped with a bidirectional cloth (with fibers in the axial and transverse directions) or spiral-wrapped. Tapered tubes can be roll-wrapped, although the orientation of the fibers is then not totally symmetric.

Figure 1.14   A composite braiding machine for advanced fiber net-shaped preforms. (*Source: Fiber Innovations, Inc., Walpole, MA.*)

Figure 1.15 Formation of a braided fiberglass preform for a composite coupling shaft. (Courtesy of Professor F. Ko, Drexel University.)

1.6 CURRENT APPLICATIONS

A number of current applications of composites are illustrated in the following. These applications show quite a variety. Two important areas for use of advanced composites are aerospace and sporting goods, areas where high performance is required. Other applications mentioned before capitalize on the excellent corrosion resistance of composites, such as in marine applications and chemical industries. The applications can be considered by area as follows.

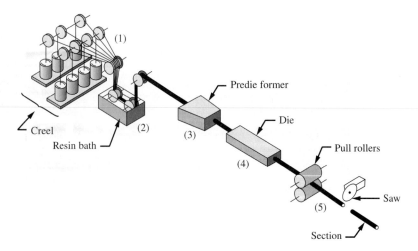

Figure 1.16 The pultrusion process. (*Source:* From [1.6].)

1.6.1 Aerospace

The aerospace industry has been a major factor in the development and application of carbon, aramid, and boron fibers. Carbon and aramid fibers have been used in solid rocket motor cases because of their high strength-to-weight properties. These cases are manufactured by filament winding. One of the earliest applications for carbon fiber was in space structures because of its very special thermal-expansion properties. Carbon fiber actually has a small but negative coefficient of thermal expansion in the fiber direction. It is possible to align the fibers so as to achieve a very low distortion associated with changes in temperature. Present-day space structures, such as illustrated in Figure 1.17, may use high-modulus carbon fiber and special resins to achieve excellent dimensional stability.

Carbon fibers, and in some instances aramid fiber, are being used extensively in military aircraft and helicoptors because of high stiffness-to-weight ratios as well as strength-to-weight ratios. For example, the USA Comanche helicopter under development uses carbon-fiber prepreg systems with toughened epoxies or BMI resins for 73% of the airframe [1.8], and carbon fiber/epoxy for the blade spars and glass fiber/epoxy for the blade skins. The V-22 Osprey tiltrotor aircraft under production, illustrated in Figure 1.18, uses intermediate-modulus, carbon-fiber IM6/3501-6 for 41% of the primary structure and glass fiber/epoxy for an additional 8%.

The applications to commercial aircraft have been much slower to come to market because of the problems associated with both material and manufacturing cost. The Airbus series of airplanes introduced a vertical stabilizer made from carbon fiber/epoxy in 1985, and incorporated this in subsequent models. As illustrated in Figure 1.19, the airbus A340 introduced in 1993 also has a carbon-fiber/epoxy horizontal rear stabilizer, and uses carbon-fiber composites for most of the control surfaces, fairings, nacelles, and access doors. The recently introduced Boeing 777 is also using carbon fiber for the horizontal and vertical rear stabilizers. The Boeing 777 horizontal stabilizer and tail have a span of 21 m and almost 10 m, respectively, and are made of carbon fiber and toughened epoxy. The Boeing 777, a 400-passenger aircraft, as illustrated in Figure 1.20 will have about 10% composites by weight

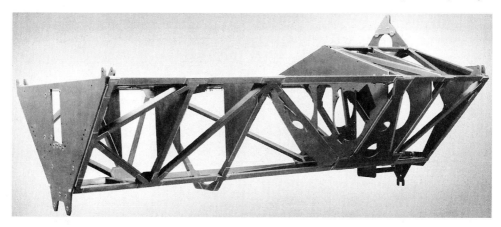

Figure 1.17 Optical bench for space application, made from carbon-fiber/epoxy laminates designed with a near zero coefficient of thermal expansion. (*Source:* Alliant Techsystems.)

Figure 1.18 The V-22 Osprey, with half of the primary structure made from fiber composites. (*Source:* Bell Helicopter Textron.)

[1.9]. Although carbon-fiber composites have been used in the primary structure of military aircraft for some time, this recent use of carbon fiber in commercial aircraft represents a significant advance. Reducing the problems of design, reliability, manufacturing, and cost to commercial practice represents a milestone in the use of composite materials. On a smaller scale, the introduction of the Beech Starship corporate jet with an all-carbon-fiber composite airframe, shown in Figure 1.21, represents another milestone in the use of fiber composites in commercial aviation.

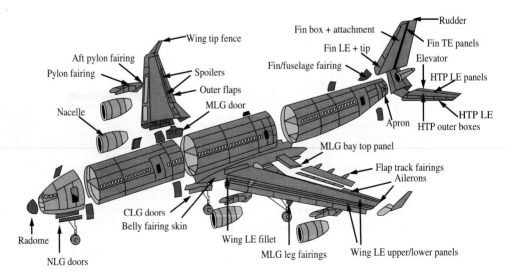

Figure 1.19 Use of fiber composites in Airbus A340 commercial aircraft. (*Source:* Deutsche Aerospace.)

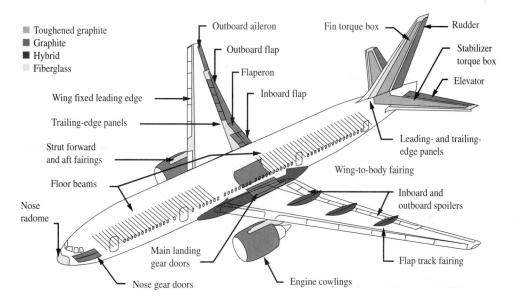

Figure 1.20 Use of fiber composites in Boeing 777 commercial aircraft. (*Source:* Boeing Commercial Airplane Group.)

Figure 1.21 The "all-composite" Beech Starship. (*Source:* Alliant Techsystems.)

A significant development has been the fan blade for the GE-90 turbine aircraft engine developed for large aircraft such as the Boeing 777. This fan blade is made of carbon fiber and a high-toughness epoxy resin. This application is driven by strength-to-weight and stiffness-to-weight ratios, but the most stringent requirement is for impact resistance. Although impact resistance is a significant design issue for carbon-fiber composites, tests have indicated that the carbon fiber, high-toughness resin combination is superior to titanium fan blades in this respect.

Many early applications used prepreg tape materials, often in conjunction with hand layup. Prepreg tape is still a viable material form, as evidenced by recent use on the Boeing 777 and the GE jet engine fan blades mentioned before, for example. However, current efforts are underway to develop more cost-effective manufacturing techniques. Processes such as braiding are being considered for smaller parts such as ribs and stringers for commercial aircraft. Stitched and woven fiber forms are being considered for wing and fuselage skins. The resin transfer molding (RTM) technique is being considered for many of these applications, in which dry fibers are placed in a mold and the resin is injected and then cured.

1.6.2 Sporting Goods

Composites have become popular in a number of applications in sporting goods. One of the early popular applications of carbon-fiber composites was for the shafts of golf clubs. The light weight and stiffness enabled a higher percentage of the weight to be concentrated in the head, giving better performance. Golf shafts are fabricated by roll wrapping with carbon/epoxy prepreg or by filament winding. Standard-modulus carbon fiber is used, and the more expensive shafts may use high-modulus carbon fiber. Glass fiber is universally used in poles used for pole vaults, taking advantage of the high strain to failure of that material to store energy. A similar application of glass fiber is in archery bows, and carbon fiber is used for the very high-performance arrow shafts. In another application involving sporting goods, polyethylene and aramid fibers are used in protective helmets. Carbon fiber is widely used in various types of tennis rackets. Typical commercial products are shown in Figure 1.22. Here the stiffness-to-weight ratio and vibration absorption are key characteristics, properties that are utilized in fishing rods as well. Carbon-fiber composite fishing rods are very popular, and are available at moderate cost due to high production.

Sailboard and sailboat masts employ glass fiber in the lower-cost models and carbon fiber in higher-performance models. Although significantly lighter than glass fiber, the carbon-fiber masts typically require more care in use to prevent accidental damage. Carbon fiber is now universally used in Formula I race-car frames, for reasons of crash protection that take advantage of the high strength-to-weight and stiffness-to-weight ratios of carbon fiber. An early model is shown in Figure 1.23. The history of using carbon fiber in this application is interesting: Once it was introduced by some of the teams, all others quickly followed because of the competitive edge that the lighter structures provided.

Glass fiber dominates the recreational boat industry because of corrosion resistance and cost. Higher-performance kayaks and canoes are available in aramid fiber. Very high-performance (and expensive) racing power and sailboat hulls are now being made with carbon fiber, including the boats for the America's Cup. The chief barrier to more widespread use is cost, and the lower-cost carbon fibers becoming available may increase the utiliza-

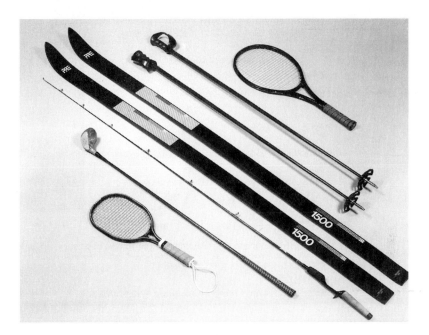

Figure 1.22   Fiber composite materials are used in sporting goods. (*Source:* Alliant Techsystems.)

tion. In some products, hybrids of carbon and Spectra-oriented polyethlyene products are being used to achieve lighter weight.

Bicycle frames are becoming available from many manufacturers in carbon fiber. The more conventional method of using carbon fibers in bicycle frames has been to retain the conventional tube and lug construction, with carbon-fiber/epoxy tubes in conjunction with secondary bonding to metal lugs, and in some cases to composite lugs. The tubes may be roll-wrapped, hand layup with prepreg materials, or braided. A typical example is illustrated

Figure 1.23   Formula I race car with a carbon-fiber/epoxy chassis. (*Source:* Alliant Techsystems.)

Figure 1.24 Bicycle frame made by braiding carbon-fiber/epoxy tows. (*Source:* Albany International.)

in Figure 1.24. More exotic frames have been made with hard tooling with either inflatable mandrels or foam cores, such as shown in Figure 1.25. Designs quite unlike those for metal construction are then available.

1.6.3 Automotive

Despite early predictions of widespread use of composites in the automotive industry by this time, actual use of composites has been quite low. Some examples are components such as springs, driveshafts, and chopped glass fiber as sheet molding compound used for body

Figure 1.25 Innovative bicycle frame made from carbon-fiber/epoxy.

Figure 1.26   Carbon- and glass-fiber truck leaf springs. (*Source:* Alliant Techsystems.)

panels. Some components are illustrated in Figure 1.26. Cost appears to be the principal barrier. There are indications that legislated requirements for fuel economy may lead to further consideration of composites. Prototypes of frame cross-members have been built, and manufacturing techniques are currently being studied with the goal of decreasing manufacturing costs. The use of resin transfer molding (RTM) with high-cure-rate polyurethane resin, with stitched cloth or braided glass-fiber preforms, looks promising at present.

Glass fiber has been emphasized in the production and prototype applications to date in the automotive industry. However, it is still an open question as to whether the weight savings with glass fiber will be adequate to justify the change from steel, or whether eventually carbon-fiber composites will be used because of the increased stiffness-to-weight ratios for that material.

Figure 1.27   A bridge column retrofitted by wrapping with fiber composite for improved earthquake resistance. (*Source:* XXsys Technologies, Inc.)

1.6.4 Infrastructure

A possible emerging market for composites is for infrastructure applications, such as bridges and buildings. For example, carbon-fiber and glass-fiber composites are being considered for use in reinforced concrete. Corrosion of steel reinforcement in concrete, particularly in bridge decks, is a significant problem that leads to deterioration of the structure. Glass fibers and carbon fibers have been used in demonstration projects as replacements for steel. Both of these materials are also being considered as reinforcement for retrofitting buildings and bridge columns for earthquake resistance. As would be expected, however, the initial cost is a significant barrier to the use of fiber composites in these applications. An example is illustrated in Figure 1.27, which shows fiber composites being investigated for use in providing circumferential reinforcement to bridge columns in California. Preliminary results indicate that the columns can be significantly strengthened by wrapping with fiber composites, and both glass-fiber and carbon-fiber systems are being proposed and investigated. This is a potentially very large market for fiber composites.

1.7 A FINAL NOTE

The composites industry, and particularly the advanced composites industry, is currently in a state of flux. Growth rates for carbon-fiber use have been on the order of 15 to 20% per year for the past decade, with consumption in 1991 being around 20 million pounds. The reductions in defense spending that followed the end of the Cold War have led to reductions in material requirements for carbon fiber in the military aerospace industry. As a consequence, the supply of carbon fiber exceeded demand. One consequence is that manufacturers have offered commercial grades of carbon fiber at significantly reduced prices, in the range of $9 to $15 per pound ($20 to $33 per kg) for carbon fiber with properties similar to that of AS4, which has been widely used in aerospace applications. Carbon fiber with larger tow sizes is currently available at prices of from $9 to $12 per pound ($20 to $26 per kg) with projections that these prices will be cut in half in the next few years. These lowered prices are making other markets feasible that do not require the certification procedures and therefore higher prices of the aerospace grades. It is possible that a greatly expanded role for fiber composites in infrastructure may open up, as well as an increased role in the automotive industry. However, in addition to the performance and cost issues, the natural resistance to change because of the uncertainties involved will have to be overcome in order for fiber composite materials to achieve widespread use in these industries.

There are signs that the industry will continue to grow, although the rate at which growth occurs depends on complex interactions between cost and performance gains. The technical need for design and analysis of composite structures remains in place, as increased use of composites will require taking full advantage of the material properties and manufacturing techniques available.

REFERENCES

1.1 W. Bishop, "High Performance Fibres," in *Advanced Composites*, ed. I. K. Partridge (London: Elsevier, 1989), pp. 111–144.

1.2 N. W. Hansen, "Carbon Fibers," in *Engineered Materials Handbook*, Vol. 1 (Metals Park, OH: ASM International, 1987), pp. 112–113.

1.3 R. J. Diefendorf, "Carbon/Graphite Fibers," in *Engineered Materials Handbook*, Vol. 1 (Metals Park, OH: ASM International, 1987), pp. 49–53.

1.4 C. D. Dudgeon, "Polyester Resins," in *Engineered Materials Handbook*, Vol. 1 (Metals Park, OH: ASM International, 1987), pp. 90–96.

1.5 J. C. Reindl, "Commercial and Automotive Applications," in *Engineered Materials Handbook*, Vol. 1 (Metals Park, OH: ASM International, 1987), pp. 832–836.

1.6 M. P. Groover, *Fundamentals of Modern Manufacturing* (Englewood Cliffs, NJ: Prentice Hall, 1996).

1.7 *High Performance Composites,* Vol. 3 (Denver: Ray Publishing, 1995).

1.8 V. P. McConnell, "Military Programs," in *High Performance Composites* (Denver: Ray Publishing, 1994), pp. 19–24.

1.9 K. H. Schreiber, and J. T. Quinlivan, "The Boeing 777 Empennage," paper presented at International Conference on Composite Materials 9, Madrid, 12–16 July 1993.

2

Stress–Strain Relationships for an Orthotropic Lamina

2.1 INTRODUCTION

The fundamental way in which fiber composites, and in particular continuous-fiber composites, differ from conventional engineering materials such as metals is that the properties are highly directional. This directionality affects the way in which the materials are used and the way in which the directions of the individual plies are selected. In this chapter, the stress–strain relationships for an individual ply or lamina are examined. These relationships form the basic building block on which all subsequent analysis and design procedures are based. It is assumed here that the material under consideration is orthotropic, that is, it has directional stiffness properties, but that certain symmetries hold. In particular, an orthotropic material has planes of symmetry and principal material axes such that loading along these principal axes in tension or compression does not induce shear stresses and strains, and the applications of shear stresses does not produce normal strains. The individual layers of a composite, whether it be a layer in a laminate or a layer in a filament-wound structure, closely follow this assumption, with the principal material axes aligned with and transverse to the fibers. When a composite is considered to be an orthotropic material, the individual constituents of fiber and matrix are no longer explicitly considered, but only average or "smeared" properties in the different directions are employed. Because many composite structures are thin in the through-the-thickness direction, the theory developed here is essentially a two-dimensional stress theory.

The major focus of this chapter is to develop the relationships between stress and strain for a thin lamina (layer) of aligned fibers in a matrix. These relationships are applicable to all continuous-fiber composites and to aligned short-fiber composites. Those short-fiber composites that have more random fiber orientations, and other materials such as continuous fibers placed in what is called a "random mat" may be considerably less directional in stiffness; in many cases, they can be analyzed as if they were conventional isotropic materials. The chapter begins by introducing the idea of orthtropic properties.

2.2 ORTHOTROPIC PROPERTIES

A unidirectional layer is shown in Figure 2.1, along with a coordinate system used to establish notation. Here directions 1 and 2 refer to the fiber direction and transverse to the fibers in the plane of the ply, and direction 3 refers to the through-the-thickness direction. The modulus of the ply in the direction of the fibers is called E_{11}, and the modulus of the ply in the transverse direction is E_{22}. The response to a uniaxial stress in the fiber direction is a strain given by

$$\epsilon_1 = \sigma_1/E_{11} \tag{2.1}$$

The response to a uniaxial stress in (transverse) direction 2 is a strain given by

$$\epsilon_2 = \sigma_2/E_{22} \tag{2.2}$$

Note that the numbers 1 and 2 indicate directions and have nothing to do with principal stresses. Similarly, an in-plane shear modulus G_{12} can be defined so that the response to a shear stress is a shear strain given by

$$\gamma_{12} = \tau_{12}/G_{12} \tag{2.3}$$

The Poisson ratios also can be defined in a similar manner. If one again considers a uniaxial stress in (fiber) direction 1, a strain in (transverse) direction 2 will result because of the Poisson effect. The appropriate Poisson ratio can be defined as

$$\epsilon_2 = -\nu_{12}\epsilon_1 \text{ (for uniaxial stress in direction 1)} \tag{2.4}$$

Conversely, if a uniaxial stress is applied in (transverse) direction 2, the strain in (fiber) direction 1 can be defined in terms of the appropriate Poisson ratio as

$$\epsilon_1 = -\nu_{21}\epsilon_2 \text{ (for uniaxial stress in direction 2)} \tag{2.5}$$

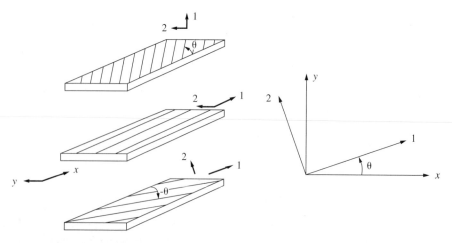

Figure 2.1   Unidirectional plies with a local 1,2 fiber coordinate system and a global x,y coordinate system.

The notation for the Poisson ratio is usually defined as given, although some authors reverse the order of the subscripts. The stress and strain in the through-the-thickness direction can be defined in a similar manner as

$$\epsilon_3 = \sigma_3/E_{33} \text{ (for uniaxial stress in direction 3)} \tag{2.6}$$

and

$$\epsilon_1 = -\nu_{31}\epsilon_3 \quad \text{and} \quad \epsilon_2 = -\nu_{32}\epsilon_3 \tag{2.7}$$

Finally, these straightforward notions can be combined by using the idea of superposition. That is, consider that the strain in direction 1 results both from a stress σ_1 and through the Poisson effect from stresses σ_2 and σ_3. Thus, consider that stresses σ_1, σ_2, and σ_3 are applied. A strain in direction 1 results from each of these stresses, and is the sum of the strains that would result from these stresses applied separately. The strains in direction 1 for each load acting separately are given by

σ_1 loading: $\epsilon_1 = \sigma_1/E_{11}$

σ_2 loading: $\epsilon_1 = -\nu_{21}\epsilon_2 = -\nu_{21}\sigma_2/E_{22}$

σ_3 loading: $\epsilon_1 = -\nu_{31}\epsilon_3 = -\nu_{31}\sigma_3/E_{33}$

Combining these loadings and adding the strains in direction 1 by superposition gives

$$\epsilon_1 = \sigma_1/E_{11} - \nu_{21}(\sigma_2/E_{22}) - \nu_{31}(\sigma_3/E_{33}) \tag{2.8}$$

and similarly,

$$\epsilon_2 = -\nu_{12}(\sigma_1/E_{11}) + \sigma_2/E_{22} - \nu_{32}(\sigma_3/E_{33}) \tag{2.9}$$

and so forth. It is convenient to arrange these in a matrix; using standard matrix notation and procedures gives

$$
\begin{Bmatrix} \epsilon_1 \\ \epsilon_2 \\ \epsilon_3 \\ \gamma_{23} \\ \gamma_{31} \\ \gamma_{12} \end{Bmatrix}
=
\begin{bmatrix}
\dfrac{1}{E_{11}} & \dfrac{-\nu_{21}}{E_{22}} & \dfrac{-\nu_{31}}{E_{33}} & 0 & 0 & 0 \\[2mm]
\dfrac{-\nu_{12}}{E_{11}} & \dfrac{1}{E_{22}} & \dfrac{-\nu_{32}}{E_{33}} & 0 & 0 & 0 \\[2mm]
\dfrac{-\nu_{13}}{E_{11}} & \dfrac{-\nu_{23}}{E_{22}} & \dfrac{1}{E_{33}} & 0 & 0 & 0 \\[2mm]
0 & 0 & 0 & \dfrac{1}{G_{23}} & 0 & 0 \\[2mm]
0 & 0 & 0 & 0 & \dfrac{1}{G_{31}} & 0 \\[2mm]
0 & 0 & 0 & 0 & 0 & \dfrac{1}{G_{12}}
\end{bmatrix}
\begin{Bmatrix} \sigma_1 \\ \sigma_2 \\ \sigma_3 \\ \tau_{23} \\ \tau_{31} \\ \tau_{12} \end{Bmatrix}
\tag{2.10}
$$

or

$$\{\epsilon\} = [S]\{\sigma\} \tag{2.11}$$

The S matrix is often referred to as the compliance matrix for the lamina, or the strain–stress form of material properties with the strains as the dependent variables. It can be shown that the matrices describing the stress–strain relationships of an elastic material must be symmetric, so that relationships such as

$$E_{11}\nu_{21} = E_{22}\nu_{12} \quad \text{or} \quad \nu_{12}/E_{11} = \nu_{21}/E_{22} \tag{2.12}$$

hold for the off-diagonal terms, so that only nine material properties are required to fully characterize the linear behavior of a lamina in 3-D stress and strain states. The zeros in the compliance matrix reflect the fact that we are describing the stress–strain behavior of an orthotropic material (rather than a generally anisotropic material) and that the description is made with respect to the principal material axes.

2.3 ORTHOTROPIC PROPERTIES IN PLANE STRESS

Because many engineering structures made of laminates are thin in the through-the-thickness direction, the two-dimensional subset of the preceding is frequently used. This can be obtained by setting $\sigma_3 = \tau_{13} = \tau_{23} = 0$ (a plane stress assumption) to get

$$\begin{Bmatrix} \epsilon_1 \\ \epsilon_2 \\ \gamma_{12} \end{Bmatrix} = \begin{bmatrix} \dfrac{1}{E_{11}} & \dfrac{-\nu_{21}}{E_{22}} & 0 \\ \dfrac{-\nu_{12}}{E_{11}} & \dfrac{1}{E_{22}} & 0 \\ 0 & 0 & \dfrac{1}{G_{12}} \end{bmatrix} \begin{Bmatrix} \sigma_1 \\ \sigma_2 \\ \tau_{12} \end{Bmatrix} \quad \text{(plane stress)} \tag{2.13}$$

The matrix of Eq. (2.13) can be inverted to give the stress–strain stiffness matrix as

$$\begin{Bmatrix} \sigma_1 \\ \sigma_2 \\ \tau_{12} \end{Bmatrix} = \begin{bmatrix} Q_{11} & Q_{12} & 0 \\ Q_{21} & Q_{22} & 0 \\ 0 & 0 & Q_{66} \end{bmatrix} \begin{Bmatrix} \epsilon_1 \\ \epsilon_2 \\ \gamma_{12} \end{Bmatrix} \quad \text{(plane stress)} \tag{2.14}$$

or

$$\{\sigma\} = [Q]\{\epsilon\} \tag{2.15}$$

where the individual terms of the matrix are given by

$$\begin{aligned} Q_{11} &= E_{11}/D & Q_{12} &= \nu_{21}E_{11}/D \\ Q_{21} &= \nu_{12}E_{22}/D & Q_{22} &= E_{22}/D \\ Q_{66} &= G_{12} & D &= 1 - \nu_{12}\nu_{21} \end{aligned} \tag{2.16}$$

so that

$$[Q] = \begin{bmatrix} \dfrac{E_{11}}{1 - \nu_{12}\nu_{21}} & \dfrac{\nu_{21}E_{11}}{1 - \nu_{12}\nu_{21}} & 0 \\ \dfrac{\nu_{12}E_{22}}{1 - \nu_{12}\nu_{21}} & \dfrac{E_{22}}{1 - \nu_{12}\nu_{21}} & 0 \\ 0 & 0 & G_{12} \end{bmatrix} \tag{2.17}$$

Note that it is conventional to identify the Q_{66} term from its location in the full 6-by-6 matrix before the plane-stress assumption was made. Although there appears to be five independent constants needed to describe the stress–strain response of the lamina, again the S and Q matrices must be symmetric. As a consequence, there are only four independent properties to be considered, and the reciprocity relation

$$E_{11}\nu_{21} = E_{22}\nu_{12} \quad \text{or} \quad \nu_{12}/E_{11} = \nu_{21}/E_{22} \tag{2.18}$$

is used.

EXAMPLE 2.1   Stress–strain matrix for an orthotropic fiber composite

Using the orthotropic properties for AS4/3501-6 carbon/epoxy, write the Q stress–strain matrix. Here AS4 is the designation for the carbon fiber and 3501-6 is the designation for the epoxy matrix. The orthotropic elasticity constants for unidirectional AS4/3501-6 at a 60% fiber volume fraction are given in Table 2.1 later in this chapter, and are as follows: $E_{11} = 131.0$ GPa (18.4 Msi), $E_{22} = 11.2$ GPa (1.60 Msi), $\nu_{12} = 0.28$, and $G_{12} = 6.55$ GPa (0.95 Msi). The value of ν_{21} is obtained from the reciprocity relationship:

$$\nu_{21} = \frac{E_{22}}{E_{11}}\nu_{12} = \frac{1.6}{18.4}(0.28) = 0.024$$

The value for the denominator term is $1 - \nu_{12}\nu_{21} = 0.993$. The Q matrix is thus

$$[Q] = \begin{bmatrix} \dfrac{18.4}{0.993} & \dfrac{0.448}{0.993} & 0 \\ \dfrac{0.448}{0.993} & \dfrac{1.6}{0.993} & 0 \\ 0 & 0 & 0.95 \end{bmatrix} = \begin{bmatrix} 18.5 & 0.451 & 0 \\ 0.451 & 1.61 & 0 \\ 0 & 0 & 0.95 \end{bmatrix} \text{Msi} = \begin{bmatrix} 128 & 3.11 & 0 \\ 3.11 & 11.1 & 0 \\ 0 & 0 & 6.55 \end{bmatrix} \text{Gpa}$$

∎

In subsequent sections of this chapter, we consider experimental tests for determining these stress–strain properties, along with typical properties of some representative materials. However, first, the important subject of determining the stress–strain relationship for a lamina when the coordinate axes do not correspond to the 1,2 or principal material axes must be considered.

2.4 TRANSFORMATION OF COORDINATES

Standard transformation procedures, such as using Mohr's circle for two dimensions, indicate how a system of stresses in one coordinate system can be related to the stress components in another coordinate system that is rotated at an angle with respect to the first system. Consider the x,y system that is at an angle θ with respect to the fiber or 1,2 system, as shown in Figure 2.1. These transformations are developed in detail in any mechanics of materials text, but it is instructive to briefly review them here. Consider a state of 2-D stress defined by σ_x, σ_y, and τ_{xy}, as illustrated in Figure 2.2, and it is desired to know how these components change with the orientation of the coordinate system. In particular, we wish to know what the components will be when the coordinate system coincides with the fiber directions, the 1,2 coordinate system shown in Figure 2.1. The relationships can be developed by cutting a cube of material at an angle θ, as illustrated in Figure 2.2, so as to expose the normal and shear stresses on the face that is normal to axis 1. Because the cube of material is in equilibrium, the stresses can be found by setting the resultant of the forces to zero. Balancing forces in direction 1 gives (with the constant thickness canceled from each term)

$$\sigma_1\,ds = \sigma_x\,dy\cos\theta + \sigma_y\,dx\sin\theta + \tau_{xy}\,dy\sin\theta + \tau_{xy}\,dx\cos\theta$$

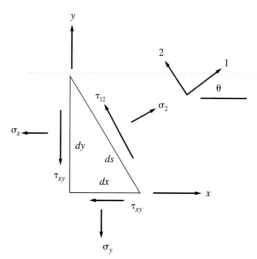

Figure 2.2 The "wedge method" for deriving the coordinate transformation equations for stress components.

using the relationships between the length of the sides given by

$$dx/ds = \sin \theta \quad \text{and} \quad dy/ds = \cos \theta$$

and dividing through by ds gives

$$\sigma_1 = \sigma_x \cos^2 \theta + \sigma_y \sin^2 \theta + 2\tau_{xy} \sin \theta \cos \theta$$

Similarly, solving for τ_{12} by using equilibrium of forces gives

$$\tau_{12} \, ds = -\sigma_x \, dy \sin \theta + \sigma_y \, dx \cos \theta + \tau_{xy} \, dy \cos \theta - \tau_{xy} \, dx \sin \theta$$

and dividing through by ds gives

$$\tau_{12} = -\sigma_x \sin \theta \cos \theta + \sigma_y \sin \theta \cos \theta + \tau_{xy} (\cos^2 \theta - \sin^2 \theta)$$

A similar method can be used to find σ_2. Rearranging these relationships in a matrix equation gives

$$\left\{ \begin{matrix} \sigma_1 \\ \sigma_2 \\ \tau_{12} \end{matrix} \right\} = [T] \left\{ \begin{matrix} \sigma_x \\ \sigma_y \\ \tau_{xy} \end{matrix} \right\} \tag{2.19}$$

where

$$[T] = \begin{bmatrix} \cos^2 \theta & \sin^2 \theta & 2\sin\theta\cos\theta \\ \sin^2 \theta & \cos^2 \theta & -2\sin\theta\cos\theta \\ -\sin\theta\cos\theta & \sin\theta\cos\theta & \cos^2\theta - \sin^2\theta \end{bmatrix} \tag{2.20}$$

The inverse of this transformation matrix is called T^{-1} and is given by

$$T^{-1} = \begin{bmatrix} \cos^2 \theta & \sin^2 \theta & -2\sin\theta\cos\theta \\ \sin^2 \theta & \cos^2 \theta & 2\sin\theta\cos\theta \\ \sin\theta\cos\theta & -\sin\theta\cos\theta & \cos^2\theta - \sin^2\theta \end{bmatrix} \tag{2.21}$$

and the inverse relation gives

$$\{\sigma\}_{x,y} = [T^{-1}]\{\sigma\}_{1,2} \tag{2.22}$$

The same transformation can be used with strain components, if one is careful to use the tensor definition for shear strain, which is just the engineering shear strain divided by 2. This can be accomplished conveniently either by dividing the engineering shear strain component by 2 prior to using the transformation of coordinates relationships or else by using a matrix R, which accomplishes the same thing but gives a more convenient notation. Defining R by [2.1]

$$[R] = \begin{bmatrix} 1 & 0 & 0 \\ 0 & 1 & 0 \\ 0 & 0 & 2 \end{bmatrix} \tag{2.23}$$

then the engineering strain is related to the tensor strain by

$$\begin{Bmatrix} \epsilon_1 \\ \epsilon_2 \\ \gamma_{12} \end{Bmatrix} = [R] \begin{Bmatrix} \epsilon_1 \\ \epsilon_2 \\ \dfrac{\gamma_{12}}{2} \end{Bmatrix} \tag{2.24}$$

The relationship between the strains in the 1,2 fiber direction coordinate system and those in the x,y coordinate system are then

$$\begin{Bmatrix} \epsilon_1 \\ \epsilon_2 \\ \gamma_{12} \end{Bmatrix} = [R] \begin{Bmatrix} \epsilon_1 \\ \epsilon_2 \\ \dfrac{\gamma_{12}}{2} \end{Bmatrix} = [R][T] \begin{Bmatrix} \epsilon_x \\ \epsilon_y \\ \dfrac{\gamma_{xy}}{2} \end{Bmatrix} = [R][T][R^{-1}] \begin{Bmatrix} \epsilon_x \\ \epsilon_y \\ \gamma_{xy} \end{Bmatrix} \tag{2.25}$$

The law describing the stress–strain relationships in an x,y coordinate system at an angle θ to the 1,2 fiber direction coordinate system then can be derived from the preceding. Starting with the ply stress–strain law in the fiber directions,

$$\begin{Bmatrix} \sigma_1 \\ \sigma_2 \\ \tau_{12} \end{Bmatrix} = [Q] \begin{Bmatrix} \epsilon_1 \\ \epsilon_2 \\ \gamma_{12} \end{Bmatrix} = [Q][R] \begin{Bmatrix} \epsilon_1 \\ \epsilon_2 \\ \dfrac{\gamma_{12}}{2} \end{Bmatrix} \tag{2.26}$$

Then premultiply both sides of this equation by T^{-1} and substitute as shown to get

$$\begin{Bmatrix} \sigma_x \\ \sigma_y \\ \tau_{xy} \end{Bmatrix} = [T^{-1}] \begin{Bmatrix} \sigma_1 \\ \sigma_2 \\ \tau_{12} \end{Bmatrix} = [T^{-1}][Q][R] \begin{Bmatrix} \epsilon_1 \\ \epsilon_2 \\ \dfrac{\gamma_{12}}{2} \end{Bmatrix} = [T^{-1}][Q][R][T] \begin{Bmatrix} \epsilon_x \\ \epsilon_y \\ \dfrac{\gamma_{xy}}{2} \end{Bmatrix} \tag{2.27}$$

and finally

$$\begin{Bmatrix} \sigma_x \\ \sigma_y \\ \tau_{xy} \end{Bmatrix} = [T^{-1}][Q][R][T][R^{-1}] \begin{Bmatrix} \epsilon_x \\ \epsilon_y \\ \gamma_{xy} \end{Bmatrix} = [\overline{Q}] \begin{Bmatrix} \epsilon_x \\ \epsilon_y \\ \gamma_{xy} \end{Bmatrix} \tag{2.28}$$

where

$$[\overline{Q}] = [T^{-1}][Q][R][T][R^{-1}] \tag{2.29}$$

This may seem like a complicated result, but it will be seen that it is easy to implement. It will also be seen that the preceding relationship between stresses and strains in an arbitrary coordinate system will be a fundamental tool in understanding the mechanical behavior of composite materials.

The preceding stiffness matrix can be simply coded as is and multiplied out by computer, but it is also possible to multiply it out by hand to get the following result for the stiffness constants in an arbitrary coordinate system:

$$
\begin{aligned}
\overline{Q}_1 &= Q_{11}\cos^4\theta + 2(Q_{12} + 2Q_{66})\sin^2\theta\cos^2\theta + Q_{22}\sin^4\theta \\
\overline{Q}_{12} &= (Q_{11} + Q_{22} - 4Q_{66})\sin^2\theta\cos^2\theta + Q_{12}(\sin^4\theta + \cos^4\theta) \\
\overline{Q}_{22} &= Q_{11}\sin^4\theta + 2(Q_{12} + 2Q_{66})\sin^2\theta\cos^2\theta + Q_{22}\cos^4\theta \\
\overline{Q}_{16} &= (Q_{11} - Q_{12} - 2Q_{66})\sin\theta\cos^3\theta + (Q_{12} - Q_{22} + 2Q_{66})\sin^3\theta\cos\theta \\
\overline{Q}_{26} &= (Q_{11} - Q_{12} - 2Q_{66})\sin^3\theta\cos\theta + (Q_{12} - Q_{22} + 2Q_{66})\sin\theta\cos^3\theta \\
\overline{Q}_{66} &= (Q_{11} + Q_{22} - 2Q_{12} - 2Q_{66})\sin^2\theta\cos^2\theta + Q_{66}(\sin^4\theta + \cos^4\theta)
\end{aligned}
\tag{2.30}
$$

Symmetry gives the terms not listed in Eq. (2.30). Note that the Q_{16} and Q_{26} terms are no longer 0, and thus a coupling exists between shear and normal stresses and strains. That is, an applied shear strain causes a normal stress and an applied normal strain causes a shear stress. This is a consequence of the fact that we are no longer referring to the principal material axes. To see this coupling more clearly, Eq. (2.28) can be written as follows:

$$
\begin{aligned}
\sigma_x &= \overline{Q}_{11}\epsilon_x + \overline{Q}_{12}\epsilon_y + \overline{Q}_{16}\gamma_{xy} \\
\sigma_y &= \overline{Q}_{21}\epsilon_x + \overline{Q}_{22}\epsilon_y + \overline{Q}_{26}\gamma_{xy} \\
\tau_{xy} &= \overline{Q}_{16}\epsilon_x + \overline{Q}_{26}\epsilon_y + \overline{Q}_{66}\gamma_{xy}
\end{aligned}
$$

It can be seen that shear strains cause normal stresses and normal strains cause shear stresses when the $\overline{Q}_{16}$ and $\overline{Q}_{26}$ terms are present. Inverting the stress–strain relationship shows that if the coupling terms are present in the stress–strain form, they will also be present in the strain–stress or inverse matrix as $\overline{S}_{16}$ and $\overline{S}_{26}$. An illustration of this type of coupling is illustrated in Figure 2.3, where the strains resulting from a uniaxial stress on an off-axis unidirectional lamina are shown. Other illustrations of coupling that has no counterpart with isotropic materials are shown in Chapter 3.

The preceding equations represent a fundamental result that forms a basic building block for analyses and design with composite materials. They are used in the development of the analysis equations in the next chapter. In the next section, it is shown how thermal expansion and moisture absorption terms can be added to the stress–strain equations. Following this, the procedures for obtaining the material constants used to describe the ply stress–strain behavior are discussed, and typical values are presented.

EXAMPLE 2.2   Change of stress–strain matrix with coordinate axis rotation

Transform the Q orthotropic elasticity stiffness matrix of Example 2.1, which refers to the 1,2 principal fiber directions, into x,y coordinates. The angle θ from the x,y coordinates to the fiber

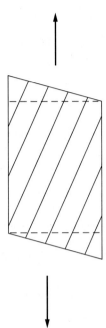

Figure 2.3   Shear strains resulting from a normal stress in a unidirectional off-axis lamina.

coordinates, as defined in Figure 2.1, is 30°. See Figure 2.4. Transformations of this type are required when laminates with multidirectional fiber layups are considered.

Solution: The coordinate transformation for the elasticity matrix is defined in either Eq. (2.29) or (2.30). Equation (2.29) is used here. The matrix operations can be simply carried out using any of the software tools such as Mathcad, MATLAB, Maple, or Mathematica. Substituting $\theta = 30°$ into the T matrix of Eq. (2.20) gives

$$[T] = \begin{bmatrix} 0.75 & 0.25 & 0.866 \\ 0.25 & 0.75 & -0.866 \\ -0.433 & 0.433 & 0.5 \end{bmatrix} \quad \text{and} \quad [T^{-1}] = \begin{bmatrix} 0.75 & 0.25 & -0.866 \\ 0.25 & 0.75 & 0.866 \\ 0.433 & -0.433 & 0.5 \end{bmatrix}$$

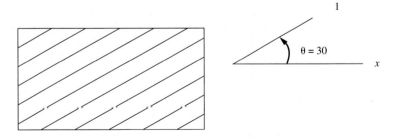

Figure 2.4   Coordinate system for Example 2.2.

and using the definitions for R and R^{-1} gives

$$[\bar{Q}] = [T^{-1}][Q][R][T][R^{-1}] = \begin{bmatrix} 11.35 & 3.38 & 5.35 \\ 3.38 & 2.91 & 1.97 \\ 5.35 & 1.97 & 3.83 \end{bmatrix} \text{Msi} = \begin{bmatrix} 78.3 & 23.3 & 36.9 \\ 23.3 & 20.1 & 13.6 \\ 36.9 & 13.6 & 26.4 \end{bmatrix} \text{GPa}$$

Note that the matrix is now fully populated. The terms in the 1,3 and 2,3 positions give a coupling between normal and shear behavior that is characteristic of an anisotropic material. The fiber composite is orthotropic when referred to fiber direction coordinates, and anisotropic in other coordinate systems.   ∎

Graphs of the various terms of the $\bar{Q}$ matrix with change of the angle θ between the fiber axis and the x axis are shown in Figures 2.5 and 2.6. As would be expected, the 1,1 and 2,2 terms interchange when the angle goes through 90°, as the axial orientation then becomes the transverse orientation. The 3,3 shear modulus term (also called the 6,6 term in the unrotated matrix) increases and goes through a maximum at 45°. This characteristic is employed in the next chapter on laminates to provide shear stiffness. The 1,3 and 2,3 coupling terms (also called the 1,6 and 2,6 terms in the unrotated matrix) are seen to be zero for 0 and 90° orientations, the principal material directions, and increase in magnitude in between.

Similar plots are shown in Figures 2.7 and 2.8 for E-glass/epoxy, using values taken from Table 2.1, presented later in this chapter. It can be seen that the results are simi-

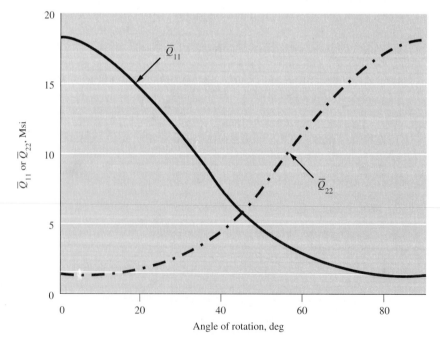

Figure 2.5   Change in the $\bar{Q}_{11}$ and $\bar{Q}_{22}$ stiffness coefficients with angle of rotation for AS4/3501-6 carbon/epoxy.

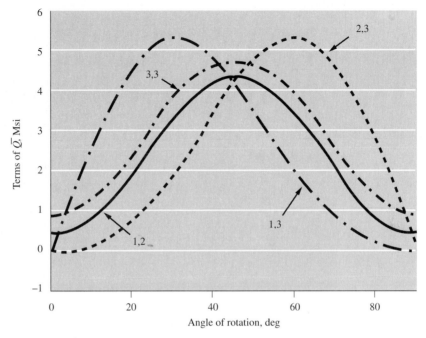

Figure 2.6 Change in the $\overline{Q}_{12}$, $\overline{Q}_{33}$, $\overline{Q}_{13}$, and $\overline{Q}_{23}$ stiffness coefficients with angle of rotation for AS4/3501-6 carbon/epoxy.

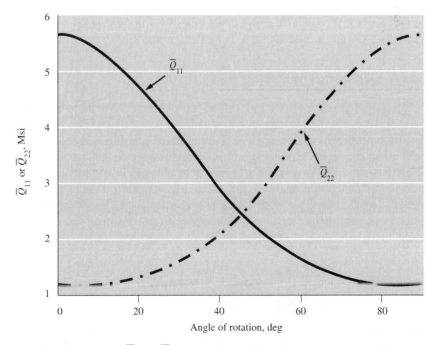

Figure 2.7 Change in the $\overline{Q}_{11}$ and $\overline{Q}_{22}$ stiffness coefficients with angle of rotation for E-glass/epoxy.

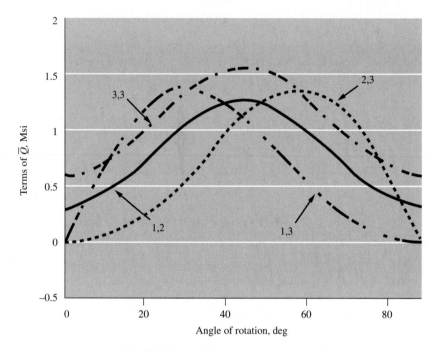

Figure 2.8   Change in the $\overline{Q}_{12}$, $\overline{Q}_{33}$, $\overline{Q}_{13}$, and $\overline{Q}_{23}$ stiffness coefficients with angle of rotation for E-glass/epoxy.

lar, although E glass is a lower-stiffness fiber, and the difference between the axial and transverse is not as pronounced as it is for carbon-fiber/epoxy systems.

2.5 THERMAL AND MOISTURE EFFECTS

It is frequently the case that thermal effects must be included in the stress–strain relationship for composite materials. In fact, polymeric matrix composites are frequently cured at an elevated temperature and then used at a different temperature such as the ambient. These changes in temperature can induce stresses into the composite. Carbon-fiber composites are utilized in space structures because of their unique properties of thermal expansion. Moisture absorption by polymeric matrices also can have a similar effect in that moisture can cause the matrix to swell, inducing stresses into the composite. All of these considerations suggest that moisture and thermal effects must be incorporated into the analysis. This can be easily accomplished, however. The stress–strain law for an orthotropic lamina can be written as

$$\left\{\begin{array}{c} \epsilon_1 \\ \epsilon_2 \\ \gamma_{12} \end{array}\right\} = [S]\left\{\begin{array}{c} \sigma_1 \\ \sigma_2 \\ \tau_{12} \end{array}\right\} + \left\{\begin{array}{c} \alpha_1 \Delta T \\ \alpha_2 \Delta T \\ 0 \end{array}\right\} + \left\{\begin{array}{c} \beta_1 \Delta m \\ \beta_2 \Delta m \\ 0 \end{array}\right\} \qquad (2.31)$$

where α_1 and α_2 are the coefficients of thermal expansion and β_1 and β_2 are the coefficients of moisture expansion in the fiber and transverse directions, respectively. Because of the mathematical similarity between the thermal and moisture effects, only the thermal effects are shown explicitly in the following. Equation (2.31) can be inverted to give

$$
\left\{\begin{array}{c} \sigma_1 \\ \sigma_2 \\ \tau_{12} \end{array}\right\} = [Q]\left\{\begin{array}{c} \epsilon_1 \\ \epsilon_2 \\ \gamma_{12} \end{array}\right\} - [Q]\left\{\begin{array}{c} \alpha_1\Delta T \\ \alpha_2\Delta T \\ 0 \end{array}\right\}
\tag{2.32}
$$

This relationship in the 1,2 principal material axes must now be converted to general x,y coordinate axes. To accomplish this, define

$$
\left\{\begin{array}{c} \alpha_x\Delta T \\ \alpha_y\Delta T \\ \alpha_{xy}\Delta T \end{array}\right\} = [R]\left\{\begin{array}{c} \alpha_x\Delta T \\ \alpha_y\Delta T \\ \dfrac{\alpha_{xy}\Delta T}{2} \end{array}\right\} = [R][T^{-1}][R^{-1}]\left\{\begin{array}{c} \alpha_1\Delta T \\ \alpha_2\Delta T \\ 0 \end{array}\right\}
\tag{2.33}
$$

Then it follows from the substitutions leading up to Eq. (2.33) that

$$
\left\{\begin{array}{c} \sigma_x \\ \sigma_y \\ \tau_{xy} \end{array}\right\} = [\overline{Q}]\left\{\begin{array}{c} \epsilon_x - \alpha_x\Delta T \\ \epsilon_y - \alpha_y\Delta T \\ \gamma_{xy} - \alpha_{xy}\Delta T \end{array}\right\}
\tag{2.34}
$$

Example 2.3   Change of apparent coefficients of thermal expansion with change of coordinate axes

Find the apparent coefficients of thermal expansion for AS4/3501-6 carbon/epoxy when referred to an x,y coordinate system with an angle θ of 30° as defined in Figure 2.1.

Solution: The coordinate transformation for the coefficients of thermal expansion (CTE) is defined in Eq. (2.33). The values of CTE for AS4/3501-6 are given in Table 2.1 at the end of this chapter. The T and T^{-1} matrices have been shown for an angle of 30° in Example 2.2. Multiplying this out gives

$$
\left\{\begin{array}{c} \alpha_x \\ \alpha_y \\ \alpha_{xy} \end{array}\right\} = [R][T^{-1}][R^{-1}]\left\{\begin{array}{c} -3.5\text{E}-8 \\ 1.6\text{E}-5 \\ 0 \end{array}\right\} = \left\{\begin{array}{c} 3.97\text{E}-6 \\ 1.20\text{E}-5 \\ -1.39\text{E}-5 \end{array}\right\}°\text{F}^{-1} = \left\{\begin{array}{c} 7.15\text{E}-6 \\ 2.16\text{E}-5 \\ -2.50\text{E}-5 \end{array}\right\}°\text{C}^{-1}
$$

The CTE values for carbon-fiber composites are very unusual in that the CTE in the fiber direction is small in absolute value, and actually negative. That means that the composite extends in length in the fiber direction as it is cooled. The CTE in the transverse direction is controlled by the matrix and is typical of polymeric materials. These unusual CTEs permit structures to be built that are dimensionally stable with respect to temperature changes; they are used in satellite structures for that reason. The CTEs also can bring about undesirable effects, such as distortion with temperature, if not accounted for in the design. Note that the term in the third row of the CTE matrix is 0 in the fiber direction coordinates, but it is not 0 in other coordinate systems.

A plot of the apparent CTE in the x direction is shown in Figure 2.9 as a function of the angle between the fiber direction and the x axis. It can be seen that the value varies between α_1 and α_2 as would be expected. An enlarged scale is shown in Figure 2.10. Here it can be seen that

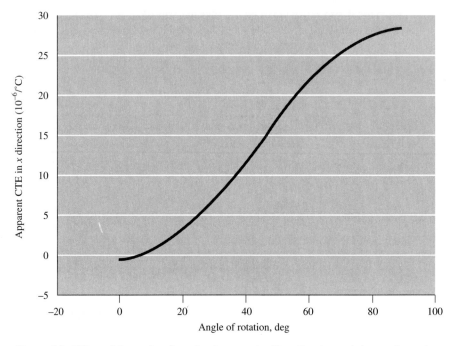

Figure 2.9   Effect of the angle of rotation between the fiber direction and the x axis on the apparent CTE in the x direction. α_x varies between the axial and transverse values.

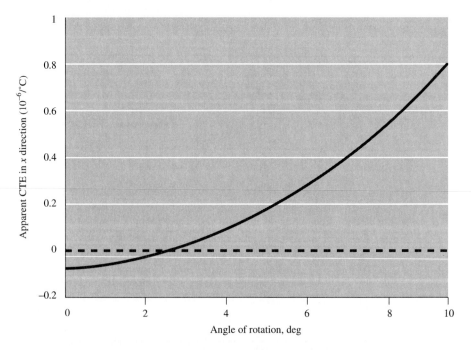

Figure 2.10   Effect of the angle of rotation between the fiber direction and the x axis on the apparent CTE in the x direction. The plot shows that a CTE of zero can be obtained for small angles of rotation.

a CTE of zero in the x direction can be obtained with a small angle of rotation. This is a unique feature of carbon-fiber composites that is utilized in the design of space structures that have extremely low distortion with temperature changes.   ■

2.6 EXPERIMENTAL PROCEDURES FOR LAMINA CHARACTERIZATION

The stiffness properties needed for a plane-stress analysis are the modulus in the fiber direction E_{11}, the modulus transverse to the fiber direction E_{22} (in the plane of the lamina), the in-plane shear modulus G_{12}, and one of the in-plane Poisson ratios v_{12} or v_{21}. These properties are routinely characterized by laboratory experiments. The experiments commonly utilized are described in what follows along with some representative properties. It may also be noted that many of these tests are used for failure properties as well. This aspect will be discussed in later chapters.

2.6.1 E_{11} and v_{12}

The modulus in the direction of the fibers E_{11} and the Poisson ratio v_{12} can be characterized by means of tension tests on unidirectional coupons that are instrumented with electric resistance strain gages. See Figure 2.11. The coupons are usually made and tested according to an ASTM specification. Because the state of stress is uniaxial in the fiber direction, the modulus is just the ratio of stress to strain in that direction. The Poisson ratio is just $v_{12} = -\epsilon_2/\epsilon_1$. It may be noted that some nonlinearity may be observed in these tests. For example,

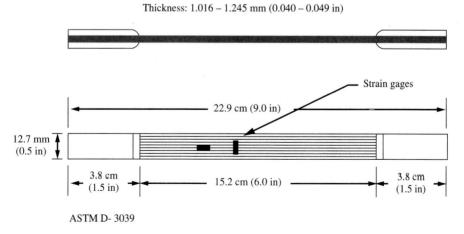

Thickness: 1.016 – 1.245 mm (0.040 – 0.049 in)

ASTM D- 3039

Figure 2.11   Tensile coupon instrumented with axial and transverse strain gages for measuring the modulus E_{11} and the Poisson ratio v_{12}, as well as tensile strength and strain to failure.

carbon-fiber lamina often stiffen somewhat in tension, so that precise measurements of the modulus depend on the procedure used for data reduction. A final secant value for modulus may be 15% higher than a value measured at low strain levels. It also should be noted that the measurement of stress in the data-reduction procedure is based on the total cross-sectional area of the combined fiber and matrix, and the fibers are contributing essentially all of the stiffness, for polymeric matrix composites. Thus, for a given combination of fiber and matrix, the modulus obtained depends on the relative fraction of the cross-section taken up by the fibers, which is also equal to the volume fraction of the fibers. The fiber volume fraction can vary somewhat with manufacturing procedure, so that adjustments for the actual fiber volume fraction may have to be made. Procedures for doing this are given later in this chapter.

2.6.2 E_{22}

Tensile coupons are also used for measuring E_{22}, but with the fibers oriented perpendicular to the direction of the applied load. See Figure 2.12. Care must be taken with these specimens, as they are quite fragile in the transverse direction, reflecting the extreme difference in strength between fiber and matrix. Although it is theoretically possible to obtain the Poisson ratio v_{21} from strain gages on this specimen, as a consistency check on the value obtained from the test described before, it is difficult to obtain accurate values in this manner because of the low value of v_{21}, which is on the order of 0.025 for polymer matrix composites. It is common practice to obtain v_{12} from the test for E_{11}, and rely on the reciprocity relationship $v_{21} = v_{12}E_{22}/E_{11}$.

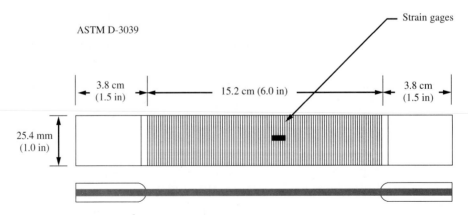

Thickness: 2.11 – 2.41 mm (0.083 – 0.095 in)

Figure 2.12 Transverse direction tensile coupon instrumented with axial strain gages for measuring the modulus E_{22}, as well as the transverse tensile strength and strain to failure.

2.6.3 G_{12}

The in-plane shear modulus can be obtained in a number of ways [2.2–2.5]. One method is to use angle ply coupons, made up of alternating layers of plies at an angle to the axis of the specimen. The theory for understanding laminates of this type will be presented in detail in Chapter 3, but for now it will be simply stated that the streas and strain response in the axial direction of a ±45° laminate can be interpreted to give G_{12} according to the following expression:

$$G_{12} = \frac{4}{\dfrac{4}{E_x} - \dfrac{1}{E_1} - \dfrac{1}{E_2} + \dfrac{2\nu_{12}}{E_1}} \tag{2.35}$$

An alternative test involves transverse tests of thicker specimens, often called the Iosipescu shear test [2.6, 2.7], as illustrated in Figure 2.13. The transverse loads are intended to introduce a state of shear stress in the center portion of the specimen, where the strain response is measured with strain gages placed at 45° to the longitudinal axis of the specimen.

A more elaborate test is for a torsion specimen of a tube layed up with the fibers in the circumferential direction, as illustrated in Figure 2.14. This test has been used by the author to compare with the Iosipescu test, with the result showing that equivalent stiffness properties are obtained from these two tests [2.8, 2.9]. Torsion tests of thin-walled tubes with fibers in the hoop direction represent a very accurate method for determining the in-plane shear stiffness, because of the well-defined stress fields and potential for minimizing confusing end effects.

It should be noted that the in-plane shear response is typically quite nonlinear. A typical result for AS4/3501-6 carbon/epoxy is shown in Figure 2.15, taken from [2.8].

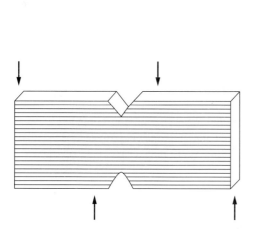

Figure 2.13 Iosipescu shear test used for in-plane shear properties determination.

Figure 2.14 Unidirectional hoop fiber torsion specimen used for in-plane shear properties determination.

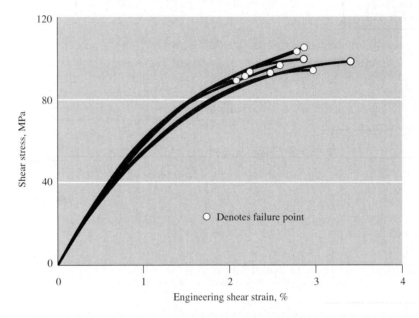

Figure 2.15   Typical in-plane shear stress–strain response for AS4/3501-6. (*Source:* From [2.8].)

2.7 MICROMECHANICS PREDICTIONS OF STIFFNESS

A considerable literature exists concerning the theoretical predictions of the various stiffness coefficients, given the properties of the individual constituents, that is, the fiber and matrix properties. These models range from very simple strength-of-materials type models to more elaborate elasticity solutions. This literature is not discussed in any detail here, but rather a few general remarks are made and some references to the literature given. It may be helpful to give some perspective on the use of theoretical models for prediction of stiffness coefficients. First of all, if the composite material under consideration is readily available, experimental tests usually will be relied on with little if any recourse to theoretical models. Model predictions are helpful to adjust for volume fraction changes over a limited range, and quite simple models can be utilized for this purpose. Where theoretical models do play a more significant role is in promoting understanding of the contributions of the constituents, and in helping to extrapolate to new and perhaps novel material systems for which both material for experimental tests and prior experience are lacking. The theoretical models may be invaluable in this latter case.

2.7.1 Simple Models

Simple models are available for the prediction of stiffness properties, which are usually known as the rule-of-mixtures models. They fall into two types called series and parallel, respectively, with the parallel models used for E_{11} and ν_{12}, and the series models used for E_{22} and G_{12}. These models are illustrated in what follows.

Figure 2.16   Parallel layers of fiber and matrix, used for the rule-of-mixtures micromechanics rule for E_{11} and v_{12}.

Model for E_{11}.   Consider the simple parallel arrangement of fiber and matrix illustrated in Figure 2.16. The specific arrangement of fibers in the matrix does not need to be specified at the present level of detail. A constant strain is imposed on the model in the fiber direction, and the total force and then the average stress are computed. The total force is the sum of the force in the fibers and the force in the matrix given by

$$F = F_f + F_m = A_f E_f \epsilon_1 + A_m E_m \epsilon_1 \tag{2.36}$$

The average stress is then just the force divided by the total area, and the composite modulus in the fiber direction is then given by

$$E_{11} = \frac{\sigma}{\epsilon_1} = \frac{A_f E_f + A_m E_m}{A} \tag{2.37}$$

and noting that the area ratio is the same as the volume ratio, there results

$$E_{11} = V_f E_f + V_m E_m \tag{2.38}$$

where V_f and V_m are fiber and matrix volume fractions, and E_f and E_m are fiber and matrix moduli. This result is called a "rule-of-mixtures" rule. For carbon fibers in an epoxy matrix, the matrix stiffness is much lower than the fiber stiffness, and it is seen that the composite modulus varies directly with the fiber volume fraction.

Model for v_{12}.   A similar result can be obtained for the major Poisson ratio by using the ratio of lateral to axial strain in conjunction with Figure 2.16. It is now necessary to be more specific about the geometry of fiber and matrix, and it is convenient to assume that the fiber and matrix are arranged as layers. The displacement of each layer then depends on the thickness h of that layer and the Poisson ratio for that layer. Finally, the average lateral strain is obtained by dividing the total lateral displacement by the total thickness to give

$$v_{12} = \frac{\delta_f + \delta_m}{h\epsilon_1} = \frac{v_{12_f} h_f \epsilon_1 + v_{12_m} h_m \epsilon_1}{h\epsilon_1} = V_f v_{12_f} + V_m v_{12_m} \tag{2.39}$$

which is again a rule-of-mixtures result.

Model for E_{22}.   Consider the model described before of parallel layers of fiber and matrix, but this time loaded by a force transverse to the fibers and matrix, as illustrated in Figure 2.17. The stress in the fiber and matrix is thus assumed to be the same, whereas the transverse displacement of the two components is additive. Thus, the average modulus in the transverse direction is given by

$$\frac{1}{E_{22}} = \frac{\epsilon_2}{\sigma_2} = \frac{\delta_f + \delta_m}{h\sigma_2} = \frac{\epsilon_{2_f} h_f + \epsilon_{2_m} h_m}{h\sigma_2} = \frac{\sigma_2 h_f / E_{2_f} + \sigma_2 h_m / E_{2_m}}{h\sigma_2} \tag{2.40}$$

or

$$\frac{1}{E_{22}} = \frac{V_f}{E_{2_f}} + \frac{V_m}{E_{2_m}} \tag{2.41}$$

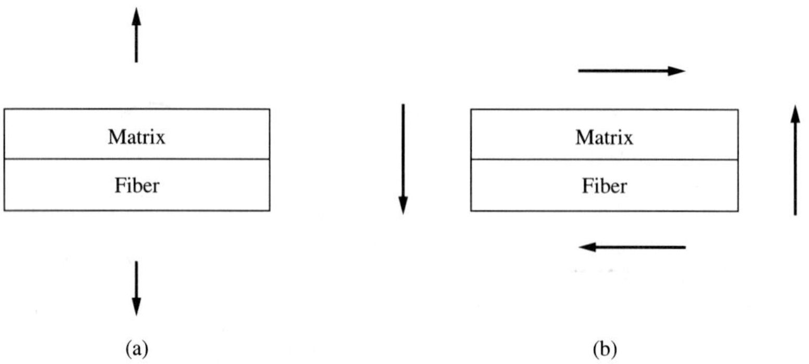

Figure 2.17. Loading for simplified micromechanics models for E_{22} and G_{12}. (a) Transverse normal loading for E_{22}; (b) in-plane shear loading for G_{12}.

Model for G_{12}.   A similar treatment gives the in-plane shear modulus. Applying a shear stress to the layers of fiber and matrix, computing the total shear displacement, and then taking the average strain as the total displacement divided by the total thickness gives

$$\frac{1}{G_{12}} = \frac{\gamma_{12}}{\tau_{12}} = \frac{\delta_f + \delta_m}{h\tau_{12}} = \frac{\gamma_{12_f}h_f + \gamma_{12_m}h_m}{h\tau_{12}} = \frac{\tau_{12}h_f/G_{12_f} + \tau_{12}h_m/G_{12_m}}{h\tau_{12}} \qquad (2.42)$$

and thus

$$\frac{1}{G_{12}} = \frac{V_f}{G_{12_f}} + \frac{V_m}{G_{12_m}} \qquad (2.43)$$

A comparison with experiments suggests that the parallel models are sufficiently accurate to be used with confidence, whereas the series models are less accurate.

2.7.2 Models Based on Elasticity Principles

More detailed investigations of micromechanical models to estimate composite stiffness properties have been carried out. The objective in all cases is to relate the constituent properties of fiber and matrix to the effective orthotropic properties of the composite. These investigations can be grouped into three categories, which are exact elasticity solutions to highly idealized models that are representative of the fiber and surrounding matrix in some sense, upper and lower bounds to properties that are established by means of energy theorems, and numerical solutions to problems that represent arrays of fiber and matrix.

Two models that are very useful in predicting composite properties are illustrated in Figures 2.18 and 2.19. The concentric-cylinder model employed by Hashin and Rosen [2.10] and Hill [2.11] is illustrated in Figure 2.18. This model, often called the composite cylinder array (CCA) model, has a number of desirable properties. Exact elasticity solutions have been obtained for the case of transversely isotropic constituents for four of the five properties that completely characterize the transversely isotropic composite [2.12]. Upper and lower bounds are available for the remaining property. The model shown in Figure 2.19 is called the three-phase cylinder model. An exact solution for the composite transverse shear modulus based on isotropic fiber and matrix properties has been found by Christensen and Lo [2.13] using this model. The transverse shear modulus is the remaining property not available for the composite cylinder model.

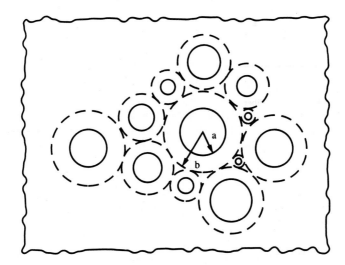

Figure 2.18 Composite cylinder array model for the micromechanics prediction of composite properties.

Before examining the specific methods of estimating the properties, let us examine the properties required. Relating the six stresses to the six strains in a three-dimensional stress–strain relationship requires 36 coefficients, but the requirement of symmetry reduces this to 21 independent material properties relating the six stresses to the six strains in a completely anisotropic medium. An orthotropic material, that is, one with principal material axes, reduces this to 9 independent material properties. If the assumption is further made that the material is transversely isotropic, the number of material properties is further re-

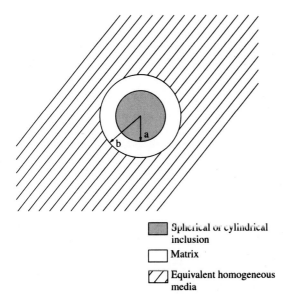

▨ Spherical or cylindrical
    inclusion

☐ Matrix

▨ Equivalent homogeneous
    media

Figure 2.19 Three-phase cylinder model. (*Source:* From Christensen and Lo [2.13].)

duced to 5. By transversely isotropic, it is meant that the transverse stiffness properties are independent of orientation in the plane normal to the axis of the fibers. The assumption of transverse isotropy is very appropriate for fiber composites on a lamina level. Note that the plane-stress assumption is not being used here; as discussed previously in Section 2.3, this gives a further reduction in the number of properties of interest that is not being considered here.

The relationship between the three-dimensional strains and stresses has been written previously for a general orthotropic material in Eq. (2.10). The inverse of this equation, written in the stress–strain form, can be written as

$$
\begin{Bmatrix} \sigma_1 \\ \sigma_2 \\ \sigma_3 \\ \tau_{23} \\ \tau_{31} \\ \tau_{12} \end{Bmatrix} =
\begin{bmatrix}
Q_{11} & Q_{12} & Q_{13} & 0 & 0 & 0 \\
Q_{21} & Q_{22} & Q_{23} & 0 & 0 & 0 \\
Q_{31} & Q_{32} & Q_{33} & 0 & 0 & 0 \\
0 & 0 & 0 & Q_{44} & 0 & 0 \\
0 & 0 & 0 & 0 & Q_{55} & 0 \\
0 & 0 & 0 & 0 & 0 & Q_{66}
\end{bmatrix}
\begin{Bmatrix} \epsilon_1 \\ \epsilon_2 \\ \epsilon_3 \\ \gamma_{23} \\ \gamma_{31} \\ \gamma_{12} \end{Bmatrix}
\tag{2.44}
$$

The reader is cautioned that the terms of the Q matrix given are not the same as those given in Eqs. (2.14) and (2.17), where the plane-stress assumption had been invoked. As discussed previously, the matrix must be symmetric. The further assumption of transverse isotropy means that properties in direction 2 must be the same as in direction 3. Thus, $Q_{12} = Q_{13}$, $Q_{22} = Q_{33}$, and $Q_{44} = Q_{55}$. Following the notation of Hashin [2.12], the stress–strain matrix for a transversely isotropic material can be written as

$$
\begin{Bmatrix} \sigma_1 \\ \sigma_2 \\ \sigma_3 \\ \tau_{23} \\ \tau_{31} \\ \tau_{12} \end{Bmatrix} =
\begin{bmatrix}
n & l & l & 0 & 0 & 0 \\
l & k + G_T & k - G_T & 0 & 0 & 0 \\
l & k - G_T & k + G_T & 0 & 0 & 0 \\
0 & 0 & 0 & G_T & 0 & 0 \\
0 & 0 & 0 & 0 & G_A & 0 \\
0 & 0 & 0 & 0 & 0 & G_A
\end{bmatrix}
\begin{Bmatrix} \epsilon_1 \\ \epsilon_2 \\ \epsilon_3 \\ \gamma_{23} \\ \gamma_{31} \\ \gamma_{12} \end{Bmatrix}
\tag{2.45}
$$

In this notation, n is Q_{11}, l is Q_{12} and Q_{13}, and k is the transverse bulk modulus, defined for plane-strain conditions ($\epsilon_{11} = 0$) by

$$
k = \frac{1}{2} \frac{\sigma_{22} + \sigma_{33}}{\epsilon_{22} + \epsilon_{33}}
\tag{2.46}
$$

The above properties can be related to the more usual engineering properties by applying uniaxial stress in direction 1 to get

$$
E_A = E_{11} = n - \frac{l^2}{k} = n - 4k\nu_{AT}^2
\tag{2.47}
$$

and

$$
\nu_A = \nu_{12} = \nu_{13} = \frac{l}{2k}
\tag{2.48}
$$

Similarly, applying a uniaxial stress in direction 2 or 3 leads to

$$
E_T = E_{22} = E_{33} = \frac{4G_T(kn - l^2)}{n(k + G_T) - l^2}
\tag{2.49}
$$

and

$$\nu_T = \nu_{23} = \frac{n(k - G_T) - l^2}{n(k + G_T) - l^2} \tag{2.50}$$

It is useful to have these relationships in inverse form, so that n, l, and k can be obtained from the more common engineering properties. These relationships can be obtained by inverting Eq. (2.44) and comparing to Eq. (2.45). Defining the combination of properties as

$$D \equiv 1 - \nu_T - 2\nu_A^2 \frac{E_T}{E_A} \tag{2.51}$$

gives

$$n = Q_{11} = \frac{E_A(1 - \nu_T)}{D} \tag{2.52}$$

$$l = Q_{12} = \frac{\nu_A E_T}{D} \tag{2.53}$$

$$k + G_T = Q_{22} = \frac{E_T\left(1 - \nu_{AE_A}^2 \frac{E_T}{E_A}\right)}{(1 + \nu_T)D} \tag{2.54}$$

$$k - G_T = Q_{23} = \frac{E_T\left(\nu_T + \nu_{AE_A}^2 \frac{E_T}{E_A}\right)}{(1 + \nu_T)D} \tag{2.55}$$

Composite cylinders model.   As mentioned before, Hashin and Rosen [2.10], Hill [2.11], and Hashin [2.12] have developed the idea of a composite cylinder model. The geometry assumed for the model is as shown in Figure 2.18, and consists of a number of cells each with a cylindrical fiber surrounded by a concentric cylindrical matrix phase. The individual cells of concentric cylinders must be of different sizes down to the infinitesimal in order to fill the volume. This obviously does not represent the actual geometry of a fiber composite, but there are indications that the results may be indicative of real fiber composites. The chief advantage of the composite cylinder model is that it provides an exact elasticity solution for four of the five stiffness properties for transversely isotropic materials, as well as thermal expansion and thermal conductivity properties, based on the properties of the constituent fiber and matrix phases.

Example of composite cylinder model solution.   A summary of the solution approach has been given by Hashin [2.12] and an example given by Christensen [2.14]. The following illustrates the solution process, using the composite cylinder model to determine the transverse bulk modulus. Consider the geometry illustrated in Figure 2.18. A state of equal biaxial strain is considered along with plane strain in the axial direction, so that

$$\epsilon = \begin{bmatrix} 0 & & \\ & \epsilon^0 & \\ & & \epsilon^0 \end{bmatrix} \tag{2.56}$$

is the average macroscopic state of strain. Consider that the material is homogenous with the elastic properties of the fiber composite, with transversely isotropic properties given by

Eq. (2.45). The state of stress would then be given by

$$
\sigma = \begin{bmatrix} 0 & & \\ & 2k^*\epsilon^0 & \\ & & 2k^*\epsilon^0 \end{bmatrix} \tag{2.57}
$$

where k^* is the transverse bulk modulus of the composite. Consider the perimeter of one of the composite cylinder cells, of radius b, and take the origin to be at the center of this region. The radial displacement obtained by integrating the average strain is

$$
u = \epsilon^0 b \tag{2.58}
$$

and the radial stress is given by

$$
\sigma_r(b) = 2k^*\epsilon^0 = 2k^*\frac{u(b)}{b} \tag{2.59}
$$

This radial stress and radial displacement serve as the boundary conditions for the model of the composite cylinder. The composite cylinder consists of a thick-walled cylinder composed of the matrix material and a solid core of the fiber material. The radial displacement and radial stress at radius a, the interface between the fiber and the matrix, is given by

$$
\sigma_r(a) = 2k_f\frac{u(a)}{a} \tag{2.60}
$$

where subscript f refers to the orthotropic elastic properties of the fiber. This provides the additional boundary conditions for the matrix material region. The solution to the problem of pressure loading of a thick-walled cylinder is then needed. The equation of equilibrium in cylindrical coordinates is given by

$$
\frac{d\sigma_r}{dr} + \frac{\sigma_r - \sigma_\theta}{r} = 0 \tag{2.61}
$$

and the strain-displacement relations are

$$
\epsilon_r = \frac{du}{dr} \quad \text{and} \quad \epsilon_\theta = \frac{u}{r} \tag{2.62}
$$

substituting the stress–strain relations given for the matrix as

$$
\begin{Bmatrix} \sigma_r \\ \sigma_\theta \end{Bmatrix} = \begin{bmatrix} k_m + G_m & k_m - G_m \\ k_m - G_m & k_m + G_m \end{bmatrix} \begin{Bmatrix} \epsilon_r \\ \epsilon_\theta \end{Bmatrix} \tag{2.63}
$$

Substituting the stress–strain and then the strain-displacement relations into the equilibrium equation gives an ordinary differential equation with variable coefficients as

$$
\frac{d^2u}{dr^2} + \frac{1}{r}\frac{du}{dr} - \frac{u}{r^2} = 0 \tag{2.64}
$$

with a solution given by

$$
u = Ar + \frac{B}{r} \tag{2.65}
$$

Again, using the strain-displacement relations and substituting in terms of the stress gives a solution for the radial stress as

$$\sigma_r = 2k_m A - 2G_m \frac{B}{r^2} \tag{2.66}$$

The unknown constants A and B are determined by equating values of the radial stress with those of the inner fiber region at $r = a$ and with that of the outer homogeneous solution at $r = b$. Substituting and solving for A and B gives

$$A = \frac{\sigma_r(b) - v_f \sigma_r(a)}{2k_m v_m} \tag{2.67}$$

$$B = \frac{[\sigma_r(b) - \sigma_r(a)]a^2}{2G_m v_m} \tag{2.68}$$

where the volume fraction of the fiber and matrix are defined by

$$c_f = \frac{a^2}{b^2} \quad \text{and} \quad c_m = 1 - c_f \tag{2.69}$$

The expressions for the radial stresses at $r = a$ and $r = b$ from Eqs. (2.59) and (2.60) are substituted into Eqs. (2.67) and (2.68), thus eliminating the radial stresses in terms of the radial displacements. The values thus determined for constants A and B are substituted into Eq. (2.65), which is then evaluated at $r = a$ and $r = b$. This gives two equations that both involve $u(a)$ and $u(b)$. Factoring for these displacements and then eliminating by dividing one equation by the other leads, after some simplification and rearrangement, to an expression for the effective composite property in terms of the properties of the fiber and matrix, as

$$k^* = \frac{k_m G_m c_m + k_f(k_m + G_m c_f)}{G_m + k_m c_f + k_f c_m} \tag{2.70}$$

which can be rearranged to get the form given by Hashin [2.12] as

$$k^* = \frac{k_m(k_f + G_m)c_m + k_f(k_m + G_m)c_f}{(k_f + G_m)c_m + (k_m + G_m)c_f} \tag{2.71}$$

Because the exterior of every fiber matrix region is compatible with the overall state of stress and strain, the material property k^* as determined in Eq. (2.71) is representative of the bulk material.

The results for three other properties are reported by Hashin as follows.

$$E_A^* = E_{Am} c_m + E_{Af} c_f + \frac{4(v_{Af} - v_{Am})^2 c_f c_m}{c_m/k_f + c_f/k_m + 1/G_{Tm}} \tag{2.72}$$

$$v_A^* = v_{Am} c_m + v_{Af} c_f + \frac{(v_{Af} - v_{Am})(1/k_m - 1/k_f)c_f c_m}{c_m/k_f + c_f/k_m + 1/G_{Tm}} \tag{2.73}$$

$$G_A^* = G_{Am} \frac{G_{Am} c_m + G_{Af}(1 + c_f)}{G_{Am}(1 + c_f) + G_{Af} c_m} \tag{2.74}$$

The first two terms of the results for E_A^* and v_A^* can be identified as the rule-of-mixtures expression.

As discussed in Section 2.3, a common type of analysis involving laminated fiber composites uses the plane-stress assumption. The properties needed for this analysis are

E_{11}, E_{22}, ν_{12}, and G_{12}. Although for many materials these properties are available from experimental tests, the previous theoretical expressions can be very useful for extending the range of properties. A frequent need is to adjust these properties for changes in the fiber volume fraction. It is hoped theoretical predictions of the effects of fiber volume fraction can be used to supplement the available experimental data. Three of these plane-stress properties are available from the preceding expressions. The properties given by the Hashin model are directly related to three of these properties by

$$E_{11} = E_A^* \qquad \nu_{12} = \nu_A^* \qquad G_{12} = G_A^* \tag{2.75}$$

The properties given by the composite cylinder model also can be manipulated to give the relationship

$$\frac{E_{22}}{1 - \nu_{12}} = \frac{E_T}{1 - \nu_T} = \frac{2k^* E_A}{E_A^* + 4(\nu_A^*)^2 k^*} \tag{2.76}$$

However, it is not possible to solve for E_{22} independently without a knowledge of the transverse shear modulus, which is not available from this model. If the transverse shear modulus were known, the additional relationship available for the isotropic transverse properties, given by

$$E_T^* = 2G_T^*(1 + \nu_T^*) \tag{2.77}$$

could be used to obtain the transverse Poisson ratio, and thus the transverse tensile modulus. A discussion of an alternative model for obtaining the transverse shear modulus follows later.

An example of the use of the preceding relationships is given here. The first problem faced is obtaining the required properties of the fiber and matrix needed for the analysis. Whereas the matrix usually can be taken as being isotropic and the properties obtained from tests on the bulk material, fiber properties are much more difficult to obtain. Although fibers such as glass are usually considered to be isotropic, carbon and aramid (Kevlar) fibers are believed to be strongly orthotropic. Some properties for fibers and matrix materials are listed in Tables 2.1 and 2.2, taken from [2.15]. It should be noted that it is very difficult to measure the transverse properties of carbon fibers, and some of the values given in the table have been back calculated from model results, rather than measured.

The predicted effect of fiber volume fraction on the G_{12} shear modulus from Eq. (2.74) is shown in Figure 2.20 using the properties listed for AS fiber and the HM (high-modulus) matrix. This prediction is in good agreement with that measured for AS4/3501-6 at a nominal 60% fiber volume fraction, and could be calibrated for an even better fit by adjusting the input material properties to fit available experimental data.

Three-phase cylinder model.   Christensen and Lo [2.13] have addressed the issue of obtaining the remaining fifth property, the transverse shear modulus. The result that follows is taken from Christensen [2.16], which corrects some typographical errors in [2.13]. Note that the solution is given only for isotropic fibers. The transverse shear modulus is then found from the solution to a quadratic given by

$$A\left(\frac{G_T^*}{G_m}\right)^2 + 2B\left(\frac{G_T^*}{G_m}\right) + C = 0 \tag{2.78}$$

Table 2.1 Typical In-Plane Lamina Stiffness Properties of Composite Materials

Material	E_{11} GPa (Msi)	E_{22} GPa (Msi)	ν_{12}	G_{12} GPa (Msi)	α_1 C^{-1} (F^{-1})	α_2 C^{-1} (F^{-1})	Density g/cc (lb/in³)	Ref.
Carbon/epoxy AS4/3501-6	131.0 (18.4)	11.2 (1.60)	0.28	6.55 (0.95)	-6.3 E -8 (-3.5 E -8)	2.88 (1.6 E -5)	1.55 (0.056)	2.22
Carbon/epoxy T300/5208	153 (22.1)	11.2 (1.60)	0.33	7.1 (1.03)				2.23
Carbon/epoxy G30-500/2431	129 (18.7)	8.6 (1.25)	0.31	4.1 (0.6)	$-.30$ E -6 (-0.17 E -6)	28.1 E -6 (15.6 E -6)	1.57 (0.0567)	2.25
Boron/epoxy	204 (29.6)	18.5 (2.70)	0.23	5.59 (0.81)				2.24
Kevlar 49/epoxy	76.0 (11.0)	5.50 (0.80)	0.34	2.30 (0.33)	-3.5 E -6 (-1.94 E -6)	60 E -6 (33.3 E -6)	1.38 (0.050)	2.25
E-glass/epoxy	38.6 (5.60)	8.27 (1.20)	0.26	4.14 (0.60)				2.24
E-glass/epoxy cloth ($vf = 0.46$)	16.6 (2.41)	16.6 (2.41)	0.05	3.1 (0.45)	11.4 E -6 (6.31 E -6)	11.4 E -6 6.31 E -6	1.92 (0.069)	2.26
Carbon/epoxy T300/2431 cloth	62.8 (9.11)	62.8 (9.11)	0.05	6.2 (0.90)	1.87 E -6 (1.04 E -6)	1.87 E -6 (1.04 E -6)	1.57 (0.0569)	2.26
Spectra 900/ 826 epoxy	24 (3.5)						1.04 (0.038)	2.27
Spectra 1000/ 826 epoxy	66 (9.50)						1.04 (0.038)	2.27

where

$$A = 3c_f c_m^2 \left(\frac{G_f}{G_m} - 1\right)\left(\frac{G_m}{G_m} + \eta_f\right)$$
$$+ \left[\frac{G_f}{G_m}\eta_m + \eta_f \eta_m - \left(\frac{G_f}{G_m}\eta_m - \eta_f\right)c_f^3\right]\left[c_f \eta_m \left(\frac{G_f}{G_m} - 1\right) - \left(\frac{G_f}{G_m}\eta_m + 1\right)\right] \quad (2.79)$$

$$B = -3c_f c_m^2 \left(\frac{G_f}{G_m} - 1\right)\left(\frac{G_f}{G_m} + \eta_f\right)$$
$$+ \frac{1}{2}\left[\frac{G_f}{G_m}\eta_m + \left(\frac{G_f}{G_m} - 1\right)c_f + 1\right]^* \left[(\eta_m - 1)\left(\frac{G_f}{G_m} + \eta_f\right)\right]$$
$$+ \frac{c_f}{2}(\eta_m + 1)\left(\frac{G_f}{G_m} - 1\right)\left[\frac{G_f}{G_m} + \eta_f + \left(\frac{G_f}{G_m}\eta_m - \eta_f\right)c_f^3\right] \quad (2.80)$$

$$C = 3c_f c_m^2 \left(\frac{G_f}{G_m} - 1\right)\left(\frac{G_f}{G_m} + \eta_f\right)$$
$$+ \left[\frac{G_f}{G_m}\eta_m + \left(\frac{G_f}{G_m} - 1\right)c_f + 1\right]\left[\frac{G_f}{G_m} + \eta_f + \left(\frac{G_f}{G_m}\eta_m - \eta_f\right)c_f^3\right] \quad (2.81)$$

where

$$\eta_m = 3 - 4c_m \quad \text{and} \quad \eta_f = 3 - 4c_f \quad (2.82)$$

Table 2.2 Fiber Properties

Property	Units	Boron	HMS	AS	T300	KEV	S-G	E-G
Number of fibers per end	—	1	10,000	10,000	3000	580	204	204
Fiber diameter	in	0.0056	0.0003	0.0003	0.0003	0.00046	0.00036	0.00036
Density	lb/in^3	0.095	0.070	0.063	0.064	0.053	0.090	0.090
Longitudinal modulus	10^6 psi	58	55.0	31.0	32.0	22	12.4	10.6
Transverse modulus	10^6 psi	58	0.90	2.0	2.0	0.6	12.4	10.6
Longitudinal shear modulus	10^6 psi	24.2	1.1	2.0	1.3	0.42	5.17	4.37
Transverse shear modulus	10^6 psi	24.2	0.7	1.0	0.7	0.22	5.17	4.37
Longitudinal Poisson's ratio	—	0.20	0.20	0.20	0.20	0.35	0.20	0.22
Transverse Poisson's ratio	—	0.20	0.25	0.25	0.25	0.35	0.20	0.22
Heat capacity	Btu/lb/°F	0.31	0.20	0.20	0.22	0.25	0.17	0.17
Longitudinal heat conductivity	Btu/h/ft^2/°F/in	22	580	580	580	1.7	21	7.5
Transverse heat conductivity	Btu/h/ft^2/°F/in	22	58	58	58	1.7	21	7.5
Longitudinal thermal expansion coefficient	10^{-6}in/in/°F	2.8	−0.55	−0.55	−0.55	−2.2	2.8	2.8
Transverse thermal expansion coefficient	10^{-6}in/in/°F	2.8	5.6	5.6	5.6	30	2.8	2.8
Longitudinal tensile strength	ksi	600	250	350	350	400	600	400
Longitudinal compression strength	ksi	700	200	260	300	75	—	—
Shear strength	ksi	100	—	—	—	—	—	—

Source: From Chamis [2.15].

Transverse, shear, and compression properties are estimates inferred from corresponding composite properties.

Note that c_f and c_m have been used for fiber and matrix volume fractions, rather than the more usual notation v_f and v_m, to avoid confusion with the Poisson ratio terms.

The preceding results given can be combined with the results given in Eqs. (2.71) to (2.74) to obtain the transverse modulus E_{22} for materials with isotropic fibers and matrix. A plot is shown for S-glass fiber/epoxy in Figure 2.21 using the properties from Tables 2.1 and 2.2 for the S-glass isotropic fiber and the matrix labeled IMLS (intermediate modulus, low strength).

2.7.3 Numerical Calculations

A number of investigators have carried out numerical solutions to obtain composite properties from the properties of the fiber and matrix, using various idealizations of the fiber and matrix geometry. Typical results have been presented by Adams and Doner for G_{12} in [2.17] and for E_{22} in [2.18], using isotropic fiber and matrix properties. Extensive studies have also been reported by Caruso and Chamis [2.19] using finite-element calculations. These calculations provide important information about composite lamina properties, but of course are limited to the specific values of fiber and matrix employed. Typical results are shown in Figures 2.22 and 2.23 for G_{12} and E_{22}.

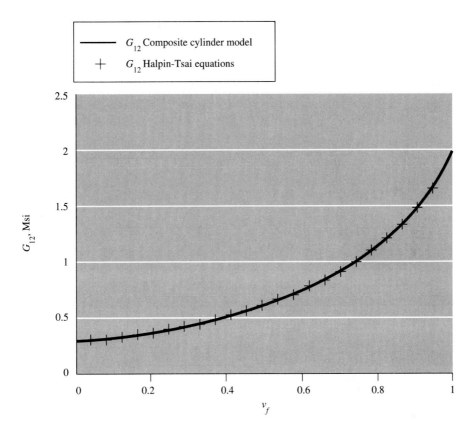

Figure 2.20   Calculation of G_{12} from the composite cylinder model for carbon fiber/epoxy, and comparison with the prediction based on the Halpin-Tsai equations.

2.7.4 Curve-Fitting Expressions

A simple expression has been developed, known as the Halpin-Tsai relationships, that serves to predict stiffness coefficients [2.20, 2.21]. It uses the simple rule-of-mixtures results given before in Eqs. (2.38) and (2.39) for E_{11} and n_{12}, but gives alternative expressions for E_{22} and G_{12}. These alternative expressions are simply curve-fitting relationships that have been calibrated against the results of the more elaborate theoretical models available in the literature, such as those mentioned before. The curve-fitting expressions are given as

$$\frac{G_{12}}{G_m} = \frac{1 + \zeta \eta V_f}{1 - \eta V_f} \tag{2.83}$$

where

$$\eta = \frac{G_{12_f}/G_{12_m} - 1}{G_{12_f}/G_{12_m} + \zeta} \tag{2.84}$$

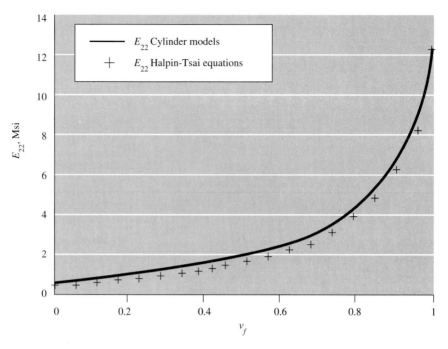

Figure 2.21 Calculation of E_{22} from three-phase cylinder and composite cylinder models for glass fiber/epoxy, and comparison with the prediction based on the Halpin-Tsai equations.

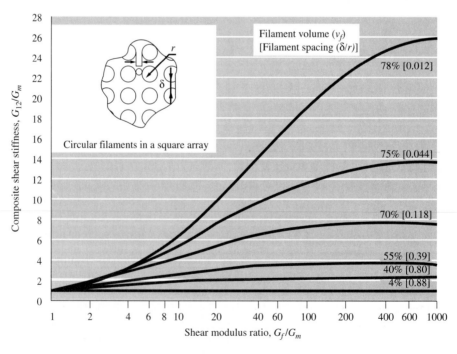

Figure 2.22 Normalized composite shear stiffness, calculated for circular fibers in a square array. (*Source:* From Adams and Doner [2.17].)

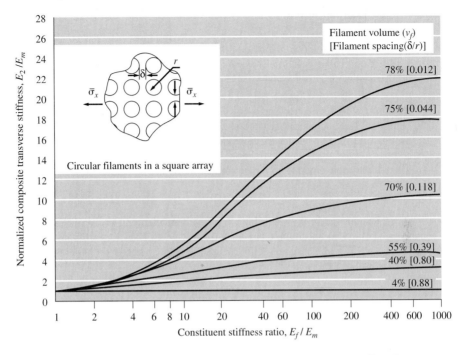

Figure 2.23   Normalized composite transverse stiffness, calculated for circular fibers in a square array. (*Source:* From Adams and Doner [2.17].)

and a similar expression for E_{22} given as

$$\frac{E_{22}}{E_m} = \frac{1 + \zeta \eta V_f}{1 - \eta V_f} \tag{2.85}$$

with

$$\eta = \frac{E_{12_f}/E_m - 1}{E_{12_f}/E_m + \zeta} \tag{2.86}$$

where ζ is a "curve-fitting factor" given as approximately 2 for E_{22} and 1 for G_{12}. Although empirical, this curve-fitting procedure has been shown to represent quite well a variety of elasticity and finite-element-model solutions. Comparisons of this curve-fitting relationship with numerical results are given in [2.21]. Comparisons with the results given previously for G_{12} for carbon/epoxy in Figure 2.20, and with the calculation for E_{22} in Figure 2.21 are shown in those figures, and indicate good agreement. The comparison for G_{12} is within plotting accuracy, and that for E_{22} is quite good over the entire range of fiber volume fraction. If used over a narrower range of volume fractions, say, those that are likely to be used in commercial practice, and calibrated to fit the measured data at a given volume fraction, the Halpin-Tsai equation appears to be very useful.

Example 2.4   Adjustment of elasticity constants for fiber volume fraction

The elasticity constants for AS4/3501-6 given in Table 2.3 are considered to be for a nominal fiber volume fraction (i.e., the ratio of the fiber volume to the total volume in a ply) of $v_f = 0.6$. Estimate new values for these constants if the fiber volume fraction is $v_f = 0.55$, using the rule-of-mixtures models for E_{11} and v_{12}, and the Halpin-Tsai relations for E_{22} and G_{12}.

Solution: The difficulty in adjusting for the fiber volume fraction is that the separate properties of the fiber and matrix may not be well known. Often, the procedure that must be used is to assume "reasonable" values for fiber and matrix that are consistent with the known measured constants at the given volume fraction. Because the fiber modulus is much larger than the matrix modulus, the relationship can be approximated as

$$E_{11} = E_{11_{ref}} \frac{v_f}{v_{f_{ref}}} = 18.4 \frac{0.55}{0.6} = 16.9 \text{ Msi} = 116 \text{ GPa}$$

The change in the value for v_{12} is much smaller, and in many cases is neglected. Although somewhat uncertain, using values of $v_{12f} = 0.23$ and $v_{12m} = 0.35$ is consistent with the value of $v_{12} = 0.28$ measured for this material. The predicted effect of the reduced fiber volume fraction is then estimated by the rule of mixtures as

$$v_{12} = v_{12f}v_f + v_{12m}v_m = (0.23)(0.55) + (0.35)(0.45) = 0.284$$

Table 2.3   Matrix Properties

Name	Units	LM	IMLS	IMHS	HM	Polyimide	PMR
Density	lb/in^3	0.042	0.046	0.044	0.045	0.044	0.044
Modulus	10^6 psi	0.32	0.50	0.50	0.75	0.50	0.47
Shear modulus	10^6 psi	—	—	—	—	—	—
Poisson ratio	—	—	0.43	0.41	0.35	0.35	0.35	0.36
Heat capacity	Btu/lb/°F	0.25	0.25	0.25	0.25	0.25	0.25
Heat conductivity	Btu/h/ft^2/°F/in	1.25	1.25	1.25	1.25	1.25	1.25
Thermal-expansion coefficient	10^{-6}in/in/°F	57	57	36	40	20	28
Diffusivity	10^{-10}in^2/s	0.6	0.6	0.6	0.6	0.6	0.6
Moisture-expansion coefficient	in/in/M	0.33	0.33	0.33	0.33	0.33	0.33
Tensile strength	ksi	8	7	15	20	15	8
Compression strength	ksi	15	21	35	50	30	16
Shear strength	ksi	8	7	13	15	13	8
Tensile fracture strain	in/in (%)	8.1	1.4	2.0	2.0	2.0	2.0
Compressive fracture strain	in/in (%)	15	4.2	5.0	5.0	4.0	3.5
Shear fracture strain	in/in (%)	10	3.2	3.5	4.0	3.5	5.0
Air heat conductivity	Btu/h/ft^2/°F/in	0.225	0.225	0.225	0.225	0.225	0.225
Glass transition temperature (dry)	°F	350	420	420	420	700	700

Source: From Chamis [2.15].

LM = low modulus; IMLS = intermediate modulus, low strength; IMHS = intermediate modulus, high strength; HM = high modulus. Thermal, hygral, compression, and shear properties are estimates only: $G_m = E_m/2(1 + v_m)$.

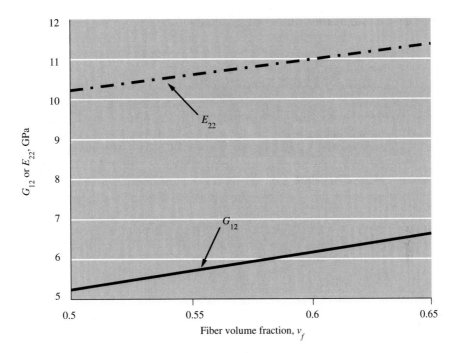

Figure 2.24   Variation of G_{12} and E_{22} for AS4/3501-6 carbon-fiber/epoxy with fiber volume fraction, predicted with the Halpin-Tsai equations.

The prediction of the changes in E_{22} and G_{12} is estimated from the Halpin-Tsai relations. The problem is in knowing what values of fiber and matrix stiffness to use. Using the orthotropic transverse fiber properties listed in Table 2.1 for AS fiber as a guide, and calculating the properties required to give agreement with the measured data values at $v_f = 0.6$ is a possible approach. By using the measured data given in Table 2.1 for E_{22} and G_{12}, a set of properties that are at least consistent with these values at a 60% fiber volume fraction are $E_{22f} = 2.2$ Msi, $G_{12f} = 2.0$ Msi, $G_m = 0.377$ Msi, $v_m = 0.35$, and $E_m = 2(1 + v_m) = 1.02$ Msi. These properties are then used with the Halpin-Tsai equations, Eqs. (2.85) and (2.86), to get values of $G_{12} = 0.83$ Msi and $E_{22} = 1.54$ Msi at a 55% fiber volume fraction. Although it is clear that uncertainty exists with regard to the fiber and matrix properties to be used, the procedure still gives a reasonable estimate of properties over a fairly narrow range of fiber volume fraction useful in typical applications. A plot of the predictions for G_{12} and E_{22} over a range of volume fractions from 0.5 to 0.65 is shown in Figure 2.24. ∎

2.8 CLOSURE

This chapter has developed fundamental ideas about the elastic stiffness properties of fiber composites. The basic material component considered is a mixture of unidirectional fibers embedded in a matrix. Because the fiber often has stiffness properties that are much different than the matrix, the mixture has highly directional properties. For example, with stiff fibers in a polymer matrix, the stiffness in the fiber direction is much higher than in the transverse direction. Because of the directional properties, the number of moduli needed to describe the elastic properties is higher than it is for more familiar isotropic materials. These constants are tabulated for popular material systems or must be measured experimentally if not already available. A further consequence of the stiffness being directional is that the components of the stiffness depend on the coordinate system, and the components change as the coordinate system is rotated. These changes in stiffness components with rotation can be described by transformation equations. Changes in the stiffness with rotation will be found to be a key element in the analysis of laminates, which is taken up in the next chapter. Finally, it was shown that the stiffness properties of the combined fiber and matrix can be estimated from a knowledge of the properties of the fiber and matrix separately. This estimation procedure is highly useful for new systems and for estimating the effect on stiffness properties of changing the relative amounts of fiber and matrix.

REFERENCES

2.1 R. M. Jones, *Mechanics of Composite Materials* (New York: Hemisphere Publishing, 1975).

2.2 Y. T. Yeow, and H. F. Brinson, "A Comparison of Simple Shear Characterization Methods for Composite Laminates," *Composites* 9 (1978): 49–55.

2.3 M. Arcan, Z. Hashin, and A. Voloshin, "A Method to Produce Uniform Plane-Stress States with Applications to Fibre-Reinforced Materials," *Exper. Mech.* 18 (1978): 141–146.

2.4 J. M. Whitney, D. L. Stansbarger, and J. B. Howell, "Analysis of the Rail Shear Test, Applications and Limitations," *J. Composite Mater.* 5 (1971): 24–34.

2.5 B. W. Rosen, "A Simple Procedure for Experimental Determination of the Longitudinal Shear Modulus of Unidirectional Composites," *J. Composite Mater.* 6 (1972): 552–554.

2.6 N. Iosipescu, "New Accurate Procedure for Single Shear Testing of Metals," *J. Mater.* (1967): 537–566.

2.7 D. E. Walrath and D. F. Adams, "The Iosipescu Shear Test as Applied to Composite Materials," *Exper. Mech.* 23 (1983): 105–110.

2.8 S. R. Swanson, M. Messick, and G. R. Toombes, "Comparison of Torsion Tube and Iosipescu In-Plane Shear Test Results for a Carbon Fibre-Reinforced Epoxy Composite," *Composites* 16 (1985): 220–224.

2.9 S. R. Swanson, M. J. Messick, and Z. Tian, "Failure of Carbon/Epoxy Lamina Under Combined Stress," *J. Composite Mater.* 21 (1987): 619–630.

2.10 Z. Hashin and B. W. Rosen, "The Elastic Moduli of Fiber-Reinforced Materials," *J. Appl. Mech.* 31 (1964): 223–232.

2.11 R. Hill, "Theory of Mechanical Properties of Fibre-Strengthened Materials: 1. Elastic Behavior," *J. Mech. Phys. Solids* 12 (1964): 199–212.

2.12 Z. Hashin, "Analysis of Properties of Fiber Composites with Anisotropic Constituents," *J. Appl. Mech.* 46 (1979): 543–550.

2.13 R. M. Christensen and K. H. Lo, "Solutions for Effective Shear Properties in Three Phase Sphere and Cylinder Models," *J. Mech. Phys. Solids* 27 (1979): 315–330.

2.14 R. M. Christensen, *Mechanics of Composite Materials* (New York: John Wiley, 1979).

2.15 C. C. Chamis, "Simplified Composite Micromechanics Equations for Mechanical, Thermal and Moisture-Related Properties," in *Engineers' Guide to Composite Materials,* ed. J. W. Weeton, D. M. Peters, and K. L. Thomas (Materials Park, OH: ASM International, 1987), pp. 3-8–3-24.

2.16 R. M. Christensen, "Mechanical Properties of Composite Materials," in *Mechanics of Composite Materials, Recent Advances,* ed. Z. Hashin and C. T. Herakovich (Oxford: Pergamon Press, 1983).

2.17 D. F. Adams and D. R. Doner, "Longitudinal Shear Loading of a Unidirectional Composite," *J. Composite Mater.* 1 (1967): 4–17.

2.18 D. F. Adams and D. R. Doner, "Transverse Normal Loading of a Unidirectional Composite," *J. Composite Mater.* 1 (1967): 152–164.

2.19 J. J. Caruso and C. C. Chamis, "Assessment of Simplified Composite Micromechanics Using Three-Dimensional Finite Element Analysis, *J. Composite Tech. and Res.* 8 (1986): 77–83.

2.20 J. C. Halpin and S. W. Tsai, "Effects of Environmental Factors on Composite Materials," AFML-TR-67-423, Air Force Materials Laboratory, Wright-Patterson Air Force Base, Ohio, June (1969).

2.21 J. C. Halpin, *Primer on Composite Materials Analysis,* 2nd ed., rev. (Lancaster: Technomic Publishing, 1992).

2.22 S. R. Swanson and A. P. Christoforou, "Response of Quasi-Isotropic Carbon/Epoxy Laminates to Biaxial Stress," *J. Composite Mater.* 20 (1986): 457–471.

2.23 N. J. Pagano and H. T. Hahn, "Evaluation of Composite Curing Stresses," in *Composite Materials: Testing and Design* (4th Conf.), ASTM STP 617 (Philadelphia: American Society for Testing and Materials, 1977), pp. 317–329.

2.24 S. W. Tsai, *Composites Design 1986* (Dayton, OH: Think Composites, 1986).

2.25 *Data Manual,* E.I. duPont de Nemours, Wilmington, DE (1980).

2.26 *Data Sheet,* Fiber Science Division of EDO Corp., Salt Lake City (1995).

2.27 *Spectra Data Sheet,* Allied Fibers Technical Center, Petersburg, VA (1994).

PROBLEMS

2.1. Write out the stress–strain matrix in plane stress for glass/epoxy unidirectional material, and compare the values with that for the carbon/epoxy given in Example 2.1.

2.2. Write out the stress–strain matrix in plane stress for aramid fiber (kevlar)/epoxy unidirectional material, and compare the values with that for the carbon/epoxy given in Example 2.1.

2.3. Divide the fiber direction lamina modulus E_{11} by the density, for AS4/epoxy, E-glass/epoxy, Kevlar/epoxy, and Spectra/epoxy, and compare the values.

2.4. What is meant by the "reciprocity relationship" for the stiffness properties of a fiber composite material?

2.5. Give the state of strain that results from the following:

(a) 1000 psi in the fiber direction (direction 1).

(b) 1000 psi in the transverse direction (direction 2).

(c) 1000 psi shear stress in the 1,2 plane.

Use the following properties that are typical of AS4/3501-6 carbon/epoxy at $V_f = 60\%$: $E_{11} = 18.4$ Msi, $E_{22} = 1.60$ Msi, $G_{12} = 0.95$ Msi, and $\nu_{12} = 0.28$.

2.6. Invert the strain–stress relationship for an orthotropic material in plane stress to get the stress–strain relationship (known as the Q matrix).

2.7. Do the Mohr's circle relationships for transformation of components with change of coordinate axes still hold for a nonisotropic material for
(**a**) change of stress components?
(**b**) change of strain components?
State why or why not.

2.8. How does "tensor" shear strain differ from "engineering" shear strain?

2.9. Review the "wedge" (equilibrium) method, often given in strength-of-materials books for change of stress components with rotation of coordinate axes. Verify that the expressions given in the text in Eq. (2.20) are equivalent to the "wedge"-method equations.

2.10. Verify that Eq. (2.25) is the standard transformation for strain components given in mechanics-of-materials texts.

2.11. Show that T and T^{-1} satisfy the relationship $TT^{-1} = T^{-1}T = I$, where I is the unit matrix.

2.12. Show in matrix form how the stress–strain matrix at an arbitrary angle can be obtained from the Q matrix that is given with respect to principal material directions.

2.13. Multiply out Eq. (2.29) to verify the terms shown in Eq. (2.30). The terms that express the change in the directional stiffness terms with rotation of coordinate axes will be a key part of the analysis of laminates in Chapter 3.

2.14. Transform the Q stress–strain matrix of Example 2.1 to coordinates that are rotated by 90°, and note the relationship to the original Q matrix.

2.15. Transform the Q stress–strain matrix of Example 2.1 to coordinates that are rotated by 60°.

2.16. Transform the Q stress–strain matrix of Example 2.1 to coordinates that are rotated by $-60°$, and compare the result with that of Problem 2.15.

2.17. Find the apparent coefficients of thermal expansion when the coordinate system is rotated by 90°, and note the relationship to the original CTE array in principal material directions.

2.18. Find the apparent coefficients of thermal expansion when the coordinate system is rotated by 45°, and with original CTE array in principal material directions.

2.19. Find the apparent coefficients of thermal expansion when the coordinate system is rotated by $-45°$, and compare with the original CTE array in principal material directions.

2.20. Calculate strains ϵ_1, ϵ_2, and γ_{12} that result in a lamina of AS4/3501-6 carbon/epoxy in a cooldown from the cure temperature of 177°C (350°F) to ambient temperature. Also calculate these same strains for aluminum under the same temperature change, and compare. Aluminum can be considered to be isotropic with a CTE of 23 μstrain/°C (13 μstrain/°F).

2.21. What is meant by "normal-shear" coupling? Write out the stress–strain relationship for an anisotropic material in plane stress to show mathematically how this coupling occurs.

2.22. Give an example of how "normal-shear" coupling could be observed experimentally.

2.23. Describe a laboratory test that could be used to determine each of the properties E_{11}, E_{22}, G_{12}, and v_{12} for a fiber-composite material unidirectional lamina.

2.24. Plot values of E_{11}, E_{22}, G_{12}, v_{12}, and v_{21} over the range of fiber volume fraction $V_f = 0.5$ to 0.65, as computed from the mechanics-of-materials simplified micromechanics formulas. Compare with lamina properties for AS4/3501-6 carbon/epoxy at $V_f = 0.6$. (V_f is the fiber volume fraction). Use the fiber and matrix properties given in Example 2.4 for AS4 fiber and the 3501-6 epoxy.

2.25. Compute G_{12} and E_{22} from the Halpin-Tsai equations over the range of V_f from 0.5 to 0.65 using the properties of Problem 2.24. Compare with the results of Problem 2.24.

3

Laminate Analysis

3.1 INTRODUCTION

Practical structures made of composite materials have fibers placed in more than one direction. Because most composites, for example, those with polymeric matrices, are extremely weak in directions transverse to the fibers, fibers must be placed in more than one direction. Otherwise, even secondary loads in transverse directions could cause failure of the structure. The proper selection of the placement angles of the different layers of fibers is a key feature in the design of composite structures. The foundation for the analysis techniques necessary to accomplish this design are explained in this chapter.

The situation with composite materials is somewhat similar to that with reinforced concrete, in that even if the overall loads are simple, such as a uniaxial load, for example, the internal stress distribution is not uniform. Rather the individual plies carry the load according to their relative stiffnesses. The situation is complicated in fiber composites, because the stiffnesses of the individual plies depend on the angles of fiber placement with respect to the loads.

The material developed in this chapter has direct application to the case in which the final composite form has distinct layers, such as the layers of a prepreg laminate or a filament-wound structure. However, other material forms, such as the various textile forms (e.g., cloth or braids), can often be analyzed using similar techniques. Thus, the material to be developed here is applicable when the material has fibers aligned within a layer. Materials such as random chopped-fiber or random mat composites have much less directionality to the various layers, and can be analyzed as if they were isotropic.

This chapter proceeds in what perhaps seems to be a roundabout way. The basic geometry to be considered is that of a flat plate under both tension (or compression) and bending, and the basic problem is to relate the applied in-plane loads and bending moments to the stresses within the individual layers. Subsequent chapters show how to apply the pro-

cedures developed here to other structural geometries. The basic approach is to first describe the geometry characterizing extension and bending of a flat plate. Strain distributions
are then obtained, and stresses related to these strains by means of the stress–strain laws
discussed in Chapter 2. Integration of the stresses gives the extension forces and bending
moments as a function of the strains. Finally, these extension forces and bending moments
are related back to the stresses in the individual plies.

3.2 DEFORMATION DUE TO EXTENSION AND BENDING

Consider a flat plate made up of a number of individual layers with an x,y coordinate system
in the plane of the plate. The basic assumption is that the individual layers are perfectly
bonded together, so that in terms of displacements, it is not necessary at this point to consider the individual layers, as they all displace together under the action of the applied loads.
In the usual (simplest) theory, which is now described, the Kirchhoff–Love hypothesis is invoked by assuming that normals to the center line remain normal after deformation. This assumption neglects through-the-thickness shear deformation. Further discussion of shear deformation is given subsequently. The displacements in the x,z plane that characterize
uniform extension are illustrated in Figure 3.1, along with those that characterize bending. A
similar situation will exist in the y,z plane for displacements in that direction. The displacements in the x, y, and z directions are called u, v, and w, respectively, and are assumed to be
described by continuous functions of x, y, and z. It is assumed that the plate displaces in the z
direction only because of the bending motion, and that no variation of w through the thickness takes place. This is a usual assumption of thin-plate (and beam) analysis.

As illustrated in the figure, the in-plane displacements u and v can be related to the
center-line displacements u_0 and v_0 and the slopes by

$$u(x,y,z) = u_0(x,y) - z\frac{\partial w(x,y)}{\partial x}$$

$$v(x,y,z) = v_0(x,y) - z\frac{\partial w(x,y)}{\partial y}$$

(3.1)

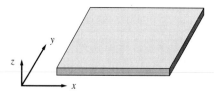

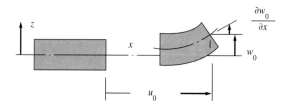

Figure 3.1   Illustration of extension and
bending-plate deformation.

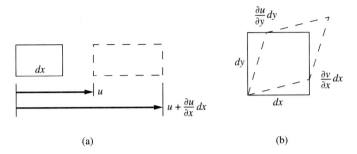

Figure 3.2   The relationship between strains and displacement gradients: (a) normal strains and (b) shear strains.

The displacements can then be used to relate to the strains by using the usual strain-displacement relationships of linear elasticity. These relationships are developed in most texts on mechanics of materials or elasticity, and can be easily obtained from Figure 3.2 by using the usual definitions for strain, that is, that normal strain is the change in length per unit length, and that engineering shear strain is the change in the angle between two initially perpendicular sides. These ideas can be written mathematically from the deformations shown in Fig 3.2:

$$\epsilon_x = \frac{\left(u + \dfrac{\partial u}{\partial x}dx\right) - u}{dx} = \frac{\partial u}{\partial x}$$

for normal strain, and the relationship

$$\gamma_{xy} = \frac{\dfrac{\partial u}{\partial y}dy}{dy} + \frac{\dfrac{\partial v}{\partial x}dx}{dx} = \frac{\partial u}{\partial y} + \frac{\partial v}{\partial x}$$

A similar relationship holds for normal strain in the y direction, so that the strain-displacement relations needed are given by

$$
\begin{aligned}
\epsilon_x &= \frac{\partial u}{\partial x} \\[2mm]
\epsilon_y &= \frac{\partial v}{\partial y} \\[2mm]
\gamma_{xy} &= \frac{\partial v}{\partial x} + \frac{\partial u}{\partial y}
\end{aligned}
\tag{3.2}
$$

Substituting the displacements gives

$$
\begin{Bmatrix} \epsilon_x \\ \epsilon_y \\ \gamma_{xy} \end{Bmatrix} =
\begin{Bmatrix} \dfrac{\partial u_0}{\partial x} \\[3mm] \dfrac{\partial v_0}{\partial y} \\[3mm] \dfrac{\partial u_0}{\partial y} + \dfrac{\partial v_0}{\partial x} \end{Bmatrix} + z
\begin{Bmatrix} -\dfrac{\partial^2 w}{\partial x^2} \\[3mm] -\dfrac{\partial^2 w}{\partial y^2} \\[3mm] -2\dfrac{\partial^2 w}{\partial x \, \partial y} \end{Bmatrix}
\tag{3.3}
$$

and defining center-line strains $\{\epsilon^0\}$ and curvatures $\{\kappa\}$, this can be expressed as

$$\{\epsilon\} = \{\epsilon^0\} + z\{\kappa\} \tag{3.4}$$

where the center-line strains $\{\epsilon^0\}$ and curvatures $\{\kappa\}$ are defined by

$$\{\epsilon^0\} = \left\{ \begin{array}{c} \epsilon^0_x \\ \epsilon^0_y \\ \gamma^0_{xy} \end{array} \right\} \tag{3.5}$$

and

$$\left\{ \begin{array}{c} \kappa_x \\ \kappa_y \\ \kappa_{xy} \end{array} \right\} = \left\{ \begin{array}{c} -\dfrac{\partial^2 w}{\partial x^2} \\[2mm] -\dfrac{\partial^2 w}{\partial y^2} \\[2mm] -2\dfrac{\partial^2 w}{\partial x\, \partial y} \end{array} \right\} \tag{3.6}$$

3.3 FORCE AND MOMENT RESULTANTS

The next step in the development is to relate the internal stresses (in overall x,y coordinates) to the applied loading, expressed in terms of stress resultants $\{N\}$ and moment resultants $\{M\}$. The term *stress resultant* refers to the stress integrated over the thickness of the laminate, and is thus the applied force per unit width. A similar interpretation can be given to the *moment resultant,* which is thus the applied moment per unit width. Using equilibrium, we equate the force and moment per unit width to the integral of the stress and stress times distance from the center line to get, for example,

$$N_x = \int_{-h/2}^{h/2} \sigma_x \, dz$$

or in compact form,

$$\left\{ \begin{array}{c} N_x \\ N_y \\ N_{xy} \end{array} \right\} = \int_{-h/2}^{h/2} \left\{ \begin{array}{c} \sigma_x \\ \sigma_y \\ \tau_{xy} \end{array} \right\} dz \tag{3.7}$$

and for the moment resultants,

$$\left\{ \begin{array}{c} M_x \\ M_y \\ M_{xy} \end{array} \right\} = \int_{-h/2}^{h/2} \left\{ \begin{array}{c} \sigma_x \\ \sigma_y \\ \tau_{xy} \end{array} \right\} z \, dz \tag{3.8}$$

where the integral is taken over the total laminate thickness by summing the integrals over each ply. That is, we take the integrals to be

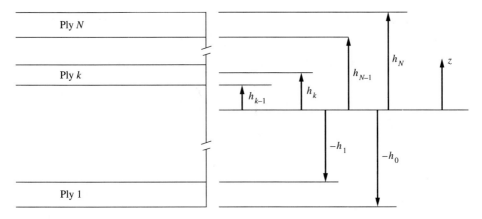

Figure 3.3   Notation for location of ply interfaces. Note that the h_k have the value of z and are negative below the center line.

$$\begin{Bmatrix} N_x \\ N_y \\ N_{xy} \end{Bmatrix} = \sum_{k=1}^{N} \int_{h_{k-1}}^{h_k} \begin{Bmatrix} \sigma_x \\ \sigma_y \\ \tau_{xy} \end{Bmatrix} dz \qquad (3.9)$$

$$\begin{Bmatrix} M_x \\ M_y \\ M_{xy} \end{Bmatrix} = \sum_{k=1}^{N} \int_{h_{k-1}}^{h_k} \begin{Bmatrix} \sigma_x \\ \sigma_y \\ \tau_{xy} \end{Bmatrix} z\, dz \qquad (3.10)$$

where the positions of the limits for each ply are illustrated in Figure 3.3. Coordinates h_k are the values of z at the interfaces and they have the sign convention of the z coordinate. Note that the integral of a matrix is just the integral of each term in the matrix.

3.4 *A, B,* AND *D* MATRICES

The force and moment resultants can be related to the strains in the laminate through the material properties for each ply group. This relationship can be expressed in terms of matrices that are labeled *A, B,* and *D* by custom. These matrices are developed in what follows. The first task in the development is to relate the stresses in each ply to the strains in the ply. The strains are given in terms of position z in Eq. (3.4). This relationship between stresses and strains must be expressed in terms of the overall x,y coordinate system, because the strains are given in terms of x,y coordinates. However, this can be done using the stress–strain relationships for a layer oriented at an arbitrary angle that were developed in Eqs. (2.28) and (2.29). Thus, from Chapter 2, we have

$$\begin{Bmatrix} \sigma_x \\ \sigma_y \\ \tau_{xy} \end{Bmatrix} = [\overline{Q}] \begin{Bmatrix} \epsilon_x \\ \epsilon_y \\ \gamma_{xy} \end{Bmatrix} \qquad (2.28)$$

where

$$[\overline{Q}] = [T^{-1}][Q][R][T][R^{-1}] \tag{2.29}$$

Substituting the stress–strain relationship in x,y coordinates into the preceding equations gives

$$\begin{Bmatrix} N_x \\ N_y \\ N_{xy} \end{Bmatrix} = \sum_{k=1}^{N} \int_{h_{k-1}}^{h_k} \overline{Q}_k \begin{Bmatrix} \epsilon_x \\ \epsilon_y \\ \gamma_{xy} \end{Bmatrix} dz = \sum_{k=1}^{N} \int_{h_{k-1}}^{h_k} \overline{Q}_k \begin{Bmatrix} \epsilon_x^0 \\ \epsilon_y^0 \\ \gamma_{xy}^0 \end{Bmatrix} dz + \sum_{k=1}^{N} \int_{h_{k-1}}^{h_k} \overline{Q}_k \begin{Bmatrix} \kappa_x \\ \kappa_y \\ \kappa_{xy} \end{Bmatrix} z \, dz \tag{3.11}$$

and

$$\begin{Bmatrix} M_x \\ M_y \\ M_{xy} \end{Bmatrix} = \sum_{k=1}^{N} \int_{h_{k-1}}^{h_k} \overline{Q}_k \begin{Bmatrix} \epsilon_x \\ \epsilon_y \\ \gamma_{xy} \end{Bmatrix} z \, dz = \sum_{k=1}^{N} \int_{h_{k-1}}^{h_k} \overline{Q}_k \begin{Bmatrix} \epsilon_x^0 \\ \epsilon_y^0 \\ \gamma_{xy}^0 \end{Bmatrix} z \, dz + \sum_{k=1}^{N} \int_{h_{k-1}}^{h_k} \overline{Q}_k \begin{Bmatrix} \kappa_x \\ \kappa_y \\ \kappa_{xy} \end{Bmatrix} z^2 \, dz \tag{3.12}$$

The integrals are easy to carry out, because the material properties are constant over each individual ply (or ply group) and the only variable is z. Thus, for example,

$$\int_{h_{k-1}}^{h_k} dz = h_k - h_{k-1} \tag{3.13}$$

$$\int_{h_{k-1}}^{h_k} z \, dz = \frac{h_k^2 - h_{k-1}^2}{2} \tag{3.14}$$

and

$$\int_{h_{k-1}}^{h_k} z^2 \, dz = \frac{h_k^3 - h_{k-1}^3}{3} \tag{3.15}$$

By using these integrals, the equations can be written in the classic relation between stress resultants, moment resultants, center-line strains, and curvatures in the following form:

$$\begin{Bmatrix} N \\ M \end{Bmatrix} = \begin{bmatrix} A & B \\ B & D \end{bmatrix} \begin{Bmatrix} \epsilon^0 \\ \kappa \end{Bmatrix} \tag{3.16}$$

where the A, B, and D matrices are each 3-by-3 matrices defined as

$$A_{ij} = \sum_{k=1}^{N} (\overline{Q}_{ij})_k (h_k - h_{k-1}) \tag{3.17}$$

$$B_{ij} = \sum_{k=1}^{N} (\overline{Q}_{ij})_k \frac{h_k^2 - h_{k-1}^2}{2} \tag{3.18}$$

$$D_{ij} = \sum_{k=1}^{N} (\overline{Q}_{ij})_k \frac{h_k^3 - h_{k-1}^3}{3} \tag{3.19}$$

where the positions of the ply surfaces are denoted by h_k, N is the number of plies (or groups of plies), and the $\overline{Q}$ matrix is the stiffness in the x,y coordinate system of each ply.

In the general case described by Eq. (3.16), there is a coupling between the in-plane behavior and the bending behavior because of the presence of the B matrix. This coupling leads to effects that are not present in isotropic materials; they are discussed in more detail subsequently. It will also be shown that the B matrix vanishes for symmetric laminates, that is, laminates that are symmetric with respect to the midplane. When the B matrix vanishes, the coupling between in-plane behavior and the bending behavior does not occur. For this case, Eq. (3.16) reduces to

$$\{N\} = [A]\{\epsilon^0\} \quad \text{or} \quad \begin{Bmatrix} N_x \\ N_y \\ N_{xy} \end{Bmatrix} = \begin{bmatrix} A_{11} & A_{12} & A_{16} \\ & A_{22} & A_{26} \\ \text{sym} & & A_{66} \end{bmatrix} \begin{Bmatrix} \epsilon_x^0 \\ \epsilon_y^0 \\ \gamma_{xy}^0 \end{Bmatrix} \tag{3.20}$$

$$\{M\} = [D]\{\kappa\} \quad \text{or} \quad \begin{Bmatrix} M_x \\ M_y \\ M_{xy} \end{Bmatrix} = \begin{bmatrix} D_{11} & D_{12} & D_{16} \\ & D_{22} & D_{26} \\ \text{sym} & & D_{66} \end{bmatrix} \begin{Bmatrix} \kappa_x \\ \kappa_y \\ \kappa_{xy} \end{Bmatrix} \tag{3.21}$$

The preceding relationships between the stress and moment resultants and the center-line strains and curvatures are well known, and are the heart of laminate analysis. Because a laminate is often made up of a number of ply groups, a certain amount of bookkeeping is involved in calculating the A, B, and D matrices. However, this can be readily implemented on a desktop computer, either in a special program or in a spreadsheet. Computer programs to accomplish the calculation of the A, B, and D matrices as well as other useful tasks also accompany this text and are discussed further later in this chapter.

It can be seen in Eq. (3.19) that the A matrix is the sum of the moduli for each layer in the overall coordinate system multiplied by the thickness of that layer. Thus, the A matrix divided by the total laminate thickness represents an average in-plane stress–strain relationship for the laminate, expressed as

$$[\overline{Q}_{\text{avg}}] = \left(\frac{1}{t}\right)[A] \tag{3.22}$$

It will be shown in later chapters that the average stress–strain properties for a laminate can be useful in a number of calculations.

The notation used in the A matrix, that of calling the term in the first row and third column A_{16} rather than A_{13} should be noted. The rationale for this is that these matrices involved integrals of the Q stress–strain matrix, and it is customary to identify the position relative to the full three-dimensional stress–strain matrix with a size of 6 by 6, before it is reduced to the 3-by-3 matrix for plane stress. Although perhaps confusing, this notation seems well established in the composites literature. Similar notation is used for the D-matrix terms.

The inverses of the previous matrix equations are required for a number of purposes, including calculating the stresses within the various plies of the laminate. In the general case of Eq. (3.16), the entire 6-by-6 ABD matrix must be inverted to get

$$\begin{Bmatrix} \epsilon^0 \\ \kappa \end{Bmatrix}_{6,1} = \begin{bmatrix} A & B \\ B & D \end{bmatrix}_{6,6}^{-1} \begin{Bmatrix} N \\ M \end{Bmatrix}_{6,1} \tag{3.23}$$

The inverse of the ABD matrix is sometimes called the $A*B*D*$ matrix; in this text it is called the F matrix to simplify notation. Thus,

$$[F]_{6,6} \equiv \begin{bmatrix} A & B \\ B & D \end{bmatrix}^{-1} \equiv \begin{bmatrix} A^* & B^* \\ B^* & D^* \end{bmatrix} \tag{3.24}$$

For symmetric laminates, which thus have a zero B matrix, the two 3-by-3 matrices can be inverted to get the following:

If

$$[B]_{3,3} = [0]_{3,3}$$

then

$$\{\epsilon^0\}_{3,1} = [A]_{3,3}^{-1}\{N\}_{3,1} \tag{3.25}$$

and

$$\{\kappa\}_{3,1} = [D]_{3,3}^{-1}\{M\}_{3,1} \tag{3.26}$$

3.5 LAMINATE CODE

Before discussion of particular laminates, it is convenient to explore a shorthand code used to specify the layup. Laminates are specified by the plies or ply groups that constitute the layup. Some examples will illustrate the procedure. A laminate consisting of a series of layers (made up of individual plies in a prepreg laminate) of one material in unidirectional form can be specified by the angles and numbers of plies in each ply group, such as $[0_2/90/90/0_2]$, where the subscript refers to the number of plies in the ply group. A $[0/45/-45/90]_s$ laminate is symmetric about the midplane, and is thus equivalent to an $[0/45/-45/90/90/-45/45/0]$ layup. Another convention is that of repeated groups of plies, such as $[(0/-60/60)_2]_s$, which is equivalent to $[0/-60/60/0/-60/60]_s$. Another convention is that of an overbar on a ply designation adjacent to the symmetry axis, which means a half ply, for example, $[0/\overline{90}]_s$ means $[0/90/0]$. The symbol T is sometimes added for clarity to show that the total stack is indicated. For example, $[0_{10}]_T$ means 10 plies of 0^0 orientation. A hybrid laminate contains more than one material, such as mixing glass-fiber plies and carbon-fiber plies. In this case, the notation must also identify the material, usually by using a material designation as a subscript for the ply group. Manufacturing techniques other than prepreg layup do not have layers composed of a discrete number of plies. For example, in filament winding, the material is applied in layers of fibers with a common angle, but the thickness of each layer depends on the processing variables. Here the amount of fiber is identified by the thickness of the layer, given as a subscript.

EXAMPLE 3.1   Calculation of A and D matrices for a unidirectional laminate

As a first example, consider the calculation of the A and D matrices for a unidirectional laminate with 10 plies of AS4/3501-6 carbon epoxy. The layup is thus designated as $[0_{10}]$. Because the laminate is symmetric about its midplane, that is, it could equally well be designated as a $[0_5]_s$ laminate, all terms of the B matrix are identically zero. The stress–strain matrix for this material is calculated from the properties given in Table 2.1, using Eq. (2.16), and has been shown previously in Example 2.1. Because the orientation of the plies coincides with the overall x,y coordinate system, the coordinate-transformation matrix of Eq. (2.29) is just the unit matrix, so that the properties are unchanged. Substituting into Eqs. (3.17) and (3.19), and noting that the sum is over the single ply group, gives

$$[A] = \begin{bmatrix} \dfrac{E_{11}}{1 - \nu_{12}\nu_{21}} & \dfrac{\nu_{21}E_{11}}{1 - \nu_{12}\nu_{21}} & 0 \\[3mm] \dfrac{\nu_{12}E_{22}}{1 - \nu_{12}\nu_{21}} & \dfrac{E_{22}}{1 - \nu_{12}\nu_{21}} & 0 \\[3mm] 0 & 0 & G_{12} \end{bmatrix} (t)$$

and

$$[D] = \begin{bmatrix} \dfrac{E_{11}}{1 - \nu_{12}\nu_{21}} & \dfrac{\nu_{21}E_{11}}{1 - \nu_{12}\nu_{21}} & 0 \\[3mm] \dfrac{\nu_{12}E_{22}}{1 - \nu_{12}\nu_{21}} & \dfrac{E_{22}}{1 - \nu_{12}\nu_{21}} & 0 \\[3mm] 0 & 0 & G_{12} \end{bmatrix} \left(\dfrac{t^3}{12}\right)$$

where t is the total laminate thickness. It is easy to see that for this case, the A matrix is just the stress–strain matrix multiplied by the total thickness. The D matrix represents the bending-stiffness properties, and, noting that it is defined on a per unit width basis, can be seen to be a two-dimensional version of the familiar "EI" stiffness of beam theory for a unit width beam.

■

The preceding example shows how the A and D matrices are calculated for a unidirectional material. The following example shows a similar calculation for a slightly more realistic laminate with two orientation angles.

EXAMPLE 3.2   Calculation of A and D matrices for a bidirectional laminate

As a second example, consider the calculation of the A and D matrices for a bidirectional cross-ply lamina with 20 plies of AS4/3501-6 carbon epoxy arranged as $[0_5/90_5]_s$. The layup is illustrated in Figure 3.4.

Because the laminate is symmetric about its midplane, all terms of the B matrix are identically zero. The stress–strain matrix for this material is calculated from the properties given in Table 2.1, using Eq. (2.16), and was shown previously in Example 2.1. The thickness of an individual ply is taken as the nominal value for this material, which is 0.132 mm (0.0052 in). The coordinate-transformation matrix of Eq. (2.29) is just the unit matrix for the 0° plies and interchanges the axial and transverse properties for the 90° plies. Substituting into Eqs. (3.17) and (3.19) and noting that the sum is over the four ply groups gives numerical values as

$$[A] = \begin{bmatrix} 18.5 & 0.451 & 0 \\ 0.451 & 1.61 & 0 \\ 0 & 0 & 0.95 \end{bmatrix}(2)(0.026) + \begin{bmatrix} 1.61 & 0.451 & 0 \\ 0.451 & 18.5 & 0 \\ 0 & 0 & 0.95 \end{bmatrix}(2)(.026)$$

$$[A] = \begin{bmatrix} 1.047 & 0.0469 & 0 \\ 0.0469 & 1.047 & 0 \\ 0 & 0 & 0.0988 \end{bmatrix}\text{Msi-in} = \begin{bmatrix} 183 & 8.21 & 0 \\ 8.21 & 183 & 0 \\ 0 & 0 & 17.3 \end{bmatrix}\text{MPa-m}$$

$$[D] = \begin{bmatrix} 18.5 & 0.451 & 0 \\ 0.451 & 1.61 & 0 \\ 0 & 0 & 0.90 \end{bmatrix}\dfrac{(-0.026)^3 - (-0.052)^3}{3} + \begin{bmatrix} 1.61 & 0.451 & 0 \\ 0.451 & 18.5 & 0 \\ 0 & 0 & 0.90 \end{bmatrix}\dfrac{(0)^3 - (-0.026)^3}{3}$$

$$+\begin{bmatrix}1.61 & 0.451 & 0\\0.451 & 18.5 & 0\\0 & 0 & 0.90\end{bmatrix}\frac{(0.026)^3-(0)^3}{3}+\begin{bmatrix}18.5 & 0.451 & 0\\0.451 & 1.61 & 0\\0 & 0 & 0.90\end{bmatrix}\frac{(0.052)^3-(0.026)^3}{3}$$

$$[D]=\begin{bmatrix}1538 & 42.3 & 0\\42.3 & 349 & 0\\0 & 0 & 89.1\end{bmatrix}\text{lb-in}=\begin{bmatrix}173.8 & 4.78 & 0\\4.78 & 39.4 & 0\\0 & 0 & 10.1\end{bmatrix}\text{N-m}$$

Several features can be noted about the A and D matrices. The terms of the A matrix are the same with respect to the x and y directions (compare the A_{11} and A_{22} terms), and the D_{11} and D_{22} matrix terms are quite different. This occurs because the A matrix terms are independent of position, and the D matrix terms depend on position to the third power. The D_{11} term, representing bending stiffness in the x direction, is much higher than the D_{22} term, representing bending stiffness in the y direction, because the plies in the 0 direction, with high stiffness in the x direction, are toward the outside of the laminate, farthest from the center line.

Dividing the A matrix terms by the total thickness gives the average stress–strain properties:

$$[Q_{\text{avg}}]=\begin{bmatrix}10.07 & 0.451 & 0\\0.451 & 10.07 & 0\\0 & 0 & 0.95\end{bmatrix}\text{Msi}=\begin{bmatrix}69.4 & 3.11 & 0\\3.11 & 69.4 & 0\\0 & 0 & 6.55\end{bmatrix}\text{GPa}$$

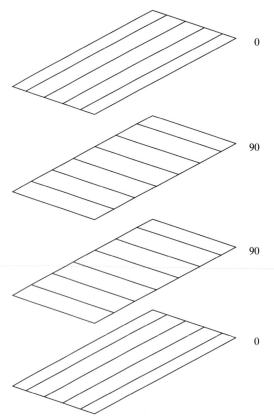

Figure 3.4 The $[0_5/90_5]_s$ layup. Each ply group is composed of five plies.

It is easy to see that the average stress–strain properties for this case of 0° and 90° plies represents the average of the axial and transverse properties. Thus, the average stiffness of this laminate is reduced by about 45% relative to the axial stiffness of the 0° plies, but is the same in both the x and y directions. This is typical of laminates in that the maximum stiffness is reduced by including plies with other orientations. However, this is usually necessary in order to provide adequate stiffness (and as will be seen later, strength) in transverse directions. It should also be noted that the shear stiffness (the 3,3 term) is unchanged from the unidirectional value. Plies with other orientation angles are needed to increase shear stiffness and strength, and plies with an orientation of ±45° are most effective in carrying shear loads.   ∎

3.6 HYGROTHERMAL BEHAVIOR

In addition to the mechanical loads described before, laminates are often subjected to thermal and moisture environments. These environments can introduce stresses into the individual plies, even if the overall laminate is subject to no additional mechanical loads. It is straightforward to include these "hygrothermal" (combined moisture and thermal) effects. The development follows exactly that given before, except that the stress–strain relations of the individual plies must now include the thermal and moisture effects. As given previously in Eq. (2.34), the stress–strain law with thermal and moisture terms, expressed in terms of the overall x,y directions, is given as

$$\left\{ \begin{array}{c} \sigma_x \\ \sigma_y \\ \tau_{xy} \end{array} \right\} = [\overline{Q}] \left\{ \begin{array}{c} \epsilon_x - \alpha_x \Delta T - \beta_x \Delta m \\ \epsilon_y - \alpha_y \Delta T - \beta_y \Delta m \\ \gamma_{xy} - \alpha_{xy} \Delta T - \beta_{xy} \Delta m \end{array} \right\} \tag{3.27}$$

where the expansion coefficients for temperature and moisture are expressed in overall x,y coordinates as given in Eq. (2.33). Substituting the preceding equation in Eqs. (3.11) and (3.12) gives

$$\left\{ \begin{array}{c} N_x \\ N_y \\ N_{xy} \end{array} \right\} = \sum_{k=1}^{N} \int_{h_{k-1}}^{h_k} \overline{Q}_k \left\{ \begin{array}{c} \epsilon_x - \alpha_x \Delta T - \beta_x \Delta m \\ \epsilon_y - \alpha_y \Delta T - \beta_y \Delta m \\ \gamma_{xy} - \alpha_{xy} \Delta T - \beta_{xy} \Delta m \end{array} \right\} dz \tag{3.28}$$

and

$$\left\{ \begin{array}{c} M_x \\ M_y \\ M_{xy} \end{array} \right\} = \sum_{k=1}^{N} \int_{h_{k-1}}^{h_k} \overline{Q}_k \left\{ \begin{array}{c} \epsilon_x - \alpha_x \Delta T - \beta_x \Delta m \\ \epsilon_y - \alpha_y \Delta T - \beta_y \Delta m \\ \gamma_{xy} - \alpha_{xy} \Delta T - \beta_{xy} \Delta m \end{array} \right\} z \, dz \tag{3.29}$$

Carrying out the integrations as before gives

$$\left\{ \begin{array}{c} N \\ M \end{array} \right\} = \left[\begin{array}{cc} A & B \\ B & D \end{array} \right] \left\{ \begin{array}{c} \epsilon^0 \\ \kappa \end{array} \right\} - \left\{ \begin{array}{c} N_{th} \\ M_{th} \end{array} \right\} \tag{3.30}$$

where the additional terms on the right-hand side contain the moisture and temperature terms, which are given by

$$\{N_{th}\} = \begin{Bmatrix} N_{x_{th}} \\ N_{y_{th}} \\ N_{xy_{th}} \end{Bmatrix} = \sum_{k=1}^{N} \int_{h_{k-1}}^{h_k} \overline{Q}_k \begin{Bmatrix} \alpha_x \Delta T + \beta_x \Delta m \\ \alpha_y \Delta T + \beta_y \Delta m \\ \alpha_{xy} \Delta T + \beta_{xy} \Delta m \end{Bmatrix} dz \tag{3.31}$$

$$\{M_{th}\} = \begin{Bmatrix} M_{x_{th}} \\ M_{y_{th}} \\ M_{xy_{th}} \end{Bmatrix} = \sum_{k=1}^{N} \int_{h_{k-1}}^{h_k} \overline{Q}_k \begin{Bmatrix} \alpha_x \Delta T + \beta_x \Delta m \\ \alpha_y \Delta T + \beta_y \Delta m \\ \alpha_{xy} \Delta T + \beta_{xy} \Delta m \end{Bmatrix} z\, dz \tag{3.32}$$

If the temperature and moisture terms are independent of the z coordinate in each ply, the integrals can be evaluated simply as shown in Eqs. (3.13) and (3.14). Note that even though the temperature and moisture may be constant through the entire thickness of the laminate, the coefficients of thermal and moisture expansion vary with the ply orientation and so must be kept inside the summation. For the case of constant temperature and moisture through the thickness, the thermal and moisture resultants simplify to

$$\begin{Bmatrix} N_{x_{th}} \\ N_{y_{th}} \\ N_{xy_{th}} \end{Bmatrix} = \sum_{k=1}^{N} [\overline{Q}_k] \begin{Bmatrix} \alpha_x \Delta T + \beta_x \Delta m \\ \alpha_y \Delta T + \beta_y \Delta m \\ \alpha_{xy} \Delta T + \beta_{xy} \Delta m \end{Bmatrix} (h_k - h_{k-1}) \tag{3.33}$$

and

$$\begin{Bmatrix} M_{x_{th}} \\ M_{y_{th}} \\ M_{xy_{th}} \end{Bmatrix} = \sum_{k=1}^{N} [\overline{Q}_k] \begin{Bmatrix} \alpha_x \Delta T + \beta_x \Delta m \\ \alpha_y \Delta T + \beta_y \Delta m \\ \alpha_{xy} \Delta T + \beta_{xy} \Delta m \end{Bmatrix} \left(\frac{h_k^2 - h_{k-1}^2}{2} \right) \tag{3.34}$$

The stress and moment resultants defined in Eqs. (3.31) and (3.32) or (3.33) and (3.34) can be considered to be loads placed on the laminate due to thermal and moisture conditions that are different from those that exist at the stress-free or reference condition. These terms can be very significant and have a number of surprising ramifications. In many cases, laminates are fabricated at elevated temperature. Cooling down to room temperature thus gives rise to the thermal terms defined before. As will be shown later, thermal stresses result from this cooldown. Also, if the laminate is nonsymmetric, significant warpage can result from unbalanced thermal stresses. This latter effect is demonstrated in the following example.

EXAMPLE 3.3   Thermal warping in an unsymmetric laminate

Consider the warping due to thermal stresses in a $[0_4/90_4]$ laminate of AS4/3501-6 carbon/epoxy that is cured at 177°C (350°F) and then cooled down to room temperature, so that $\Delta T = -156°C$ ($-280°F$). Unbalanced thermal stresses result because of the unsymmetric layup, and the laminate has a noticeable curvature at room temperature. This thermal distortion can be estimated by using the preceding relationships. The thermal stress and moment resultant are calculated from Eqs. (3.33) and (3.34). The *ABD* matrix and the inverse of this matrix must also be calculated, noting that the B matrix does not vanish because the laminate is unsymmetric. Denoting the inverse of the ABD matrix as F, as in Eq. (3.24), Eq. (3.30) can be written as

$$\left\{ \begin{matrix} \epsilon^0 \\ \kappa \end{matrix} \right\} = \begin{bmatrix} A & B \\ B & D \end{bmatrix}^{-1} \left(\left\{ \begin{matrix} N \\ M \end{matrix} \right\} + \left\{ \begin{matrix} N_{th} \\ M_{th} \end{matrix} \right\} \right) = [F] \left(\left\{ \begin{matrix} N \\ M \end{matrix} \right\} + \left\{ \begin{matrix} N_{th} \\ M_{th} \end{matrix} \right\} \right)$$

If no external stress resultants are applied to the plate, the N mechanical load stress resultants are all zero. Additionally, because no external mechanical loads are applied, it would seem that the mechanical-load-moment resultants also are all identically zero. Whereas this would be true in a very narrow-beam geometry, this is not true in typical plate geometries. It has been shown by analysis and can be easily verified by experiment that a composite plate will curve in either of the x or y axes, but not both at the same time. The plate is stable in either of these two configurations. With thin plates, they can be easily manipulated by hand and snap into either configuration. Say that the plate is placed in the configuration with curvature in the x direction. Internal moments M_y are then set up everywhere except at the y edges of the plate, in order to keep the curvature in the y direction at zero. The x-direction curvature can then be solved from the following relation:

$$\left\{ \begin{matrix} \epsilon_x^0 \\ \epsilon_y^0 \\ \gamma_{xy}^0 \\ \kappa_x \\ 0 \\ \kappa_{xy} \end{matrix} \right\} = \begin{bmatrix} - & - & - & - & - & - \\ - & - & - & - & - & - \\ - & - & - & - & - & - \\ F_{41} & F_{42} & F_{43} & F_{44} & F_{45} & F_{46} \\ F_{51} & F_{52} & F_{53} & F_{54} & F_{54} & F_{54} \\ - & - & - & - & - & - \end{bmatrix} \left\{ \begin{matrix} N_{x_{th}} \\ N_{y_{th}} \\ N_{xy_{th}} \\ M_{x_{th}} \\ M_y + M_{y_{th}} \\ M_{xy_{th}} \end{matrix} \right\}$$

Here only the terms needed are written in the F matrix. Calculating the thermal-stress resultant terms shows that the N_{xy} and M_{xy} terms vanish, and the N_{xth} and N_{yth} terms are equal. Writing the fourth and fifth equations from the preceding gives

$$\left\{ \begin{matrix} \kappa_x \\ 0 \end{matrix} \right\} = \begin{bmatrix} (F_{41} + F_{42}) & F_{44} & F_{45} \\ (F_{51} + F_{52}) & F_{54} & F_{55} \end{bmatrix} \left\{ \begin{matrix} N_{th} \\ M_{x_{th}} \\ M_y + M_{y_{th}} \end{matrix} \right\}$$

Using the second of these equations to eliminate the unknown moment M_y gives the relationship between the curvature in the x direction and the thermal resultants as

$$\kappa_x = \left((F_{41} + F_{42}) - \frac{F_{45}}{F_{55}}(F_{51} + F_{52}) \right) N_{th} + \left(F_{44} - \frac{F_{45}F_{54}}{F_{55}} \right) M_{x_{th}}$$

The plate thus deforms into a cylindrical shape with a radius of curvature $R = 1/\kappa_x$. Substituting values gives $R = 1.749$ m (68.9 in). If a plate of length L in the x direction were lying on a flat surface, the ends would curl up a distance given by

$$h = R(1 - \cos \theta) \qquad \text{where} \qquad \theta = \frac{L/2}{R}$$

Substituting values with $L = 305$ mm (12 in) gives $h = 6.63$ mm (0.261 in). Repeating for a thinner $[0_2/90_2]$ laminate gives $h = 15.3$ mm (0.602 in). These are very noticeable displacements and they indicate the significant amount of thermal distortion that can take place with nonsymmetric laminates. A thin AS4/3501-6 unsymmetrical specimen is shown in Figure 3.5. The thermal distortions are in good agreement with the calculations given here. ■

Figure 3.5   An unsymmetric layup of AS4/3501-6 carbon/epoxy at ambient temperature, showing curvature induced by thermal stresses.

3.7 SPECIAL LAMINATES

Certain special cases of laminates with particular classes of ply orientations are of significant interest. These are described in what follows.

3.7.1 Symmetric Laminates

If the lamimate is symmetric with respect to the midplane, the B matrix will vanish. This can be seen in the definition of the B-matrix terms given in Eq. (3.18) and the notation used for the location of the interfaces as illustrated in Figure 3.3. In a symmetric layup, each ply group above the center line will be paired with a similar ply group below the center line. As illustrated in Figure 3.6, the location of the interfaces of these two groups can be identified as

Upper layer:

$$h_k = \xi + t \qquad h_{k-1} = \xi$$

Lower layer:

$$h_k = -\xi \qquad h_{k-1} = -(\xi + t)$$

so that when this pair of ply groups is substituted into the definition of the B matrix as

$$B = \sum_k (\overline{Q}_{ij})_k \left(\frac{h_k^2 - h_{k-1}^2}{2} \right) = \ldots + \overline{Q}_{\text{lower}} \left\{ \frac{(-\xi)^2 - [-(\xi + t)]^2}{2} + \ldots \right.$$

$$+ \overline{Q}_{\text{upper}} \left[\frac{(\xi + t)^2 - \xi^2}{2} \right] + \ldots$$

Because from symmetry the stiffness terms are the same for the lower and upper members of the pair, the contribution from each pair cancels, and the entire B matrix vanishes.

The vanishing of the B matrix gives an uncoupling of the extensional and bending responses. If the laminate is not symmetric, bending and extension are coupled through the B matrix, as can be seen in the earlier Eqs. (3.16) and (3.23). If the B matrix is present, bending stresses can result from uniform extensional strains. It will be shown in later chapters that having the B matrix vanish simplifies many types of analyses.

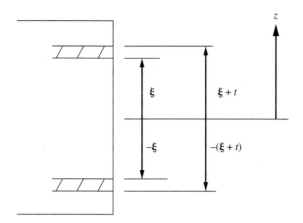

Figure 3.6 Location of interfaces for a pair of ply groups in a symmetric layup. The interfaces are located by the z values, which are negative below the center line.

3.7.2 Balanced Laminates

A balanced laminate results when the number of plies in a given θ direction is equal to the number of plies in the $-\theta$ direction, assuming that the plies are of the same material and thickness. As a result, in a balanced laminate, the A_{16} and A_{26} terms are zero, thus uncoupling the in-plane shear and extension response. To see that the A_{16} and A_{26} terms are zero for a balanced laminate, refer to the definition of the A matrix in Eq. (3.17), and note that the A matrix is just the sum of the $\overline{Q}$ matrix for each layer multiplied by the thickness of that layer. Now refer to the definition of the $\overline{Q}$ matrix given in Eq. (2.30). It can be seen that the $\overline{Q}_{16}$ and the $\overline{Q}_{26}$ terms both have terms that contain only odd powers of $\sin \theta$, so that the sign of these terms change with the sign of θ. Thus, for a balanced layup, the A_{16} and A_{26} terms are zero.

An example of the coupling that occurs in an unbalanced laminate is shown in Figure 3.7, where shear strain is depicted to result from an applied normal stress. To see more clearly why this effect is predicted to occur, consider an applied stress resultant N_x, with $N_y = N_{xy} = 0$. The center-line strains can be obtained from the inverse of the A matrix. The predicted strains are given by

$$
\left\{ \begin{array}{c} \epsilon^0_x \\ \epsilon^0_y \\ \gamma^0_{xy} \end{array} \right\} = \left[\begin{array}{ccc} A_{11}^{-1} & A_{12}^{-1} & A_{16}^{-1} \\ A_{12}^{-1} & A_{22}^{-1} & A_{26}^{-1} \\ A_{16}^{-1} & A_{26}^{-1} & A_{66}^{-1} \end{array} \right] \left\{ \begin{array}{c} N_x \\ 0 \\ 0 \end{array} \right\} \tag{3.35}
$$

where N_x is the applied force per unit length or the applied stress times the thickness of the material. Note that the terms in the A^{-1} matrix are not the reciprocal of the corresponding terms in the A matrix. It is easy to verify that if A_{16} is present, a corresponding term will be present in A^{-1}. It can be clearly seen that γ^0_{xy} does not vanish unless the A_{16}^{-1} vanishes. Although the extensional-shear coupling is unusual and has no counterpart in isotropic materials such as metals, it is a well-documented feature of composite materials. It should be also noted that whereas in a balanced, symmetric laminate both the entire B matrix and the A_{16} and A_{26} terms go to 0, the D_{16} and D_{26} terms are not zero. This is so because the D matrix depends on the relative position of each ply, and it is not possible to make the laminate layup both symmetric and have the plies that are balanced have the same relative position. An exception to this is the special case of laminates that contain only 0° and 90° plies, which are

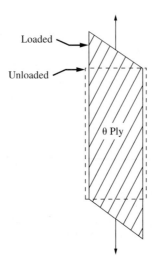

Loaded

Unloaded

θ Ply

Figure 3.7 Coupling normal and shear
effects in unbalanced laminates.

often called "cross-ply laminates." Thus, bending–twisting coupling occurs in unbalanced
laminates, and also to a lesser degree in balanced, symmetric laminates (or any other laminate where the balancing does not occur in plies of the same relative position from the center line). The relative size of the D_{16} and D_{26} terms becomes smaller as more plies are added,
if the plies at different angles are dispersed rather than being stacked together. It will be
shown later that assuming D_{16} and $D_{26} = 0$ offers a simplification in analysis, and thus this
assumption is often made whether it is strictly true or not.

Figure 3.8 X-29 aircraft with forward swept wings. The wings rely on bending–twisting coupling
to maintain stability, and this configuration could not fly at speed without fiber-composite wings.
(*Source:* Grumman Corp.)

The couplings cited above that result from A_{16}, A_{26}, D_{16}, and D_{26} are features of composite structures that have no counterpart in isotropic materials and can be taken advantage of to achieve unique characteristics. For example, the forward swept wing design of the X-29 aircraft shown in Figure 3.8 uses coupling between bending and torsion to achieve aeroelastic stability, and the design probably could not function using metallic wings. The couplings available with composites have probably not been fully explored.

It is also easy to verify experimentally that the bending–twisting coupling occurs in an unbalanced laminate. For example, a thin laminated strip made with a $[45_2/0_2]_s$ layup can be held against a desktop as a cantilever beam. Depressing the end reveals twisting as well as bending deformation that can easily be observed visually.

3.7.3 Quasi-Isotropic Laminates

An interesting category of laminates is achieved by having equal numbers of plies at 0, 45, −45, and 90 degrees, or at 0, 60, and −60 degrees, as shown in Figure 3.9. Both of these laminate families display in-plane stiffnesses that are independent of orientation. They are

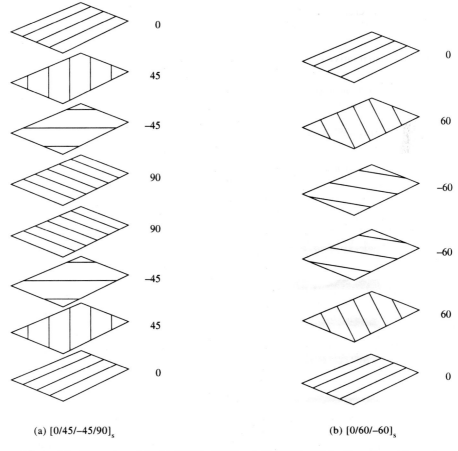

(a) $[0/45/{-}45/90]_s$ (b) $[0/60/{-}60]_s$

Figure 3.9 Illustration of the (a) $[0/45/{-}45/90]$ and (b) $[0/60/{-}60]$ families of quasi-isotropic laminates.

thus called quasi-isotropic because they display isotropic properties within the plane of the laminate, but, of course, have a different modulus in the through-the-thickness direction. These classes of laminates are often used for those cases in which the loading directions are not well known in advance, so that no particular directions can be favored. The quasi-isotropic layup is also often used in what is called "black aluminum" design, in which composite materials (black refers to carbon-fiber composites) are substituted for conventional metals without significant redesign.

It is a straightforward exercise to show that quasi-isotropic behavior results from the layups cited. The procedure is to explicitly write all the terms of the A matrix with, say, the angle between the fibers in the 0 degree ply set at an angle θ to the x axis, the 45 degree ply at $(45 + \theta)$, and so on. By means of trigonometric identities, it can then be shown that the explicit dependence on θ vanishes, showing independence of the A matrix with respect to θ. A less elegant way to demonstrate the same property is to add an arbitrary angle to each of the orientations, and then to calculate the A and $\bar{Q}_{avg}$ matrices, and to observe that the terms do not change, so that the A and $\bar{Q}_{avg}$ matrices are independent of orientation.

3.8 STRESSES WITHIN THE PLIES

The stresses within the individual plies can be highly nonuniform, even for very simple loadings. However, these stresses can be easily determined from the equations given before. The basic idea is that the strain distribution in the laminate can be determined and typically has a simple form such as a uniform-strain distribution through the thickness in some cases, or perhaps a linearly varying bending-strain distribution in other cases. These strain distributions can be determined as part of the solution process for the particular problem. As a simple example, consider a statically determinate problem in which the stress resultants and moment resultants are known. The center-line strains and curvatures then can be found by inverting Eq. (3.16). For shorthand, define the inverse of the ABD matrix as F, as given previously, that is, let

$$[F] \equiv \begin{bmatrix} A & B \\ B & D \end{bmatrix}^{-1} \tag{3.24}$$

Then the center-line strains and curvatures are found from

$$\left\{ \begin{matrix} \epsilon^0 \\ \kappa \end{matrix} \right\} = [F] \left\{ \begin{matrix} N \\ M \end{matrix} \right\} \tag{3.36}$$

The strain distribution throughout the thickness of the laminate then can be obtained from Eq. (3.4), which repeated here, as

$$\{\epsilon\} = \{\epsilon^0\} + z\{\kappa\} \tag{3.4}$$

The strains in the principal material directions then can be obtained for any (or all) of the plies from the strains above that are referred to the overall x,y coordinates by the coordinate-transformation equations given previously.

$$\left\{ \begin{matrix} \epsilon_1 \\ \epsilon_2 \\ \gamma_{12} \end{matrix} \right\} = [R][T][R^{-1}] \left\{ \begin{matrix} \epsilon_x \\ \epsilon_y \\ \gamma_{xy} \end{matrix} \right\} = [R][T][R^{-1}](\{\epsilon^0\} + z\{\kappa\}) \tag{3.37}$$

This expression uses the R matrix of Eq. (2.23) to take into account that the transformation must involve the tensor strains. The stresses in the principal material directions then can be found by multiplying the strains in those directions by the material property matrix for the ply:

$$\left\{ \begin{array}{c} \sigma_1 \\ \sigma_2 \\ \tau_{12} \end{array} \right\} = [Q] \left\{ \begin{array}{c} \epsilon_1 \\ \epsilon_2 \\ \gamma_{12} \end{array} \right\} \tag{3.38}$$

Often, the calculation of the ply stresses (or strains) is the objective of the analysis and is the basis for strength design in fiber composites.

3.9 COMPUTER PROGRAMS FOR *A, B,* AND *D* MATRICES

The computation of the A, B, and D matrices is needed for essentially all analyses with fiber-composite materials. Although it is a straightforward task, it is lengthy enough to warrant having a computer program to carry out the calculations. Computer programs for this purpose are available on the web for use with this text, and are described in the Appendix. These programs are written in Fortran (as well as other languages) and have been compiled and run on Macintosh and PC machines. In addition, a MATLAB version is also provided, in the form of m files. For those who have MATLAB available, these files provide an equivalent approach. Either version of the programs can be used, but the MATLAB format makes it easy to make modifications if desired or to use the basic ingredients to customize solutions for specialized problems.

The basic format of the program is that it asks the user to specify the layup with respect to direction and materials. Standard properties are furnished, but can be independently specified by the user. The program then calculates the A, B, and D matrices. For those cases in which these matrices will be used in other analyses, this is all that is required. For cases in which the stress and moment resultants are already known (perhaps from equilibrium, for example), the program continues by asking for these resultants. The program then finds the inverse of the combined ABD matrix, calculates the center-line strains and curvatures, and calculates the stresses and strains in each ply along the 1,2 (fiber) axes. Finally, the program predicts what the failure loads will be, using failure criteria, which are discussed in Chapter 4.

Programs are also available elsewhere from a number of sources. The calculation of the A, B, and D matrices is standard, but the programs differ in the range of features and the type of implementation. The reader can also easily write a program using the mathematical software packages such as Mathcad, MATLAB, Maple, or Mathematica. The convenient matrix capabilities of these programs are ideally suited for computations that are required for the analysis of fiber composites.

3.10 EXAMPLES

Although other examples of analysis and design are given in subsequent chapters, it is worthwhile to consider a number of simple examples. In all of these examples, the procedure is the same. The center-line strains are first calculated from the mechanical and/or thermal or moisture loadings. The strain distributions throughout the laminate are then found. These strains in global coordinates are then transformed into fiber-direction strains and finally into fiber-direction stresses.

The first example is concerned with stresses in a 0/90 symmetric laminate under axial loading.

EXAMPLE 3.4   Stresses in a $[0_5/90_5]_s$ laminate under uniaxial loading

Consider the task of finding the fiber-direction stresses in a $[0_5/90_5]_s$ laminate made of AS4/3501-6 under a uniformly distributed tensile force applied in the x direction of 17,790 N (4000 lb), as shown in Figure 3.10. The dimensions of the sheet of fiber-composite material are 254 by 50.8 mm (10 by 2 in) in the x and y directions, respectively.

Solution: The applied stress resultant is a force per unit length and is obtained by dividing the total force by the length of the x face to get $N_x = 350$ kN/m (2000 lb/in). The applied moment resultants are all zero. Because the laminate is symmetric, the B matrix vanishes and the center-line strains in the x,y coordinate system are calculated from Eq. (3.23). The curvatures, calculated from Eq. (3.24), all vanish, because no moments are applied. Using the properties given previously in Example 3.2 gives

$$\begin{Bmatrix} \epsilon^0_x \\ \epsilon^0_y \\ \gamma^0_{xy} \end{Bmatrix} = [A^{-1}] \begin{Bmatrix} N_x \\ 0 \\ 0 \end{Bmatrix}$$

The A matrix for this layup has been previously calculated in Example 3.2. In general, the strain distributions would then be calculated from Eq. (3.4), although for this case the curvatures are all zero. The strains are then transformed into the stress directions using Eq. (3.37), and the stresses in the fiber-direction coordinates are then calculated from Eq. (3.38), using the ply stress–strain law. The results are as follows.

0 ply:

$$\begin{Bmatrix} \epsilon_1 \\ \epsilon_2 \\ \gamma_{12} \end{Bmatrix} = \begin{Bmatrix} 0.00191 \\ -8.57\,E-5 \\ 0 \end{Bmatrix} \quad \text{and} \quad \begin{Bmatrix} \sigma_1 \\ \sigma_2 \\ \tau_{12} \end{Bmatrix} = \begin{Bmatrix} 244 \\ 5.0 \\ 0 \end{Bmatrix} \text{MPa} = \begin{Bmatrix} 35.4 \\ 0.725 \\ 0 \end{Bmatrix} \text{ksi}$$

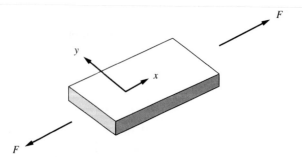

Figure 3.10   Uniaxial force loading of a $[0_5/90_5]_s$ laminate.

90 ply:

$$
\left\{ \begin{array}{c} \epsilon_1 \\ \epsilon_2 \\ \gamma_{12} \end{array} \right\} = \left\{ \begin{array}{c} -8.57\,E-5 \\ 0.00191 \\ 0 \end{array} \right\} \quad \text{and} \quad \left\{ \begin{array}{c} \sigma_1 \\ \sigma_2 \\ \tau_{12} \end{array} \right\} = \left\{ \begin{array}{c} -5.0 \\ 21.0 \\ 0 \end{array} \right\} \text{MPa} = \left\{ \begin{array}{c} -0.725 \\ 3.04 \\ 0 \end{array} \right\} \text{ksi}
$$

Several features of these results should be noted. First, consider that the average applied stress is just the applied force P divided by the area = (width $\times$ thickness), or, equivalently, the applied stress resultant divided by the thickness, which would give $\sigma_{x,\mathrm{avg}} = 132.6$ MPa (19.2 ksi). However, the stress in the 0° plies in the fiber direction is almost twice this average value. This is because the 0° fibers are much stiffer in the x direction than are the 90° plies, which have their transverse direction in the x direction. If the transverse stiffness of the 90's were actually 0, they would not carry any x-direction load, and the axial stress in the 0's would be exactly double the average applied stress. Next, note that both the 0° and the 90° plies have stress in the transverse direction, even though there is no external load in this direction. These stresses occur because of the Poisson ratio mismatch that occurs between the two plies. The contraction of the 0° plies in the y direction would result from ν_{12} if they were acting alone, and the contraction of the 90° plies would be governed by ν_{21} if acting alone, under the x-direction strain. Because these two Poisson ratios are markedly different, a system of transverse-direction stresses must be set up in order to make the transverse strains the same. It can be seen that this sets up a transverse tension in the 0° plies, and an equal but opposite axial compression in the 90° plies. This is a general result, in that laminates are under multiaxial states of stress even when the applied loading is uniaxial. ∎

Another example illustrates the calculation of stresses due to thermal effects in cooldown of a laminate. Consider the warping due to thermal stresses in a $[0_5/90_5]$ laminate of AS4/3501-6 carbon/epoxy that is cured at 177°C (350°F) and then cooled down to room temperature, so that $\Delta T = -156$°C (-280°F).

EXAMPLE 3.5   Thermal stresses in a $[0_5/90_5]_s$ laminate

Consider the calculation of the stresses that result from cooldown in a $[0_5/90_5]_s$ laminate made of AS4/3501-6 carbon/epoxy. The calculation follows that given previously in Example 3.3, however, this problem is simpler because the laminate is symmetric. Thus, the geometry is not distorted due to cooldown, but internal stresses are set up due to the different coefficients of thermal expansion in the different directions. The thermal-stress resultant vector is calculated from Eq. (3.31), and the thermal-moment resultant vector is found from Eq. (3.32) to be identically zero. The overall strains are then calculated by inverting Eq. (3.30) (note that because the B matrix is zero and the moment loading is also zero, only A has to be inverted), to get

$$
\left\{ \begin{array}{c} \epsilon_x \\ \epsilon_y \\ \gamma_{xy} \end{array} \right\} = [A^{-1}] \left\{ \begin{array}{c} N_{x_{th}} \\ N_{y_{th}} \\ N_{xy_{th}} \end{array} \right\} = \left\{ \begin{array}{c} -4.30\,E-4 \\ -4.30\,E-4 \\ 0 \end{array} \right\}
$$

The strains in the plies are calculated from Eq. (3.37), and the ply stresses are calculated from the stress–strain law, including the temperature effects, as

0 ply:

$$\begin{Bmatrix} \epsilon_1 \\ \epsilon_2 \\ \gamma_{12} \end{Bmatrix} = [R][T][R^{-1}] \begin{Bmatrix} \epsilon_x \\ \epsilon_y \\ \gamma_{xy} \end{Bmatrix} = \begin{Bmatrix} -4.30\,\text{E}-4 \\ -4.30\,\text{E}-4 \\ 0 \end{Bmatrix}$$

$$\begin{Bmatrix} \sigma_1 \\ \sigma_2 \\ \tau_{12} \end{Bmatrix} = [Q] \begin{Bmatrix} \epsilon_1 \\ \epsilon_2 \\ \gamma_{12} \end{Bmatrix} - [Q] \begin{Bmatrix} \alpha_1 \Delta T \\ \alpha_2 \Delta T \\ 0 \end{Bmatrix} = \begin{Bmatrix} -43.6 \\ 43.6 \\ 0 \end{Bmatrix} \text{MPa} = \begin{Bmatrix} -6.33 \\ 6.33 \\ 0 \end{Bmatrix} \text{ksi}$$

90 ply:

$$\begin{Bmatrix} \epsilon_1 \\ \epsilon_2 \\ \gamma_{12} \end{Bmatrix} = [R][T][R^{-1}] \begin{Bmatrix} \epsilon_x \\ \epsilon_y \\ \gamma_{xy} \end{Bmatrix} = \begin{Bmatrix} -4.30\,\text{E}-4 \\ -4.30\,\text{E}-4 \\ 0 \end{Bmatrix}$$

and

$$\begin{Bmatrix} \sigma_1 \\ \sigma_2 \\ \tau_{12} \end{Bmatrix} = [Q] \begin{Bmatrix} \epsilon_1 \\ \epsilon_2 \\ \gamma_{12} \end{Bmatrix} - [Q] \begin{Bmatrix} \alpha_1 \Delta T \\ \alpha_2 \Delta T \\ 0 \end{Bmatrix} = \begin{Bmatrix} -43.6 \\ 43.6 \\ 0 \end{Bmatrix} \text{MPa} = \begin{Bmatrix} -6.33 \\ 6.33 \\ 0 \end{Bmatrix} \text{ksi}$$

It can be seen that at the ply level, the stresses and strains are the same. This has to be, of course, because 0° and 90° are arbitrary labels and could be interchanged, as the temperature is uniform everywhere. Further, the total forces (stress × area) in both the x and y directions must equal zero, because there are no external forces. Finally, the direction of the stresses can be easily explained by remembering that the coefficient of thermal expansion (CTE) in the fiber direction is small in magnitude and actually negative in sign for carbon-fiber plies. Thus, the fibers try to expand slightly along their length, but are opposed by the adjacent plies, which contract in the transverse direction. This puts the plies in compression in the fiber direction and in tension in the transverse direction. Also, a rough approximation to the stress state can be made by one-dimensional "strength of materials" procedures by calculating the transverse stress as

$$\sigma_2 = E_2 \alpha_2 \Delta T$$

which gives a value about 13% higher than the value given before. This approximation is based on the fact that because the stiffness in the fiber direction is much higher than that of the matrix-dominated, transverse-direction stiffness, the overall strains are small. Thus, the material acts, in a rough sense, as if it were held fixed on the edges while it cools, and thus gives rise to the thermal stresses. Also, it should be noted that whereas the stresses calculated before are small compared to fiber allowable stresses, they are much more significant with respect to matrix properties for polymer-matrix composites. Thermal stresses can play a significant role in matrix microcracking.   ■

The final example shows the calculation of stresses in a $[0_2/\pm45]_s$ laminate under a direct tension load and also a bending moment.

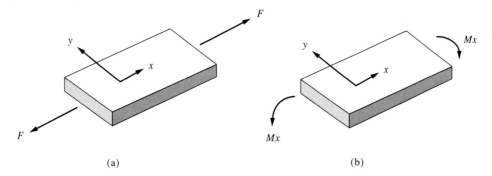

Figure 3.11   Combined (a) direct tension load and (b) moment load in x direction of laminate.

EXAMPLE 3.6   Calculation of stresses in a $[0_2/\pm 45]_s$ laminate

Consider a $[0_2/\pm 45]_s$ laminate of AS4/3501-6 carbon/epoxy under a direct tension load and also in a subsequent calculation under a bending moment, as shown in Figure 3.11. The properties of this carbon/epoxy material have been given previously in Table 2.1. The A and D matrices are then calculated as in Eqs. (3.17) and (3.19), transforming the material properties to the overall x,y coordinates that coincide with the 0° fibers. The B matrix is identically zero because of the symmetry of the laminate. Inverting these matrices and substituting into Eqs. (3.25) and (3.26) give the center-line strains and curvatures, which then permit the strain to be calculated for each ply from Eq. (3.4). Finally, the strains at a given location can be transformed into the ply directions using Eq. (3.37). The ply stresses then can be calculated from the ply-direction strains using the stress–strain relationship for the ply, as shown in Eq. (3.38). The results of these computations for ply stresses are given in Tables 3.1 and 3.2 for the direct tension and bending loads, respectively. Superposition can be used to combine the direct tension and bending stresses. Note that the z distance used for the bending case is to the outer surface of the ply.

Direct tension load: By using a value of $N_x = 17.51$ kN/m (100 lb/in), the laminate strains are then calculated as

$$\left\{ \begin{array}{c} \epsilon_x \\ \epsilon_y \\ \gamma_{xy} \end{array} \right\} = [A^{-1}] \left\{ \begin{array}{c} N_x \\ 0 \\ 0 \end{array} \right\} = \left\{ \begin{array}{c} 2.20\,\mathrm{E}-4 \\ -1.340\,\mathrm{E}-4 \\ 0 \end{array} \right\}$$

The ply-direction strains and stresses are then given in Table 3.1.

Table 3.1   Ply Strains and Stresses for N_x Loading

Ply	ϵ_1	ϵ_2	γ_{12}	σ_1 MPa	σ_1 psi	σ_2 MPa	σ_2 psi	τ_{12} MPa	τ_{12} psi
−45	4.31 E−5	4.31 E−5	3.54 E−4	5.64	817	0.612	88.8	2.32	337
45	4.31 E−5	4.31 E−5	3.54 E−4	5.64	817	0.612	88.8	−2.32	−337
0	2.20 E−4	−1.34 E−4	0	27.7	4020	−0.804	−116.6	0	
0	2.20 E−4	−1.34 E−4	0	27.7	4020	−0.804	−116.6	0	

Table 3.2 Ply Strains and Stresses for M_x Loading

Ply	z mm	z in	ϵ_1	ϵ_2	γ_{12}	σ_1 MPa	σ_1 psi	σ_2 MPa	σ_2 psi	τ_{12} MPa	τ_{12} psi
−45	0.1321	0.0052	2.02 E−5	1.143 E−5	7.315 E−5	2.61	379	0.190	27.5	0.479	69.5
45	0.264	0.0104	2.28 E−5	4.03 E−5	−1.46 E−4	3.04	442	0.519	75.3	−0.958	−139
0	0.396	0.0156	1.57 E−4	−6.23 E−5	2.62 E−5	19.9	2880	−0.204	−29.6	−0.172	−24.9
0	0.528	0.0208	2.09 E−4	−8.31 E−5	−3.50 E−5	26.5	3840	−0.272	−39.4	−0.229	−33.2

Bending load: By using a value of $M_x = 4.45$ N-m/m (1 in-lb/in), the laminate curvatures are then calculated as

$$\begin{Bmatrix} k_x \\ k_y \\ k_{xy} \end{Bmatrix} = [D^{-1}] \begin{Bmatrix} M_x \\ 0 \\ 0 \end{Bmatrix} = \begin{Bmatrix} 3.97\ E-4 \\ -1.573\ E-4 \\ -6.63\ E-5 \end{Bmatrix} \text{mm}^{-1} = \begin{Bmatrix} 1.007\ E-2 \\ -4.00\ E-3 \\ -1.682\ E-3 \end{Bmatrix} \text{in}^{-1}$$

The ply-direction strains and stresses are then given in Table 3.2. ∎

3.11 CLOSURE

This chapter has introduced the idea of lamination, which is the stacking together of layers, each containing unidirectional fibers. Typically, the orientation varies from layer to layer, that is, the fibers in the various layers are placed at different angles with respect to an overall coordinate system. This is necessary to give stiffness (and strength) in more than one direction. Relationships were developed that relate the in-plane loads and bending-moment resultants to the center-line strains and the bending curvatures of the laminate, through what are called the *A*, *B*, and *D* matrices. Here *A* is an extensional-stiffness matrix, *D* is a bending-stiffness matrix, and *B* is a coupling-stiffness matrix that has no counterpart with isotropic materials. Special classes of laminates are examined, called symmetric, balanced, and quasi-isotropic. Finally, the chapter concludes with the development of procedures to calculate the stresses and strains with the separate layers of the laminate under external mechanical or thermal loads. In typical cases, the stresses are seen to vary considerably from layer to layer in the laminate, even under simple loadings, and this must be taken into account in designing the laminate. For example, even under a simple tension loading, the stresses in individual plies can be higher or lower than the average by significant factors. Thus, the relationships developed in this chapter must be employed to obtain reasonable estimates of the stress distribution in the laminate.

REFERENCE

3.1 Swanson, S. R., "Analysis of Structures," in *Engineered Materials Handbook, Vol. 1, Composites* (Metals Park, OH: ASM International, 1987), pp. 458–462.

PROBLEMS

3.1. Draw sketches illustrating how displacements u and v in the x,y plane are related to displacement w in a plate. From this, derive the strain-displacement relationship for ϵ_x, ϵ_y, and γ_{xy} in a plate.

3.2. List and illustrate the major steps in developing the A, B, and D matrices.

3.3. Compute by hand A_{11}, A_{16}, B_{11}, and D_{11} for a single layer of isotropic material. Use the properties of aluminum ($E = 10$ Msi, $\nu = 0.33$). Explain the significance of these terms, that is, are they what you would expect?

For the following problems, use the properties of AS4/3501-6, which are $E_1 = 18.4$ Msi, $E_2 = 1.60$ Msi, $G_{12} = 0.95$ Msi, $\nu_{12} = 0.28$, and use a standard ply thickness of 0.1321 mm (0.0052 in) per ply. (*Note:* You may also wish to use computer programs such as those that accompany this text on the web to check the answers of Problems 3.4 through 3.7.)

3.4. Compute by hand A_{11}, A_{16}, B_{11}, and D_{11} for a [0/0/90] layup. Although the A, B, and D matrices are most easily obtained by means of computer programs, it is useful to carry out some computations by hand to be sure that one fully understands how the calculation is done.

3.5. Compute by hand A_{11}, A_{16}, B_{11}, and D_{11} for a [0/90/0] layup. Comment on the difference between the answers in Problem 3.4 and this problem.

3.6. Compute by hand the A_{16} term for a [0/45] laminate.

3.7. Compute by hand the A_{16} term for a [−45/45] laminate.

3.8. Calculate the A and D matrices for a $[0_2/90_2]_s$ laminate and a $[90_2/0_2]_s$ laminate, both of AS4/3501-6 carbon/epoxy. Compare the values for the two layups.

3.9. Calculate the A and D matrices for a $[0_2/\pm 45_2]_s$ laminate and a $[\pm 45_2/0_2]_s$ laminate, both of AS4/3501-6 carbon/epoxy. Compare the values for the two layups.

3.10. Consider and list the major categories of operations that must be carried out in a computer program to calculate the A, B, and D matrices. Either identify the operations that could be then used in a program (or MATLAB file) that you would write or alternatively check one of the programs furnished with this text to see if these operations are included.

3.11. Use a computer program to calculate the A, B, and D matrices for the following laminates, all made of AS4/3501-6 carbon/epoxy material.
  (a) $[0/\pm 45/90]_s$
  (b) $[0/\pm 60]_s$
  (c) $[0_2/\pm 45]_s$

3.12. Show by the use of trigonometric identities that the A_{11} and A_{12} terms for a [0/±45/90] laminate have a constant value with the rotation of coordinate axes. This family of laminates and the [0/±60] family are called "quasi-isotropic" because of this property.

3.13. Calculate the A matrix for a $[0/\pm 45/90]_s$ and a $[10/+55/-35/100]_s$ laminate using the properties of AS4/3501-6 carbon/epoxy. Comment on why the results must be the same for the two layups.

3.14. Calculate the D matrix for a $[0/\pm 45/90]_s$ and a $[10/+55/-35/100]_s$ laminate using the properties of AS4/3501-6 carbon/epoxy. Comment on why the results are not exactly the same for the two layups.

3.15. Calculate the A matrix for a $[0/\pm 60]_s$ and a $[10/+70/-50]_s$ laminate using the properties of AS4/3501-6 carbon/epoxy. Comment on why the results must be the same for the two layups.

3.16. Calculate the D matrix for a $[0/\pm 60]s$ and a $[10/+70/-50]_s$ laminate using the properties of AS4/3501-6 carbon/epoxy. Comment on why the results are not exactly the same for the two layups.

3.17. Outline the procedure used to obtain stresses in the fiber directions for each of the plies in a laminate under in-plane and moment resultant loading.

3.18. Calculate by hand the stresses in each of the plies in a [0/90/0] laminate under a uniaxial stress in the direction of the 0° fibers. Express stress σ_1 in the 0° plies as a ratio to the overall applied stress σ_x.

For the problems that follow, use the properties of AS4/3501-6, which are $E_1 = 18.4$ Msi, $E_2 = 1.60$ Msi, $G_{12} = 0.95$ Msi, and $\nu_{12} = 0.28$.

3.19. Follow and outline the procedure for calculating stresses in the plies that is used in the accompanying computer programs and show that it corresponds to that of Problem 3.18.

3.20. Use the computer programs to check the answers of Problem 3.18.

3.21. Use the computer programs to calculate the stresses in a $[0_2/\pm45]_s$ laminate under a loading $N_x = 17.51$ kN/m (100 lb/in) in the direction of the 0° fibers.

3.22. Calculate the stresses in the plies of a $[0_2/(+45)_2/(-45)_2/90_2]_s$ AS4/3501-6 laminate under a moment resultant of 448 N-m/m (100 in-lb/in) in the direction of the 0° fibers using the computer programs.

3.23. Apply an N_{xy} loading to a $[0_2/90_2]_s$ laminate of AS4/3501-6 carbon/epoxy and examine the stresses in the plies. Note that the shear loading is carried by the shear stress in the matrix, and the fibers are not used effectively.

3.24. Apply an N_{xy} loading to a $[45_2/-45_2]_s$ laminate of AS4/3501-6 carbon/epoxy and examine the stresses in the plies. Note that the shear loading is carried by the fibers, which makes this layup very effective in carrying shear loading.

3.25. Show the steps needed to calculate stresses in laminates when temperature changes are involved.

3.26. Calculate the stresses in a $[0_2/90_2]_s$ laminate of AS4/3501-6 carbon/epoxy, during cooldown from the cure temperature of 177°C (350°F) to room temperature of 21°C (70°F). Explain why the stresses have the signs that they have.

3.27. Consider a "thought experiment" in which a ply of AS4/3501-6 carbon/epoxy is held fixed in the transverse direction and cooled down as in Problem 3.26. Estimate by hand the stresses that would result, making the problem one-dimensional by neglecting Poisson effects. Compare the transverse stress with that calculated in Problem 3.26.

4

Static Strength of Laminates

4.1 INTRODUCTION

Advanced fiber composites have excellent strength-to-weight properties, and are often used in strength-critical applications. This chapter presents procedures for relating the strength of fiber composites to the strength of the constituent materials. Some typical fiber properties are presented first, followed by discussions of failure of unidirectional composites under tensile loading and under compressive loading. The failure of multidirectional fiber composites under multiaxial loading is then considered, and typical experimental data are presented.

4.2 FIBER PROPERTIES

The strength of fiber composites is determined by the fibers, although the apparent fiber strength is influenced by the matrix. Typical strengths of fibers are shown in Table 4.1, taken from [4.1] and manufacturers' literature. The high strengths shown in this table, combined with the relatively light weight, illustrate why fiber composites are advantageous for strength-to-weight-critical applications.

Tensile stress–strain curves are shown in Figure 4.1 for a number of fibers, taken from [4.2]. The fibers differ significantly in their strength, modulus, and strain to failure. The fibers tend to be relatively brittle and do not show significant ductility in their stress–strain response. The stress–strain curves of carbon fibers are interesting in that they stiffen with increasing tensile strain, and so the final stress–strain ratio may be about 10% higher than the initial modulus.

Table 4.1   Mechanical Properties of Typical Fibers

Fiber	Fiber Diameter (μm)	Fiber Density		Tensile Strength		Tensile Modulus	
		(lb/in^3)	(g/cc)	(ksi)	(GPa)	(Msi)	(GPa)
E-glass	8–14	0.092	2.54	500	3.45	10.5	72.4
S-glass	8–14	0.090	2.49	665	4.58	12.5	86.2
Polyethylene	10–12	0.035	0.97	392	2.70	12.6	87.0
Aramid (Kevlar 49)	12	0.052	1.44	525	3.62	19.0	130.0
HS Carbon, T300	7	0.063	1.76	514	3.53	33.6	230
AS4 Carbon	7	0.065	1.80	580	4.00	33.0	228
Panex 33 Carbon		0.064	1.78	525	3.60	33.0	228
IM7 Carbon	5	0.065	1.80	785	5.41	40.0	276
XUHM Carbon	—	0.068	1.88	550	3.79	62.0	428
GY80 Carbon	8.4	0.071	1.96	270	1.86	83.0	572
Boron	50–203	0.094	2.60	500	3.44	59.0	407

The strength of the actual fiber composite is lower than shown in the table because of a number of factors. The first is that the usually lower stiffness and strength matrix acts to dilute the overall apparent strength. Although the matrix is obviously necessary to bind everything together, the strength of the fiber composite in the fiber direction is generally reduced by the ratio of the area of the matrix to the total cross-sectional area of the composite. By using the usual fiber-volume fraction, the strength of the composite in the fiber direction relative to the strength of the fibers can be approximated by

$$\sigma_{\text{composite}} = V_f \sigma_{\text{fiber}} \qquad (4.1)$$

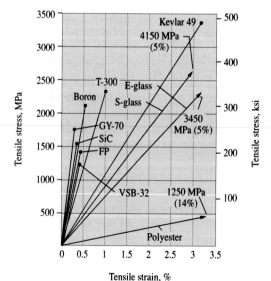

Figure 4.1   Tensile stress–strain curves for various fibers. (*Source:* From [4.2].)

where V_f is the fiber-volume fraction. Composite systems with less difference between the fiber and the matrix do not follow this relationship, but for high-strength fibers in polymeric matrices, it is a good approximation. A second major factor in strength reduction is that structures typically must have fibers oriented in more than one direction. For example, even if the load is primarily in one direction, secondary loads in transverse directions require fibers to be oriented to carry those loads also. Significant shear loads typically are carried by $\pm 45°$ fibers, or at least fibers with components other than $0°$ or $90°$ with respect to the shear loading, which would require the matrix to carry the shear load. As a consequence of the necessary requirement of multidirectional fiber layups, the fibers available to carry the load in any particular direction are less than the total number of fibers, and the apparent strength of the layup is lowered accordingly. Information on how to predict the strength of multidirectional fiber layups will be given subsequently.

4.3 TENSILE FAILURE OF FIBER COMPOSITES

One of the most interesting aspects of fiber composites is the role of the matrix in determining tensile strength. As mentioned before, clearly the load-carrying ability of fiber composites with relatively weak matrices, such as the polymer-matrix composites, is determined primarily by the fibers. The most important design rule for composites of this type is that one must orient fibers such that they can carry the primary loads. A comparison of the tensile strengths illustrates this point. High-strength carbon fibers have tensile strengths that approach 6900 MPa (one million psi), whereas the tensile strength of typical polymer matrices may be on the order of 200 MPa (30,000 psi) or less. Clearly, the tensile strength of the matrix is insignificant in comparison. In spite of this, the matrix plays a vital role in determining tensile strength, as indicated by the experimental observation that the strength of matrix-impregnated fiber bundles can be on the order of a factor-of-2 higher than the measured tensile strength of dry fiber bundles without matrix impregnation. The key to this apparently contradictory evidence lies in a synergistic effect between fiber and matrix.

The explanation for this has been offered by the work of a number of investigators. The mechanism is explained by noting that the strength of individual brittle fibers varies widely because of a statistical distribution of flaws. The fibers are brittle and sensitive to surface imperfections that are randomly distributed over the length of a fiber. The strength of individual fibers varies widely and can show reductions in strength with increasing length. These characteristics are typical of brittle materials failing at random defects. However, these characteristics are modified dramatically with the addition of the matrix. Surprisingly, the matrix acts to increase the apparent strength of a fiber bundle by as much as a factor of 2. Also, the variability is significantly reduced.

One possible explanation is as follows. In a dry fiber bundle, when a fiber breaks, it loses all load-carrying ability over its entire length and this load is shifted to the remaining fibers. When enough of the weaker fibers have failed, the strength of the remaining fibers is exceeded, and the bundle fails.

In matrix-impregnated fiber bundles, it is believed that the matrix acts to bridge around individual fiber breaks, so that the fiber quickly picks up load-carrying ability. Thus, the adjacent fibers only have to carry an increased load over a small axial distance. The statistical distribution of fiber defects makes it unlikely that the weakest location of each fiber would have the same axial location, so that failure must occur at a higher load value, after enough fibers have failed in adjacent locations. It must be remembered that because of the small diameter of individual fibers (5 to 7 microns for typical carbon fibers), there are many millions of fibers in a typical structure. Thus, there is ample opportunity for statistical effects to be important.

4.3.1 Model for Bridging Around a Fiber Break

It is possible to consider simple shear lag models to obtain an estimate of the axial distance along the fiber required for the load to be restored to the fiber after a fiber break. Consider the schematic of a fiber break shown in Figure 4.2.

Consider the fiber to be idealized as a simple axial rod under tension, with shear transmitted into the fiber from the surrounding matrix, as shown in Figure 4.3.

A statement of equilibrium for the fiber can then be given as

$$\left(\sigma_f + \frac{\partial \sigma_f}{\partial x} dx\right)A_f - \sigma_f A_f - \tau_m L_p\, dx = 0 \tag{4.2}$$

where σ_f is the axial stress in the fiber, $A_f (=\pi r_f^2)$ is the cross-sectional area of the fiber, and $L_p (=2\pi r_f)$ is the circumference of the fiber. The stresses in fiber and matrix are taken as related to the strains by simple one-dimensional linear elastic stress–strain laws, and the strains in turn are related to the displacement of the fiber. The displacement of the surrounding field is taken to be uniform and given by $u = \epsilon_0 x$, so that the composite away from the broken fiber has a uniform strain $\epsilon_x = \epsilon_0$. The average shear strain in the matrix surrounding the broken fiber can be expressed as

$$\gamma_m = \frac{u_f - u}{h} \tag{4.3}$$

where again u is the far field displacement, taken to apply to the adjacent fibers, u_f is the displacement of the broken fiber away from the break, and h is the characteristic distance between the broken fiber and adjacent fibers. Substituting these displacement relations into Eq. (4.2) gives

$$\frac{d^2 u_f}{dx^2} - \beta^2 u_f = -\beta^2 \epsilon_0 x \tag{4.4}$$

where

$$\beta^2 \equiv \frac{2G_m}{E_f r_f h} \tag{4.5}$$

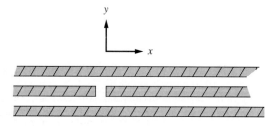

Figure 4.2 Broken fiber and adjacent unbroken fibers.

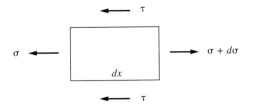

Figure 4.3   Equilibrium diagram for a segment of fiber.

where G_m is the matrix shear modulus and E_f is the fiber axial modulus. The solution to Eq. (4.4) is easily obtained as

$$u_f = c_1 e^{-\beta x} + c_2 e^{\beta x} + \epsilon_0 x \qquad (4.6)$$

Noting that c_2 must be zero for the displacements to remain finite for large x, differentiating to get fiber strain, and again using Hooke's law for the fiber gives the preceding equation in terms of the fiber stress. Using the boundary condition that the fiber axial stress is zero at the broken end (a free surface for the fiber) gives

$$\sigma_f = E_f \epsilon_0 [1 - e^{-\beta x}] \qquad (4.7)$$

When βx has a value of 3, the fiber stress has returned to about 95% of its original value, as shown in Figure 4.4. A value for β can be estimated by using the known material properties for fiber and matrix listed in Table 2.1 Using the characteristic distance between fibers as about 1/2 of the fiber radius gives a value $\beta = 0.43/D_f$, where D_f is the fiber diameter. Thus,

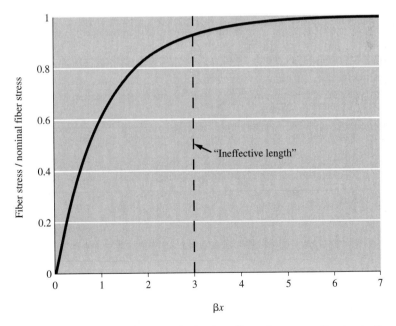

Figure 4.4   Estimate for axial stress distribution in a fiber adjacent to a fiber break. Stress is returned to the fiber by shear stress in the matrix.

by a distance of about seven fiber diameters away from the fiber break, the fiber stress has returned to 95% of its original value. This length is often called the "ineffective length," or, more precisely, the ineffective half-length, as the stresses would return to their original value on each side of the fiber break. Because fibers are very small, this is an exceedingly short distance. For example, carbon fibers are typically in the range of 5 to 7 microns in diameter. With a 7-micron fiber, this ineffective length is only 98×10^{-6} m, or 0.0039 inch.

The preceding analysis does indicate matrix stress concentrations adjacent to the fiber break. A more detailed analysis could limit these stresses, perhaps to values limited by frictional or matrix inelastic effects. However, the overall conclusion still remains that the matrix can be very effective in localizing the effects of individual fiber breaks. Thus, this simple shear lag model supports the failure mechanism postulated before, that the matrix can act to bridge around individual fiber breaks.

4.3.2 Statistical Models of Tensile Failure

A natural extension of the ideas given before would be to develop a statistical failure theory for tensile fiber failure. The goal would be to model the failure process as initiating in one of the fibers and then growing as breaks in adjacent fibers link together. Unfortunately, this has proven to be a difficult task. Rosen [4.3] assumed that the distribution of fiber strength was characterized by a Weibull statistical function, but did not consider any stress-concentration effect on adjacent fibers. Zweben [4.4] and Zweben and Rosen [4.5] added detail to this model, including a proposed stress-concentration effect. Harlow and Phoenix [4.6] carried out computer simulations limited to a small number of fibers because of numerical complexity.

The essential features of these models have been described by Batdorf [4.7]. Individual fibers are assumed to have a statistical population of weak regions characterized by a Weibull distribution function. As the composite is stressed, these weak points fail in an isolated manner. Although the fibers adjacent to a broken fiber are subject to increased stress, it is only over a small region, as described before. Thus, it is statistically unlikely that weak regions interact. As the stress is increased, fibers in the overload region eventually fail, giving a "doublet" of two fibers with breaks next to each other. At still higher stress, further doublets occur, as well as a "triplet" of three adjacent fiber breaks. At some stress level, enough fiber breaks accumulate to propagate to catastrophic failure of the entire structure.

It has proven difficult to establish a realistic model based on the statistical approach. However, considerable insight can be gained from the general approach. An example is the work of Otani, Phoenix, and Petrina [4.8] on creep rupture of carbon-fiber/polymer-matrix composites. Here creep rupture refers to the time-dependent failure under constant load. As the carbon fibers are essentially insensitive to time effects, it might be considered that there are no time effects in the composite. However, the preceding clearly shows the effect of the matrix in the failure process. As polymer matrices show time-dependent effects, it is not surprising that the composite shows time-dependent failure characteristics.

4.3.3 Size Effects on Tensile Strength

The question of whether there is a size effect on the tensile strength of fiber composites has been quite controversial, with evidence presented on both sides. It is widely accepted that in brittle materials such as ceramics, the strength tends to decrease with increased size. The usual explanation is that there is increased likelihood of more severe defects with increased volume, and that brittle failure is directly related to defect size. The Weibull statistical failure theory gives a direct result for this size effect as

$$\frac{s}{s_0} = \left(\frac{V_0}{V}\right)^{1/m} \tag{4.8}$$

where s and s_0 are mean strengths of volumes of stressed material V and V_0, respectively, and m is the Weibull shape parameter. As pointed out by Zweben [4.9], this size effect could have significant implications for the performance of large composite structures. Zweben notes that for a coefficient of variation (COV) of composite strength of 5% (and using the approximate relationship that $m = 1.2/COV$) gives $m = 24$, and this would predict strength reductions of 25 to 40% for large structures relative to coupon tests. Zweben also gives references to support a size effect. On the other hand, Cohen [4.10] has compared the apparent failure strain of large rocket motors under internal pressure loading with that of tow tests (resin-impregnated fiber bundles) of the same fiber lot and epoxy resin. The large rocket motors had a mean strain to failure that was about 3% less than the mean of the tow tests, although the stressed volume was estimated to differ by a factor of 10^7. Thus, the experimental evidence here showed minimal size effect.

4.4 COMPRESSIVE FAILURE OF FIBER COMPOSITES

The compressive strength of fiber composites is often less than the tensile strength and thus can be a limiting factor in strength-critical applications. As is discussed in more detail in what follows, experimental measurements of compressive strength can differ widely, depending on the type of test. Thus, it would appear advantageous to consider theoretical models of compressive failure to gain further understanding of the failure mechanisms involved. It is obvious that the matrix plays an important role in compressive failure, as dry fibers would not support a compressive load. One of the important early developments was the micromechanics model of compressive failure by Rosen [4.3], who assumed that the failure mode was microbuckling of the fibers and that buckling was resisted by the matrix. Although this model will be found to overpredict the compressive strength of fiber composites, it is the starting point for much additional work. In the following, the basic ideas of Rosen's model are examined, followed by a discussion of more recent developments.

4.4.1 Micromechanics Model for Fiber Compressive Strength

The model set out by Rosen [4.3] assumes a 2-D geometry in which the fibers are idealized as slabs of thickness h, separated by matrix whose space between fibers is $2c$. Fibers are considered to be initially straight and loaded in compression by a force P. At a critical value of the load, the fibers are assumed to buckle, as illustrated in Figure 4.5. The fibers are assumed to act cooperatively (which minimizes the buckling load), and two different deformation modes are distinguished. The first is called the *extension mode* and is shown in Figure 4.5(a), and the second is called the *shearing mode* and is shown in Figure 4.5(b).

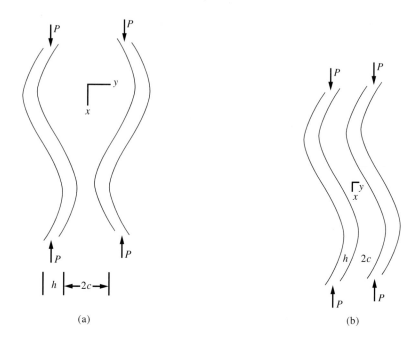

(a)　　　　　　　　　　　　　　　　　　　(b)

Figure 4.5　Deformation modes assumed for fiber microbuckling in compression: (a) extension mode and (b) shearing mode.

Fiber microbuckling occurs at a force that just produces neutral equilibrium. This condition is established by using energy principles, by equating the work done by force P in acting through the additional deformation associated with going from the straight fiber to the buckled fiber configuration, to the additional strain energy in the fiber and matrix.

The transverse displacement of the fiber in the buckled state is

$$v(x) = A_n \sin \frac{n \pi x}{L} \tag{4.9}$$

The work done by P in going from the straight to the buckled state is

$$W = P\delta \tag{4.10}$$

and the deformation is given by

$$\delta = \int_0^L \sqrt{1 + (v')^2}\, dx - L \approx \int_0^L \frac{(v')^2}{2}\, dx \tag{4.11}$$

Taking the derivative of Eq. (4.9), substituting in Eq. (4.11), and integrating gives

$$W = P \frac{\pi^2 n^2 A_n^2}{4L} \tag{4.12}$$

The strain energy from bending of the fiber is given by

$$U_f = \int_0^L \frac{EI}{2} (v'')^2\, dx = \frac{EI\pi^4}{4L^3} n^4 A_n^2 = \frac{\pi^4 E_f h^3}{48L^3} n^4 A_n^2 \tag{4.13}$$

If the fiber is taken as a slab of unit thickness into the plane with width h, the moment of inertia is given as $I = h^3/12$, as used before. The final term needed is the strain energy in the matrix from the additional deformation resulting from the microbuckling. Here the two cases of assumed fiber cooperative deformation must be distinguished, as shown in Figure 4.5.

Extension mode.   The strain energy in the matrix is assumed to be due entirely to transverse normal stresses that are taken to be uniaxial and uniform in the transverse direction. The transverse strain is given by

$$\epsilon_y(x) = \frac{(v(x)|_c - v(x)|_{-c})}{2c} = \frac{1}{c}A_n \sin \frac{n\pi x}{L} \tag{4.14}$$

The strain energy is then given by

$$U_m = \frac{1}{2}\int_V E_m \epsilon_y^2 \, dV = \frac{1}{2}\int_0^L 2c E_m \epsilon_y^2 \, dx = \frac{E_m L}{2c}A_n^2 \tag{4.15}$$

Equating the work and energy terms gives

$$W = U_f + U_m \tag{4.16}$$

Substituting from Eq. (4.16) and rearranging gives

$$P = \frac{\pi^2 E_f h^3}{12L^2}\left[n^2 + \frac{\beta}{n^2}\right] \tag{4.17}$$

where

$$\beta \equiv \frac{24L^4 E_m}{\pi^4 c h^3 E_f} \tag{4.18}$$

Assuming tentatively that n is large, it can be taken as a continuous parameter. Thus, the minimum value of P can be found by differentiating Eq. (4.17) with respect to n:

$$\frac{\partial P}{\partial n} = \frac{\pi^2 E_f h^3}{12L^2}\left[2n - \frac{2\beta}{n^3}\right] = 0 \tag{4.19}$$

getting

$$n^4 = \beta \tag{4.20}$$

Substituting this value for n into Eq. (4.17) gives a value for the fiber buckling load. Noting that the cross-sectional width of the fiber is h and that of the matrix is $2c$, the fiber volume fraction is given by

$$V_f = \frac{h}{h + 2c} \tag{4.21}$$

Using the above, the critical force on the fiber is given by

$$P = 2h\sqrt{\frac{V_f E_m E_f}{3(1 - V_f)}} \tag{4.22}$$

and the composite stress is given by

$$\sigma_c = 2V_f\sqrt{\frac{V_f E_m E_f}{3(1 - V_f)}} \tag{4.23}$$

This is an expression for the compressive strength of a fiber composite under the assumptions given before and in particular the assumption of the extension mode of cooperative fiber displacement. Before examining this result further, the shearing mode is discussed.

Shearing mode.   The shearing mode of cooperative fiber microbuckling is now considered. The assumption is that only shear stresses occur in the matrix, and that they are uniform in the y direction. The in-plane shearing strain is related to the displacements by

$$\gamma_{xy} = \frac{\partial u}{\partial y} + \frac{\partial v}{\partial x} \tag{4.24}$$

Assuming that the matrix follows the fiber deformation, the second term can be easily obtained as

$$\frac{\partial v}{\partial x} = A_n \frac{n\pi}{L} \cos \frac{n\pi x}{L} \tag{4.25}$$

The first term of Eq. (4.24) is approximated with the help of Figure 4.6. From the illustration, the approximation for the first term of the matrix shear strain can be taken as

$$\frac{\partial u}{\partial y} \approx \frac{1}{2c} [u(c) - u(-c)] \tag{4.26}$$

but $u(c)$ is due to bending in the fiber, as

$$u(c) = -u(-c) = \frac{h}{2} \frac{dv}{dx} = \frac{h}{2} A_n \frac{n\pi}{L} \cos \frac{n\pi x}{L} \tag{4.27}$$

Substituting Eqs. (4.25) and (4.27) into Eq. (4.24) gives the shear strain in the matrix as

$$\gamma_{xy_m} = \left(1 + \frac{h}{2c}\right) A_n \frac{n\pi}{L} \cos \frac{n\pi x}{L} \tag{4.28}$$

The strain energy in the matrix is then given by

$$U_m = \frac{1}{2} \int_0^L 2cG_m \gamma_{xy_m}^2 \, dx = G_m c \left(1 + \frac{h}{2c}\right)^2 \frac{\pi^2 n^2 A_n^2}{2L} \tag{4.29}$$

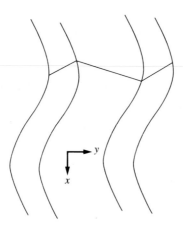

Figure 4.6   Assumed u displacement in the matrix shearing mode.

The energy balance is then similar to that given before, and the terms are the same as for the previous extension mode case, with the exception that the strain energy in the matrix is given in Eq. (4.29). The result is that the critical buckling load is given as

$$P = h\left[\frac{G_m}{v_f(1 - v_f)} + \frac{\pi^2 E_f}{12}\left(\frac{nh}{L}\right)^2\right] \tag{4.30}$$

The second term within the square brackets is much smaller than the first and can be neglected under the usual condition when L/n is greater than h. The result then can be given in terms of the composite compressive failure stress as

$$\sigma_c = \frac{G_m}{1 - v_f} \tag{4.31}$$

A comparison of Eqs. (4.23) and (4.31) shows that the extension mode used for Eq. (4.23) is favored at low fiber-volume fractions, but for realistic fiber-volume fractions typical of practical polymer matrix laminates, Eq. (4.31) provides the lower and thus controlling estimate of the compressive strength. This is a well-known result in the mechanics of composite materials and is an important result in understanding compressive failure of fiber composites. However, it is generally considered too high an estimate, perhaps by a factor of 2 to 4 [4.11, 4.12]. It can perhaps be considered to be an upper bound and shows that an elastic matrix can provide support to perfectly straight fibers, and perhaps thus answering how the very thin fibers can provide any significant compressive strength. A number of approaches have been taken to attempt to improve the prediction of compressive strength. Some of this work is described in the following.

Further developments in models of compressive strength.   As mentioned before, the Rosen model appears to give too high an estimate of the compressive strength of fiber composites. Several investigators have examined the inherent compressive strength of the fibers experimentally, by supporting the fibers so that microbuckling is suppressed. DeTeresa et al. [4.13] have shown that the relatively low compressive strength of aramid fibers may indeed be limited by the fibers themselves, as they tend to come apart laterally. Prandy and Hahn [4.14] have shown that carbon fibers made from a pitch precursor also have an inherently low strain to failure and fail by shear through the fiber. On the other hand, DeTeresa [4.15] has measured failure strains for PAN precursor fibers such as AS4 that are in excess of −3%, far exceeding values seen in laminate tests. Thus, for typical PAN precursor carbon fibers, it appears that the fiber-matrix system is the limiting factor and not the inherent properties of the fibers.

A number of investigators have attempted to add detail to the basic Rosen model. Often, the approach has been to incorporate a nonlinear stress–strain law for the matrix or initial defects in the fibers [4.16–4.24]. As would be expected, a lower and thus more realistic compressive strength is achieved. Another general approach has been to incorporate defects of various types, such as partial bonding of the fibers [4.25]. A recent review of this work has been presented by Guynn, Ochoa, and Bradley [4.26].

Many investigators have considered fibers that have initial waviness. Examinations of micrographs typically show that carbon fibers are not perfectly straight, although it is often difficult to quantify the description of just how wavy they are. The models with initially wavy fibers address an important weakness of the Rosen model, which is that as shown before, it predicts that the compressive strength (for materials with sufficiently strong fibers) is affected only by the matrix shear modulus. However, experimental evidence by Madhukar and Drzal [4.27] and Swanson and Colvin [4.28] indicates that the fiber-matrix adhesion is also important. Models with initial fiber waviness provide a natural avenue for incorporating additional parameters into the model. With initially wavy fibers, increased loading produces additional deformation in the fiber. A limit is reached when either the fiber fails in bending or the fiber-matrix bond is exceeded. The failure mode is typically shown to be associated with the fiber-matrix adhesion for carbon-fiber composites, in agreement with the experimental data mentioned before.

A weakness of the initially wavy-fiber approach is that it is difficult to characterize the waviness experimentally. The models typically show that the misalignment angle of the fiber is important and that values on the order of 3° provide agreement with laboratory data. Jelf and Fleck [4.29] report that values of 3° were observed in laboratory specimens. It has been shown that the results from models for perfectly straight fibers can be modified to allow for a misalignment angle [4.30].

It is clear that the calculation of matrix stresses in the Rosen model is approximate. One problem is exhibited in the predicted behavior at very low volume fractions. As the fibers go farther apart, the distinction between the extension mode and the shear mode should become less important, and in the limit of a single isolated fiber, the solutions should coincide. However, they do not. Zhang and Latour [4.31] have presented an elasticity model for the matrix stresses that is exact within the assumptions characteristic of the 2-D approximation. Their solution does show that the extension and shearing modes do coincide in the limit of 0 fiber-volume fraction and interestingly also predict that the shearing mode is favored over all values of fiber-volume fraction.

An entirely different approach to predicting critical compression-failure loads has been taken in models of the fiber-kinking process. Fiber kinking, as shown in Figure 4.7, is typically characteristic of compression failure. An examination of the equilibrium of kink bands leads to conditions necessary for propagation of compression failure [4.32–4.35].

Usefulness of models of compression failure.   In view of the uncertainties of the various models of compression failure in fiber composites, it is fair to ask just how useful are the models. It is true that experimental tests are needed to obtain or verify any strength values needed for design. However, a major contribution of the models is to identify the variables involved, to aid in understanding and interpreting the test data as well as to suggest possible improvements in material systems.

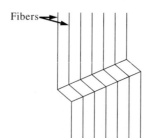

Fibers

Figure 4.7   Kink-band formation in compression failure of fiber composites.

As an example, it is widely noted that compression failure values vary widely with the type of test performed. Some of this may be associated with experimental difficulties, as Berg and Adams [36] have demonstrated that careful attention to detail can result in higher measured failure strengths. However, there also seem to be systematic differences between tests. For example, the axial sandwich column tests reported by Shuart [4.37] and by Whitney, Crasto, and Kim [4.38] give very high apparent strengths, with a compressive strain to failure of −2% for AS4 carbon/epoxy. Another example is in the bending tests reported by Jackson [4.39] and by Wisnom [4.40], in which the bend specimens failed in tension rather than in compression, implying that the compressive strengths are as high as or higher than the tensile strengths. It has also been shown that the strain to failure of critical plies can depend on the overall layup in a laminate [4.41, 4.42]. Some models have explained these results by incorporating through-the-thickness effects in supporting the fiber [4.43, 4.44, 4.28]. The conclusion is that the compressive strength is expected to vary with the support conditions characteristic of each type of test.

4.5 EFFECT OF MULTIAXIAL STRESSES

The effect of multiaxial stresses must be considered in assessing the strength of fiber composites. The various plies or layers of a fiber composite with fibers in more than one direction are in multiaxial stress even for uniaxial load, because of Poisson ratio effects. Because of the many possible laminates or layups of interest, it is clearly desirable to be able to relate the strength of the entire layup to the properties of the individual layers. This approach is utilized in the following. However, in this approach, the particular mode of failure of the individual plies must be carefully considered. In general, matrix cracking may or may not lead directly to failure, and fiber failure usually corresponds to the ultimate failure of the laminate. Examples are given to clarify these points.

The stress analysis of the laminate furnishes an overall state of strain in the laminate, from which the strains in each individual ply can be calculated. The strains in each ply are then transformed into the directions of the fibers, using standard formulas for rotation of strain components with rotation of coordinate directions. Finally, the in-plane stresses in each ply can be obtained by using the stress–strain relationship for the ply. The stresses and strains are then known for each ply in the laminate. The final product of these manipulations is the ply stresses and strains, referred to in the direction of the fiber and transverse to the fiber, in each ply of the laminate. The remaining step in the strength assessment is to compare the calculated ply stresses and strains with allowable values, using material properties in conjunction with suitable failure theories. This important step is discussed in the following section.

4.5.1 Ply-Failure Theories

Before discussing the various possible failure theories that can be applied to the individual plies of a laminate, it is useful to consider the physical processes involved in failure. In typical polymer-based composites, the resin has sufficient elongation capability so that fiber failure occurs before resin failure in the usual unidirectional tension coupon test with the load parallel to the fibers. On a more detailed level, as discussed before, it is believed that the matrix plays a significant role in bridging around the individual fiber breaks that occur at weak points in the fibers, and that the ultimate fiber failure occurs when a sufficient amount of these individual fiber breaks are coupled together. From a macroscopic, ply-level viewpoint, fiber failure is characterized by either the tensile stress or tensile strain at failure in the unidirectional specimen. The situation is more complicated in compression, as both fiber and matrix play a role in determining the strength, again as discussed before.

When tested in a direction transverse to the fibers, the composite typically fails in the matrix at a transverse strain level often significantly less than the failure strain of neat resin, and also much lower than the fiber failure strain under axial loading. The higher-modulus fibers are thought to serve as stress-concentration points so that the ply transverse failure strain is much lower than the neat matrix failure strain. As a consequence of this lower transverse strain to failure, a laminate may exhibit matrix failure in the transverse plies (relative to the major loading axis) well before failure of the fibers that are in the loading direction. Thus, for example, matrix cracking will occur in a [0/90] laminate in the 90° plies, if the loading is in the 0 direction. This matrix cracking is the first manifestation of laminate failure and has been studied extensively [4.45–4.49]. As the loading is increased, further matrix cracking occurs, forming a more or less regular spacing [4.46]. Although transverse strain (or stress) is often used to characterize the propensity to produce matrix cracks, energetic approaches have also been applied [4.47]. The energy approach indicates that the in situ matrix strength actually depends on the thickness of adjacent ply groups, which has been reported in experiments [4.45–4.49]. Further discussion of matrix cracking is given in Chapter 5.

Matrix cracking has a number of effects on the laminate. For example, it increases permeability to moisture. It also tends to reduce the effective transverse properties of the ply. A number of studies have in fact attempted to model the reduction in transverse stiffness with matrix cracking, using averaged continuum properties [4.50–4.52]. It has been shown that the matrix cracks can serve as initiation sites for delamination under fatigue loading [4.53].

It is important to note, however, that matrix cracking may or may not lead directly to ultimate laminate failure. If the laminate loading is carried primarily by the matrix, then matrix cracking and subsequent softening can lead directly to failure. An example would be shear loading of a [0/90] laminate. However, in most practical situations, the laminate is designed so that the load is carried by fibers, to take advantage of the strength of the fibers relative to the weak matrix. In these cases, the ultimate strength of the laminate may be several times that of the load corresponding to the initiation of ply cracking and is caused by the failure of fibers. In typical carbon/epoxy laminates under static tension loading, the stress–strain response may be quite linear up to failure (say, within 5%), with the softening of the transverse properties due to matrix cracking being counterbalanced by the stiffening of the fiber with loading.

The conclusion to be drawn from the preceding is that matrix cracking and ultimate laminate failure are typically separate events and must be considered separately. Thus, separate failure criteria must be established for matrix cracking and fiber failure. There are a large number of possible failure criteria that have been suggested for use with composite materials. However, almost all of these are derived from applications to materials other than laminated composites and as a consequence do not differentiate between the modes of failure. As such, they cannot be applied in a rational manner to composite laminates on a ply basis, where it is necessary to distinguish between matrix and fiber failure.

Several failure criteria have been suggested for direct application to composites. The stress polynomial due to Tsai and Wu [4.54] is given in the usual quadratic form as

$$F_1\sigma_1 + F_{11}\sigma_1^2 + F_2\sigma_2 + F_{22}\sigma_2^2 + 2F_{12}\sigma_1\sigma_2 + F_{66}\tau_{12}^2 = 1 \tag{4.32}$$

where the F terms are material constants, and the stresses are the in-plane ply stresses. The various F terms can be easily related to experimental data on ply failure by evaluating the preceding expression for the various simple material property test conditions. This gives

$$F_1 = 1/X_t + 1/X_c \qquad F_{11} = -1/X_tX_c \qquad F_{66} = 1/S^2$$
$$F_2 = 1/Y_t + 1/Y_c \qquad F_{22} = -1/Y_tY_c \tag{4.33}$$

where X_t and X_c are unidirectional strengths parallel to the fibers in tension and compression, respectively, Y_t and Y_c are transverse strengths, and S is the shear strength. The F_{12} term must be obtained from multiaxial tests on a lamina and is usually taken as either of the following two values:

$$F_{12} = 0 \tag{4.34}$$

or

$$F_{12} = -0.5\sqrt{F_{11}F_{22}} \tag{4.35}$$

This polynomial can be used directly to predict first ply failure, which may correspond to ultimate laminate failure if the major load is in compression and will usually correspond to matrix cracking if the major load is tension. This criterion does not directly differentiate between matrix and fiber failure, but can be interpreted as doing so indirectly by assuming that first ply failure corresponds to matrix failure and last ply failure corresponds to ultimate failure of the laminate [4.55].

Two additional criteria available for ply-failure prediction are based on separating the preceding polynomial into two parts, one describing matrix failure and the other describing fiber failure. Hahn, Erikson, and Tsai [4.56] recommend the following:

Fiber failure:

$$F_1\sigma_1 + F_{11}\sigma_1^2 = 1 \tag{4.36}$$

Matrix failure:

$$F_2\sigma_2 + F_{22}\sigma_2^2 + F_{66}\tau_{12}^2 = 1 \tag{4.37}$$

A similar proposal has been made by Hashin [4.57], who recommends the following:

Fiber failure:

$$F_1\sigma_1 + F_{11}\sigma_1^2 + F_{66}\tau_{12}^2 = 1 \tag{4.38}$$

Matrix failure:

$$F_2\sigma_2 + F_{22}\sigma_2^2 + F_{66}\tau_{12}^2 = 1 \tag{4.39}$$

In either of the preceding forms, there is no ambiguity about what type of failure is being predicted.

A failure criterion that is widely used for predicting fiber failure on a ply basis is that of maximum fiber-direction strain. Because composites are often notably weaker in compression than in tension, two material property values are needed and the criterion becomes

$$\epsilon_{1c} < \epsilon_1 < \epsilon_{1t} \tag{4.40}$$

where ϵ_{1c} and ϵ_{1t} are fiber-direction failure strains in compression and tension, respectively.

4.5.2 Comparison with Experimental Data

Matrix failure.   Before considering specific failure criteria, it is useful to review some experimental evidence on ply and laminate failure. Figure 4.8, taken from [4.58], shows the transverse failure envelopes in 2-D stress space for AS4/55A and IM7/8551-7 carbon/epoxy systems. The first of these systems is filament-wound, and the second is prepreg with a "high-toughness" resin system. Both are unidirectional and tested in the

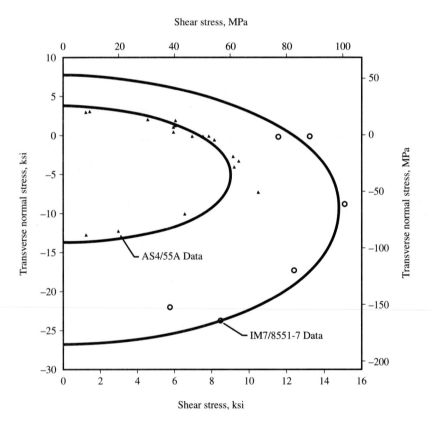

Figure 4.8   Transverse ply-failure properties for AS4/55A and IM7/8551-7 carbon/epoxy lamina. (*Source:* From [4.58].)

form of tubes subject to torsion combined with axial tension or compression. The results show that the matrix-dominated transverse strength properties are dependent on both the transverse normal stress and the shear stress. Further, there is a strong interaction between these stress components. Thus, any criterion applicable to transverse failure by matrix cracking must account for this interaction of stress components.

The matrix mode of failure shown in Figure 4.8 can be represented by either the Tsai–Wu criterion [Eq. (4.32)], the expression for matrix failure by Hahn et al. [Eq. (4.37)], or the equivalent expression for matrix failure by Hashin [Eq. (4.39)]. In fact, these criteria all reduce to the same expression for the state of stress of Figure 4.8, which represents combinations of transverse normal and in-plane shear stresses. The correlation of these three criteria with the data is quite good, as they represent the interaction of the transverse normal and shear stresses seen in the experimental results.

As mentioned before, experimental evidence suggests that the matrix failure strength within the laminate is different than it is in unidirectional laminae due to the restraint offered by the adjacent plies [4.46–4.49]. It has been suggested that the lamina strength values can be adjusted for this in-situ effect. One alternative is to abandon the concept of a stress-based failure criterion and use energy release rates in conjunction with the assumption of inherent flaws to determine matrix cracking [4.46]. This latter approach is of course much more complex. More detail on matrix cracking is given in Chapter 5.

Ultimate laminate failure.   Experimental evidence on ultimate laminate failure is given in Figure 4.9 for AS4/3501-6 carbon/epoxy [4.58, 4.59] and IM7/8551-7 carbon/epoxy [4.58]. The laminates for both materials are quasi-isotropic $[0/\pm45/90]_s$ and were tested in the form of 96-mm (3.8-in) ID cylinders with the applied loading being internal pressure and axial tension or compression. Additional data of this type have been obtained on other laminates and materials, including $[0/\pm60]$, and quasi-isotropic laminates loaded at an angle to the fibers for biaxial tension loading [4.59–4.62]. Additional failure data under biaxial loading are given in Figure 4.10 for T800/3900-2 carbon/epoxy in three different laminate layups, taken from [4.63]. Data on the failure of fiberglass/epoxy cross-ply laminates under biaxial compression are shown in Figure 4.11, taken from Wang and Socie [4.64].

The data given in Figures 4.6 to 4.8 indicate that the failure of laminates can be correlated within the accuracy of the experimental data by the maximum fiber strain criterion. This is a fundamental conclusion of the experimental studies reported in [4.58–4.63]. Fiber strain has long been used as a laminate failure criterion in practical applications, so that the results shown in Figures 4.9 to 4.11 and in [4.58–4.63] are not particularly surprising. However, this carefully controlled experimental work does add credibility to a criterion that is sometimes regarded as being "too simple." The laminate ultimate stress predicted on the basis of the maximum fiber-direction strain criterion is shown compared with the data for AS4/3501-6 in Figure 4.9. Figure 4.10 shows the comparison of the maximum fiber-strain failure criterion with the experimental data, where the same values for allowable fiber strain have been used for all three different laminate layups of T800/3900-2 carbon/epoxy.

The value of the fiber failure strain in the laminates composed of AS4/3501-6 appears to be nearly the same as that measured in unidirectional tensile coupons. However, the lam-

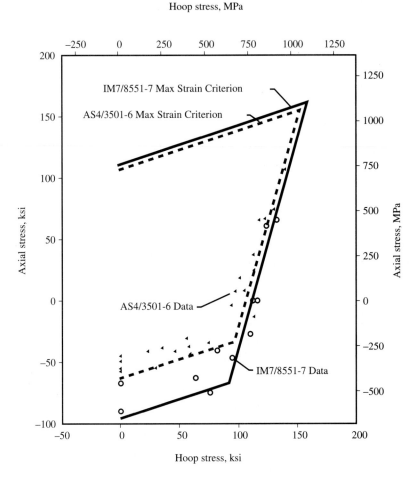

Figure 4.9   Laminate failure stresses for AS4/3501-6 and IM7/8551-7 carbon/epoxy laminates in quasi-isotropic [0/±45/90] configuration under biaxial loading. (*Source:* From [4.58].)

inate fiber-strain value for IM7/8551-7 and for T800/3900-2 appears to be about 20 to 30% lower than the values measured in tensile coupons. Thus, it may be necessary in general to establish allowables from laminate tests, rather than simply from using tensile coupon values. This creates a fundamental difficulty in that it is difficult to test laminates without introducing free-edge effects. This loss of fiber-strain capability from tensile coupon to laminate is believed to be related to the high-toughness resin systems used for both of these two material systems [4.65].

Fiber stress as a laminate failure criterion.   Stress values also can be used as the basis for a laminate failure criterion. The use of a maximum fiber-direction ply stress criterion can give accuracy equal to that of the strain criterion, if used properly. Although it is true that the value of stress in the fiber direction depends not only on the fiber-direction

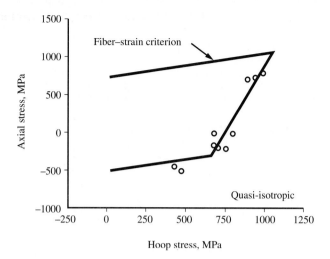

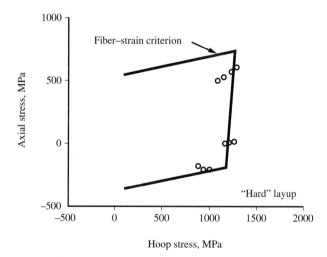

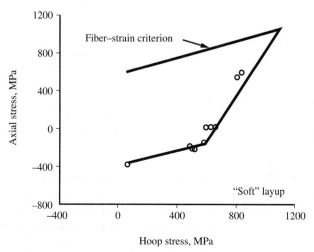

Figure 4.10 Comparison of data with failure envelopes predicted using the maximum fiber-strain criterion for T800/3900-2 carbon/epoxy under biaxial stress loading. Layups are $[0/\pm45/90]_{ns}$ (quasi-isotropic), $[0_3/\pm45/90]_s$ (hard), and $[0/(\pm45)_2/90]_s$ (soft). The same critical strain values are used for all three layups. (*Source:* From [4.63].)

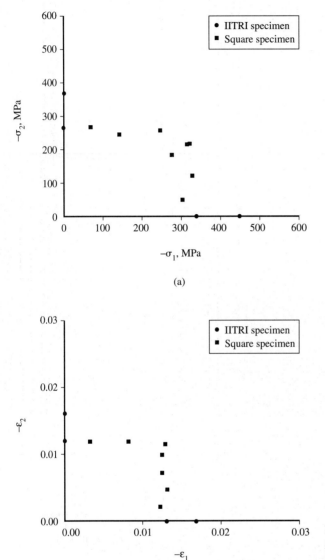

Figure 4.11   (a) Failure in stress space and (b) failure strains of cross-ply glass/epoxy laminates under biaxial compression loading. (*Source:* From [4.64].)

strain but also on the transverse strain, in fact this dependence on transverse strain is quite small due to the very low value of the minor in-plane Poisson ratio characteristic of fiber composites. Over the range of variables shown in the experimental data of Figures 4.6 and 4.7, the difference between a maximum fiber-stress and -strain criterion is only a few percent and is within the scatter of the data.

A problem exists because of the nonlinearity of the composite laminate stress–strain response. Although the stress–strain curves of laminates appear to be reasonably linear under tension loads, say, within 5 or 10% to failure, in fact, this is in part due to two counterbalancing sources of nonlinearity. In detail, carbon fibers show a stiffening behavior in tension such that the final secant modulus may be on the order of 15% higher than the initial modulus. Conversely, matrix cracking and nonlinearity in shear can soften the off-axis plies. These effects tend to offset each other, so that the overall laminate response appears linear. If either an accurate nonlinear laminate theory is used, or adjustment is made to the allowable fiber-stress values to account for the nonlinearity in an approximate manner, the fiber-direction stress can be used with equal accuracy to that of fiber strain.

The fiber failure criterion of Hahn, Erikson, and Tsai given in Eq. (4.36) is equivalent to the use of two separate values for tensile and compressive fiber-direction stress and is thus identical to the fiber-direction stress criterion discussed before. Thus, if proper stress allowables are used, this criterion gives excellent agreement with the experimental data, essentially equivalent to the use of the strain criterion. An easy way to account for the laminate nonlinearity discussed before is to use fictitious values of stress that are taken as the initial modulus multiplied by the strain at failure.

The Hashin fiber failure criterion of Eq. (4.38) has an additional shear term, in addition to the fiber normal stress terms. For conditions in which this shear stress is not large, this criterion is equivalent to the maximum fiber stress criterion and thus gives acceptable agreement with the data. However, for other conditions, the shear term is apparently overly conservative and agreement with the data is decreased [4.62].

As mentioned before, the Tsai–Wu criterion of Eq. (4.32) can be used as a fiber failure criterion by making special assumptions. In particular, the first ply to fail is assumed to be transverse, matrix-dominated failure, and the last ply failure is considered to coincide with ultimate laminate failure. An illustration of this is shown in Figure 4.12. As can be seen in the figure, the Tsai–Wu approach for predicting ultimate laminate failure is conservative by large factors under conditions of multiaxial laminate tensile stress and nonconservative for predicting multiaxial laminate compressive stress. The inherent problem is that the matrix and fiber failure modes are not clearly differentiated. The transverse stress terms are overly weighted with respect to fiber failure by being based on matrix failure. Fiber failure may indeed be influenced by the transverse stresses, but the magnitude of these stresses is essentially limited by the ability of the matrix to transmit these stresses into the fiber. In general, a transverse stress that is large with respect to matrix allowables can still be small with respect to fiber allowables.

Because the Tsai–Wu criterion is sensitive to the transverse stresses and overly conservative under conditions of multiaxial tensile stress, any reduction in the calculated transverse stresses may serve to improve the accuracy of the criterion when applied to tensile-stress states. For example, using the presumed reduction of effective transverse properties with matrix cracking and nonlinear shear response of [4.51] gives a small improvement in the comparison of the Tsai–Wu criterion with experiment. An alternative procedure is suggested in [4.55] in which the transverse properties E_{22}, G_{12}, and ν_{12} are multiplied by a degradation factor (DF), usually taken as 0.3, and the criterion of Eq. (4.32) is used as a "first-ply" failure criterion. As can be seen in Figure 4.13, this empirical approach does improve the predictive capability somewhat, although the comparison with the experimental data is still not really satisfactory. This procedure is quite empirical, as the degradation factor essentially becomes a free constant. Also, the failure is predicted to be controlled by

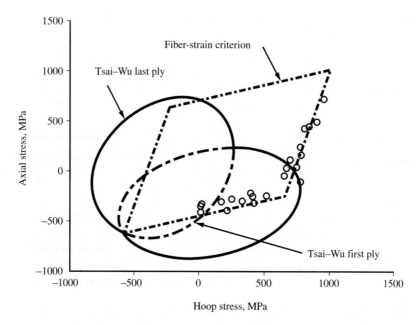

Figure 4.12 Comparison of data with failure envelopes predicted for AS4/3501-6 carbon/epoxy quasi-isotropic [0/±45/90] laminates. Prediction given using the maximum fiber-direction strain, Tsai–Wu first-ply, and Tsai–Wu last-ply criteria.

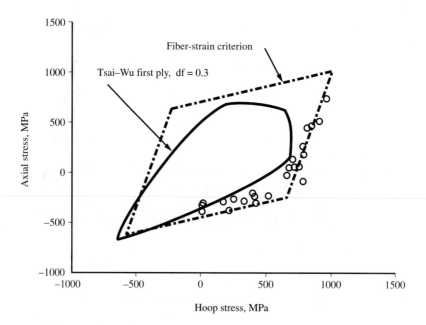

Figure 4.13 Comparison of data with failure envelopes predicted for AS4/3501-6 carbon/epoxy quasi-isotropic [0/±45/90] laminates. Prediction given using the maximum fiber-direction strain and Tsai–Wu first ply, with transverse stiffness degradation factor df = 0.3.

transverse plies rather than the plies in the loading directions, contrary to the usual interpretation of the experimental evidence.

Textile-form materials.   Fiber composites are often used in the form of textile products such as woven or braided fibers combined with various resin-impregnation techniques, such as resin transfer molding (RTM). The results of a set of biaxial tests on a particular 2-D triaxial braid of AS4/1895 carbon/epoxy are shown in Figure 4.14, taken from Smith and Swanson [4.66]. The triaxial braid is composed of a number of braided layers, each with straight axial fibers enclosed within the $\pm$ angle braids. A simplified method of analyzing the failure properties of the triaxial braid is to consider it to be analogous to a $[0/\pm\theta]$ laminate. A calculation of this type is illustrated in Figure 4.14, where a critical maximum-strain criterion has been used for the 0 and θ directions. The failure strain values are taken from uniaxial loadings of the braid material. It can be seen that this procedure provides an excellent correlation to the failure data. As can be seen in Figure 4.15, the Tsai–Wu approach does not fit the data nearly as well as the fiber-direction strain criterion.

Textile forms are often used to reduce fabrication costs or to provide reinforcement through the thickness. However, the in-plane properties are somewhat lower than in comparable straight-fiber laminates. The strength properties shown in Figure 4.14 for the 2-D triaxial braid are lower than would be expected for similar laminates, particularly in the braid direction, where apparent strength reductions exceed a factor of 2. This is believed to be due to stress concentrations associated with the fiber paths as well as stress concentrations associated with the heterogeneous microstructure.

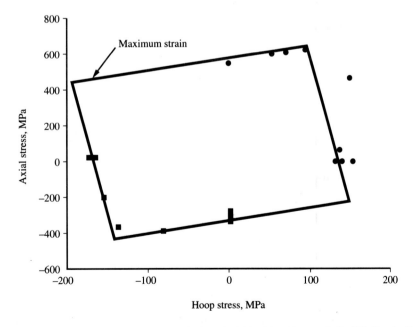

Figure 4.14   Biaxial stress failure envelope for 2-D triaxial braid, architecture B. Braid is $[0_{47\%}/\pm45]$ AS4/1895 carbon/epoxy. The line is a prediction based on the maximum fiber-direction strain failure criterion.

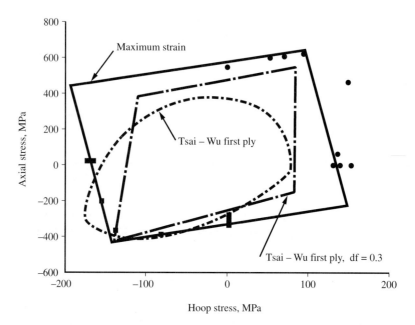

Figure 4.15 Biaxial stress failure envelope for 2-D triaxial braid, architecture B. Braid is $[0_{47\%}/\pm45]$ AS4/1895 carbon/epoxy. Predictions are based on the maximum fiber-direction strain, Tsai–Wu first-ply, and Tsai–Wu first ply with transverse stiffness degradation factor df = 0.3 failure criteria.

4.6 DISCUSSION

The major result of the evidence presented is that laminate ultimate failure can be represented on a ply-level analysis, which is thus applicable to all laminates. The most accurate failure criterion appears to be either maximum fiber-direction stress or strain. These criteria have been used extensively in practical applications, and thus it is reassuring that the laboratory data also verify the validity of these criteria. To a more or less extent, criteria that include transverse normal or shear stress effects on fiber failure appear to be less applicable. Although, in general, it would be expected that the transverse stresses do have an effect on fiber strength, the difficulty is in establishing how to accurately calculate these stresses. Clearly, the maximum transverse stresses are limited by the strength of the matrix or matrix-fiber interphase. This stress level may be quite low with respect to the fiber strength of carbon fibers. Thus, failure theories that include the effect of these stresses appear to be conservative, perhaps by as much as a factor of 4, as shown before. It may be that the transverse stresses are more important in the failure of aramid-fiber laminates, because of the weaker transverse strength of that fiber relative to carbon or glass fibers.

    The use of a ply-level criterion is of course desirable in that the criterion is presumed to apply to all fiber-dominated laminates of interest. Although the number of laminates for which valid failure properties are available is not large, the data that exist appear to support this contention. Certainly more data are needed for compressive-stress states, as the complicated failure mechanisms involved in laminate compressive failure might need additional treatment.

The question of how fiber strength or strain capability, say, as measured in a unidirectional coupon test, translates into a "delivered" value in a laminate is not settled. Although with the AS4/3501-6 carbon/epoxy system the fibers in the laminate appeared to have nearly the same strength properties as in a coupon, there was an apparent loss of strength of approximately 20% with the toughened resins of the IM7/8551-7 and T800/3900-2 carbon/epoxy systems. Thus, it appears that at least two laminate tests are necessary to determine tension and compression in-situ delivered fiber strengths.

The difference in delivered fiber strengths may be related to the fiber-matrix interphase properties. It has been conjectured that ply cracks in adjacent off-axis plies have a stress-concentration effect and thus reduce the strength of the load-carrying fibers. A mechanism for relieving this stress concentration has been proposed by Cook and Gordon [4.67], in which a microdelamination around the fiber at the tip of the crack relieves the stress, as shown in Figure 4.16. It is possible that higher matrix strength and toughness may tend to suppress this delamination and thus reduce the delivered fiber strength. Calculations to support this mechanism are given in [4.64].

The failure of fiber composites under compression is clearly very complicated, and not well understood. The available experimental data as well as the theoretical models suggest that failure values can depend on a number of variables. As a practical matter, it would seem that the best procedure is to have experimental data for compression strength under conditions as close as possible as that to be seen in the actual structure.

4.6.1 Complicating Effects

The case of statically applied uniform stress discussed before is, of course, the simplest possible situation involving failure of laminates. Obvious complications are those of fatigue, in which matrix cracking is believed to lead to delamination and thus can directly influence failure [4.53].

Another complicating effect is that of free edges. Stress-free edges in composite laminates (such as the edges of a laminate coupon) produce interlaminar stress distributions that die out a short distance from the edge. This well-known phenomenon has been studied extensively [4.68–4.70]. In many cases, the stresses cause delamination and the associated stress concentration in the fibers causes premature failure of the laminate. There is some evidence that tough resins may suppress this failure mode, in which case, the failure strength of laminate flat-coupon specimens should be the same as that of laminate tubular specimens (which do not have edges).

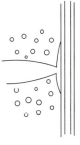

Figure 4.16   Potential stress-concentration effect of matrix crack on the fiber. Cook and Gordon [4.67] postulated that the stress concentration would be lowered by microdelaminations at the tip of the matrix crack.

Another complication is that associated with nonuniform stresses around stress concentrations. Typical cases are stresses around cutouts and pin-loaded holes, for example. Although composites tend to be brittle in their overall stress–strain response, simply using elastic stress-concentration factors has been shown to be overly conservative. The "point" and "average" stress methods have been introduced as empirical ways to use stress values lower than the peak stresses [4.71]. This approach has been applied on a ply level, using the fiber-strain criterion [4.72]. This latter procedure was shown to give reasonable comparisons with experiment for pin-loaded holes, if delamination adjacent to the hole was suppressed by lateral loads in the experiments [4.73].

In some laminates and loadings, it is not clear whether or not ultimate laminate failure can be produced by matrix failure alone or if fiber failure is required. This difficult area has been addressed by a number of investigators [4.50, 4.52, 4.74, 4.75]. A typical approach has been to formulate a nonlinear response model that includes softening due to matrix degradation, coupled with appropriate matrix and fiber failure properties and criteria. The nonlinear model then can predict the mode of failure, which may be either excessive deflection due to matrix softening or fiber failure.

4.7 CLOSURE

Recent experimental evidence has shown that the ultimate failure of carbon/epoxy and glass/epoxy laminates can be approached on a ply-level basis, so that a ply criterion can presumably be used for all laminates. If the laminate and loading is "fiber-dominated," fiber failure is required to cause ultimate laminate failure. The ply-level failure criterion that best represents the experimental data on the failure of a number of carbon/epoxy laminates as of this writing is either fiber-direction strain or stress. Allowable values for compression are often lower than for tension and are not well understood. Criteria that include interactions with transverse stresses tend to be conservative, in some cases, by large factors.

REFERENCES

4.1 Bishop, W., "High Performance Fibres," in *Advanced Composites*, ed. I. K. Partridge (New York: Elsevier, 1989), pp. 111–144.

4.2 Rosen, B. W., and N. F. Dow, "Overview of Composite Materials Analysis and Design," in *Engineered Materials Handbook, Vol. 1, Composites* (Metals Park, OH: American Society for Metals, 1987), pp. 175–180.

4.3 Rosen, B. W., "Mechanics of Fiber Strengthening," in *Fiber Composite Materials* (Metals Park, OH: American Society for Metals, 1965), pp. 37–75.

4.4 Zweben, C., "Tensile Failure of Fiber Composites," *AIAA J.* 6 (1968): 2325–2331.

4.5 Zweben, C., and B. W. Rosen, "A Statistical Theory of Material Strength with Application to Composite Materials," *J. Mech. Phys. Solids* 18 (1970): 189–206.

4.6 Harlow, D. G., and S. L. Phoenix, "The Chain-of-Bundles Probability Model for the Strength of Fibrous Materials II: A Numerical Study of Convergence," *J. Composite Mater.* 12 (1978): 314–334.

4.7 Batdorf, S. B., "Statistical Fracture Theories," in *International Encyclopedia of Composites*, ed. S. M. Lee (New York: VCH, 1991), Vol. 6, pp. 395–404.

4.8 Otani, H., S. L. Phoenix, and P. Petrina, "Matrix Effects on Lifetime Statistics for Carbon Fibre-Epoxy Microcomposites in Creep Rupture," *J. Mater. Sci.* 26 (1991): 1955–1970.

4.9 Zweben, C., "Size Effect in Composite Materials and Structures: Basic Concepts and Design Considerations," In *Proceedings of the NASA Workshop on Scaling Effects in Composite Materials and Structures*, ed. K. E. Jackson (Hampton, VA: National Aeronautics and Space Administration, 1994), pp. 197–217.

4.10 Cohen, D., "Application of Reliability and Fiber Probabilistic Strength Distribution Concepts to Composite Vessel Burst Strength Design," *J. Composite Mater.* 26 (1992): 1984–2014.

4.11 Greszczuk, L. B., "Microbuckling of Lamina-Reinforced Composites," in *Composite Materials: Testing and Design (Third Conference)*, ASTM STP 546 (Philadelphia: American Society for Testing and Materials, 1974), pp. 5–29.

4.12 Greszczuk, L. B., "On Failure Modes of Unidirectional Composites under Compressive Loading," in *Fracture of Composite Materials*, ed. G. C. Sih and V. P. Tamuzs (The Hague: Martinus Nijhoff, 1982), pp. 231–244.

4.13 DeTeresa, S. J., S. R. Allen, R. J. Farris, and R. S. Porter, "Compressive and Torsional Behavior of Kevlar 49 Fibre," *J. Mater. Sci.* 19 (1984): 57–72.

4.14 Prandy, J. M., and H. T. Hahn, "Compressive Strength of Carbon Fibers," *Sampe Quarterly* 22 (1991): 47–52.

4.15 DeTeresa, S. J., "Piezoresistivity and Failure of Carbon Filaments in Axial Compression," *Carbon* 29 (1991): 397–409.

4.16 Chaplin, C. R., "Compressive Fracture in Unidirectional Glass-Reinforced Plastics," *J. Mater. Sci.* 12 (1977): 347–357.

4.17 Piggott, M. R., "A Theoretical Framework for the Compressive Properties of Aligned Fibre Composites," *J. Mater. Sci.* 16 (1981): 2837–2845.

4.18 DeFerran, E. M., and B. Harris, "Compression Strength of Polyester Resin Reinforced with Steel Wires," *J. Mater. Sci.* 4 (1970): 62–72.

4.19 Wang, A. S. D., *A Non-Linear Microbuckling Model Predicting the Compressive Strength of Unidirectional Composites,* ASME Paper 78-WA/Aero 1 (New York: American Society of Mechanical Engineers, 1978).

4.20 Lanir, Y., and Y. C. B. Fung, "Fiber Composite Columns Under Compression," *J. Composite Mater.* 6 (1972): 387–401.

4.21 Herrman, L. R., W. E. Mason, and T. K. Chan, "Response of Reinforcing Wires to Compressive States of Stress," *J. Composite Mater.* 1 (1967): 212–226.

4.22 Hahn, H. T., and J. G. Williams, "Compression Failure Mechanisms in Unidirectional Composites," in *Composite Materials: Testing and Design (7th Conference)*, ASTM STP 893, ed. J. M. Whitney (Philadelphia: American Society for Testing and Materials, 1986), pp. 115–139.

4.23 Hayashi, T., "Compressive Strength of Unidirectionally Fibre Reinforced Composite Materials," in *Proceedings of the Seventh International Reinforced Plastics Conference of the British Plastics Federation*, 1970, pp. 11/1–11/3.

4.24 Chaudhuri, R. A., "Prediction of the Compressive Strength of Thick-Section Advanced Composite Laminates," *J. Composite Mater.* 25 (1991): 1244–1276.

4.25 Barber, J., and N. Triantafyllidis, "Effect of Debonding on the Stability of Fiber-Reinforced Composites," *J. Appl. Mech.* 52 (1985): 235–237.

4.26 Guynn, E. G., O. O. Ochoa, and W. L. Bradley, "A Parametric Study of Variables That Affect Fiber Microbuckling Initiation in Composite Laminates: Part 1—Analyses," *J. Composite Mater.* 26 (1992): 1594–1643.

4.27 Madhukar, M. S., and L. T. Drzal, "Fiber-Matrix Adhesion and Its Effect on Composite Mechanical Properties. III. Longitudinal (0°) Compressive Properties of Graphite/Epoxy Composites," *J. Composite Mater.* 26 (1992): 310–333.

4.28 Swanson, S. R., and G. E. Colvin, "Compression Failure in Reduced Adhesion Fiber Laminates," *ASME J. Eng. Mater. Tech.* 115 (1993): 187–192.

4.29 Jelf, P. M., and N. A. Fleck, "Compression Failure Mechanisms in Unidirectional Composites," *J. Composite Mater.* 26 (1992): 2706–2726.

4.30 Yeh, J. R., and J. L. Teply, "Compressive Response of Kevlar/Epoxy Composite," *J. Composite Mater.* 3 (1988): 245–257.

4.31 Zhang, G., and R. A. Latour, "FRP Composite Compressive Strength and Its Dependence upon Interfacial Bond Strength, Fiber Misalignment, and Matrix Nonlinearity," in *Proceedings of the American Society for Composites, 8th Technical Conference* (Lancaster, PA: Technomic Publishing, 1993), pp. 519–528.

4.32 Argon, A. S., "Fracture of Composites," in *Treatise on Materials Science and Technology*, Vol. 1, ed. H. Herman (New York: Academic Press, 1972), pp. 79–114.

4.33 Evans, A. G., and W. F. Adler, "Kinking as a Mode of Structural Degradation in Carbon Fiber Composites," *Acta Metall.* 26 (1978): 725–738.

4.34 Budiansky, B., "Micromechanics," *Computers Struct.* 16 (1983): 3–12.

4.35 Maewal, A., "Postbuckling Behavior of a Periodically Laminated Medium in Compression," *Intl. J. Solids Struct.* 17 (1981): 335–344.

4.36 Berg, J. S., and D. F. Adams, "An Evaluation of Composite Material Compression Test Methods," *J. Composites Tech. Res.* 11 (1989): 41–46.

4.37 Shuart, M. J., "An Evaluation of the Sandwich Beam Compression Test Method for Composites," in *Test Methods and Design Allowables for Fibrous Composites*, ASTM STP 734, ed. C. C. Chamis (Philadelphia: American Society for Testing and Materials, 1981), pp. 152–165.

4.38 Whitney, J. M., A. S. Crasto, and R. Y. Kim, "Failure Criteria for Laminated Composites Subjected to Compression Loading," in *Proceedings of the American Society for Composites, 7th Technical Conference* (Lancaster, PA: Technomic Publishing, 1992), pp. 604–612.

4.39 Jackson, K. E., "Scaling Effects in the Flexural Response and Failure of Composite Beams," *AIAA J.* 30 (1992): 2099–2105.

4.40 Wisnom, M. R., "The Effect of Specimen Size on the Bending Strength of Unidirectional Carbon Fibre-Epoxy," *Composite Struct.* 18 (1991): 47–63.

4.41 Sohi, M. M., H. T. Hahn, and J. G. Williams, "The Effect of Resin Toughness and Modulus on Compressive Failure Modes of Quasi-Isotropic Graphite/Epoxy Laminates," in *Toughened Composites*, ASTM STP 937, ed. N. J. Johnston (Philadelphia: American Society for Testing and Materials, 1987), pp. 37–60.

4.42 Colvin, G. E., and S. R. Swanson, "In-Situ Compressive Strength of Carbon/Epoxy AS4/3501-6 Laminates," *ASME J. Eng. Mater. Tech.* 115 (1993): 122–128.

4.43 Swanson, S. R., "A Micro-Mechanics Model for In-Situ Compression Strength of Fiber Composite Laminates," *ASME J. Eng. Mater. Tech.* 114 (1992): 8–12.

4.44 Swanson, S. R., "Constraint Effects in Compression Failure of Fiber Composites," in *Proceedings of the Tenth International Conference on Composite Materials*, eds. A. Poursartip and K. Street (Cambridge, England: Woodhead Publishing Ltd., 1995), pp. I-739–I-746.

4.45 Piggott, M. R., in *Developments in Reinforced Plastics* (London: Elsevier, 1984), Vol. 4, p. 131.

4.46 Wang, A. S. D., "Fracture Mechanics of Sublaminate Cracks in Composite Materials," *Composites Tech. Rev.* 6 (1984): 45–62.

4.47 Masters, J. E., and K. L. Reifsnider, "An Investigation of Cumulative Damage Development in Quasi-Isotropic Graphite/Epoxy Laminates," in *Damage in Composite Materials*, ASTM STP 775, ed. K. L. Reifsnider (Philadelphia: American Society for Testing and Materials, 1982), pp. 40–62.

4.48 Flaggs, D. L., and M. H. Kural, "Experimental Determination of the In Situ Transverse Lamina Strength in Graphite/Epoxy Laminates," *J. Composite Mater.* 16 (1982): 103–116.

4.49 Parvizi, A., K. W. Garrett, and J. E. Bailey, "Constrained Cracking in Glass Fibre-Reinforced Epoxy Cross-Ply Laminates," *J. Mater. Sci.* 13 (1978): 195–201.

4.50 Nuismer, R. J., and S. C. Tan, "The Role of Matrix Cracking in the Continuum Constitutive Behavior of a Damaged Composite Ply," in *Proceedings of the IUTAM Symposium on Mechanics of Composite Materials: Recent Advances*, eds. Z. Hashin and C. T. Herakovich (New York: Pergamon Press, 1983), pp. 437–448.

4.51 Laws, N., G. J. Dvorak, and M. Hejazi, "Stiffness Changes in Unidirectional Composites Caused by Crack Systems," *Mech. Mater.* 2 (1983): 123–137.

4.52 Swanson, S. R., and A. P. Christoforou, "Progresssive Failure in Carbon/Epoxy Laminates Under Biaxial Stress," *J. Eng. Mater. Tech.* 109 (1987): 12–16.

4.53 Reifsnider, K. L., K. Schulte, and J. C. Duke, "Long-Term Fatigue Behavior of Composite Materials," in *Long Term Behavior of Composites*, ASTM STP 813, ed. T. K. O'Brien (Philadelphia: American Society for Testing and Materials, 1983), pp. 136–159.

4.54 Tsai, S. W., and E. M. Wu, "A General Theory of Strength of Anisotropic Materials," *J. Composite Mater.* 5 (1971): 58–80.

4.55 Tsai, S. W., *Composites Design*, 3rd. ed. (Dayton, OH: Think Composites, 1987).

4.56 Hahn, H. T., J. B. Erikson, and S. W. Tsai, "Characterization of Matrix/Interface-Controlled Strength of Unidirectional Composites," in *Fracture of Composite Materials*, ed. G. Sih and V. P. Tamuzs (The Hague: Martinus Nijhoff, 1982), pp. 197–214.

4.57 Hashin, Z., "Failure Criteria for Unidirectional Fiber Composites," *J. Appl. Mech.* 102 (1980): 329–334.

4.58 Colvin, G. E., and S. R. Swanson, "Characterization of the Failure Properties of IM7/8551-7 Carbon/Epoxy Under Multiaxial Stress," *ASME J. Eng. Mater. Tech.* 112 (1990): 61–67.

4.59 Swanson, S. R., and M. Nelson, "Failure Properties of Carbon/Epoxy Laminates Under Tension-Compression Biaxial Stress," in *Proceedings of the Third Japan-U.S. Conference on Composite Materials,* eds. K. Kawata, S. Umekawa, and A. Kobayashi (Tokyo: Japan Society for Composite Materials, 1986), pp. 279–286.

4.60 Swanson, S. R., and A. P. Christoforou, "Response of Quasi-Isotropic Carbon/Epoxy Laminates to Biaxial Stress," *J. Composite Mater.* 20 (1986): 457–471.

4.61 Swanson, S. R., and B. Trask, "Biaxial Tests of Off-Axis Quasi-Isotropic Laminates," in *Proceedings of the American Society for Composites, 2nd Technical Conference* (Lancaster, PA: Technomic Publishing, 1987), pp. 225–234.

4.62 Swanson, S. R., and B. C. Trask, "An Examination of Failure Strength in [0/±60] Laminates Under Biaxial Stress," *Composites* 19 (1988): 400–406.

4.63 Swanson, S. R., and Y. Qian, "Multiaxial Characterization of T800/3900-2 Carbon/Epoxy," *Composites Sci. Tech* 43 (1992): 197–203.

4.64 Wang, J. Z., and D. F. Socie, "Failure Strength and Damage Mechanisms of E-Glass/Epoxy Laminates Under In-Plane Biaxial Compressive Deformation," *J. Composite Mater.* 27 (1993): 40–58.

4.65 Swanson, S. R., "Biaxial Failure Criteria for Toughened Resin Carbon/Epoxy Laminates," in *Proceedings of the American Society for Composites, 7th Technical Conference* (Lancaster, PA: Technomic Publishing, 1992), pp. 1075–1083.

4.66 Smith, L. V., and S. R. Swanson, "Strength Design with 2-D Triaxial Braid Textile Composites," in *Proceedings of the American Society for Composites, 9th Technical Conference* (Lancaster, PA: Technomic Publishing, 1994), pp. 727–734.

4.67 Cook, J., and J. E. Gordon, "A Mechanism for the Control of Crack Propagation in All-Brittle Systems," *Proc. R. Soc. London A* 282 (1964): 508–520.

4.68 Pipes, R. B., and N. J. Pagano, "Interlaminar Stresses in Composite Laminates Under Uniform Axial Extension," *J. Composite Mater.* 4 (1970): 538–548.

4.69 Wang, S. S., and I. Choi, "Boundary-Layer Effects in Composite Laminates: Part 2, Free-Edge Stress Solutions and Basic Characteristics," *J. Appl. Mech.* 49 (1982): 549–560.

4.70 Herakovich, C. T., "On the Relationship Between Engineering Properties and Delamination of Composite Materials," *J. Composite Mater.* 15 (1981): 336–348.

4.71 Whitney, J. M., and R. J. Nuismer, "Stress Fracture Criteria for Laminated Composites Containing Stress Concentrations," *J. Composite Mater.* 8 (1974): 253–265.

4.72 Poe, C. C., Jr., "A Unifying Strain Criterion for Fracture of Fibrous Composite Laminates," *Eng. Fract. Mech.* 17 (1983): 153–171.

4.73 Swanson, S. R., and J. S. Burns, "Analysis of Pin Loading of Carbon/Epoxy Plates," in *Proceedings of the 31st National SAMPE Symposium* (Covine, CA: Society for the Advancement of Material and Process Engineering, 1986), pp. 1078–1086.

4.74 Nuismer, R. J., "Predicting the Performance and Failure of Multidirectional Polymeric Matrix Composite Laminates: A Combined Micro-Macro Approach," *Proceedings of the Third International Conference on Composite Materials* (New York: Pergamon Press, 1980), pp. 436–452.

4.75 Sandhu, R. S., R. L. Gallo, and G. P. Sendeckyj, "Initiation and Accumulation of Damage in Composite Laminates," in *Composite Materials: Testing and Design (6th Conference)*, ASTM STP 787 (Philadelphia: American Society for Testing and Materials, 1982), pp. 163–182.

PROBLEMS

4.1. Calculate the ratio of tensile strength to density for the fibers listed in Table 4.1

4.2. Fill in the steps leading to an estimate for the "ineffective length" using Eq. (4.7) for the stress recovery away from a single broken fiber that is loaded in tension.

4.3. Calculate the "ineffective length" for stress recovery away from a single broken fiber that is loaded in tension using a best estimate for the properties of AS4/3501-6 carbon/epoxy.

4.4. Give an estimate of the change in tensile strength with size predicted by Weibull theory in going from the tow test specimens to large-scale pressure vessels using Eq. (4.8). Compare with the values reported in [4.10].

4.5. Give a full derivation of the equations that are developed in the text for predicting axial compressive strength in the fiber direction based on fiber microbuckling in the extension mode.

4.6. Give a full derivation of the equations that are developed in the text for predicting axial compressive strength in the fiber direction based on fiber microbuckling in the shear mode.

4.7. Compare the values predicted for compressive strength of a unidirectional fiber composite using the "extension mode" and "shear mode" expressions given in Eqs. (4.23) and (4.31). Also compare with typical laboratory results.

4.8. Give some possible reasons why the microbuckling expressions such as Eq. (4.31) tend to overpredict the measured compressive strength of fiber composites. Consider both aramid and intermediate-modulus carbon-fiber composites.

4.9. Derive the expressions used for obtaining the Tsai–Wu constants F_1, F_{11}, F_2, F_{22}, and F_{66} from simple laboratory tests.

4.10. Consider the matrix failure data shown in Figure 4.5 for AS4/3501-6 carbon/epoxy unidirectional material. Compare these data with the predictions of the Tsai–Wu and the modified Tsai–Wu expression for matrix failure, Eqs. (4.32) and (4.37).

4.11. Consider the matrix failure data shown in Figure 4.5 for AS4/3501-6 carbon/epoxy unidirectional material. Compare these data with the predictions of a noninteractive matrix failure criterion in which either transverse normal or in-plane shear values are taken as critical.

4.12. Consider in-plane shear loading of a $[0/\pm 45/90]_s$ laminate made of AS4/3501-6 carbon/epoxy. Calculate the maximum applied average shear stress for ultimte laminate failure according to the following:
(a) The Tsai–Wu first-ply failure criterion.
(b) The maximum fiber-strain failure criterion and identify which plies are considered critical.

4.13. Consider in-plane shear loading of a $[0/(\pm 45)_3/90]_s$ laminate made of AS4/3501-6 carbon/epoxy. Calculate the maximum applied average shear stress for ultimte laminate failure according to the following:
(a) The Tsai–Wu first-ply failure criterion.
(b) The maximum fiber-strain failure criterion and identify which plies are considered critical.

4.14. Consider in-plane shear loading of a $[0_3/\pm 45/90]_s$ laminate made of AS4/3501-6 carbon/epoxy. Calculate the maximum applied average shear stress for ultimate laminate failure according to the following:
(a) The Tsai–Wu first-ply failure criterion.
(b) The maximum fiber-strain failure criterion and identify which plies are considered critical.

4.15. Calculate the ultimate average applied stresses when the applied loads are in a 2-to-1 ratio for a $[0_2/\pm 30]_s$ laminate made of AS4/3501-6 carbon/epoxy. Calculate the maximum applied average shear stress for ultimate laminate failure according to the following:
(a) The Tsai–Wu first-ply failure criterion.
(b) The maximum fiber-strain failure criterion and identify which plies are considered critical.

4.16. Compare the ultimate failure stresses for a $[0/\pm 45/90]_s$ laminate made of AS4/3501-6 carbon/epoxy, for uniaxial tension N_x loading and equal biaxial ($N_x = N_y$) tension loading according to the following:
(a) The Tsai–Wu first-ply failure criterion.
(b) The maximum fiber-strain failure criterion and identify which plies are considered critical.

For Problems 4.17 to 4.24, consider in-plane loading of a $[0/\pm 45/90]_s$ laminate made of AS4/3501-6 carbon/epoxy. Construct failure plots to compare with the biaxial failure data shown in Figures 4.6, 4.9, and 4.10 based on the criteria listed. Compare with the data given and comment. The computer programs available on the web are useful for these problems (see the Appendix).

4.17. Calculate first-ply failure according to the Tsai–Wu criterion of Eq. (4.32) using $F_{12} = 0$.

4.18. Calculate first-ply failure according to the Tsai–Wu criterion of Eq. (4.32) using F_{12} as given in Eq. (4.35).

4.19. Calculate last-ply failure according to the Tsai–Wu criterion of Eq. (4.32) using $F_{12} = 0$.

4.20. Calculate last-ply failure according to the Tsai–Wu criterion of Eq. (4.32) using F_{12} as given in Eq. (4.35).

4.21. Calculate first-ply failure according to the Tsai–Wu criterion of Eq. (4.32) using $F_{12} = 0$. Use degraded-matrix transverse stiffness properties with DF = 0.3.

4.22. Calculate first-ply failure according to the Tsai–Wu criterion of Eq. (4.32) using F_{12} as given in Eq. (4.35). Use degraded-matrix transverse stiffness properties with DF = 0.3.

4.23. Calculate ultimate failure as predicted by the critical fiber-direction-strain criterion.

4.24. Calculate ultimate failure as predicted by the critical fiber-direction-stress criterion.

For problems 4.25 to 4.27, consider in-plane loading of the following laminates made of AS4/3501-6 carbon/epoxy. Construct failure plots for in-plane loading in the tension–tension quadrant for the layups given. The results should be generally comparable with those given for T800/3900-2 in Figure 4.7, except that the T800 is a higher-strength carbon fiber. Use the failure criterion of your choice.

4.25. Use a $[0/\pm45/90]_s$ (quasi-isotropic) layup.

4.26. Use a $[0_3/\pm45/90]_s$ layup.

4.27. Use a $[0/(\pm45)_2/90]_s$ layup.

5

Delamination, Matrix Cracking, and Durability

5.1 INTRODUCTION

The problem of delamination can be a significant one with laminated composites. As the layers of the laminate are held together by the matrix, the strength of this bond is of course limited by the matrix strength. If the laminated structure is required to resist bending loads, the stiffness and strength may be largely lost if the structure delaminates. Further, various environmental and loading factors such as thermal and moisture effects, damage caused by accidental transverse impacts, and fatigue loads may influence the lamination strength. However, it is possible to design against delamination failure if proper attention is paid to the variables of loading and environment. Certainly one tool to use in this design procedure is to calculate the interlaminar stresses and compare these with interlaminar stress allowables. Another viewpoint is to use fracture mechanics principles. Both of these viewpoints are complementary and may be employed together in a design situation. Both approaches are discussed in the following. It should also be pointed out that textile-form composites may minimize or eliminate the delamination problem; this may be one of the advantages with these material forms.

Matrix cracking is often part of the failure process in fiber composites. It typically manifests itself as cracking in the off-axis plies of a laminate, for example, in the 90° plies of a laminate loaded in the 0° direction. The matrix cracks affect the stress distribution within the plies of the laminate by lowering the transverse stiffnesses of the plies. Matrix cracks also can serve as flaws for delamination initiation. Although matrix cracking was mentioned briefly in the previous chapter on failure of laminates, this chapter gives a more detailed examination of the subject.

The last part of this chapter deals with issues of durability in fiber composites, and specifically with impact damage and fatigue loading. The durability of fiber composites is becoming of increased importance as composites are used in strength-critical applications, and the general newness of many of the current applications makes these issues very timely.

5.2 DELAMINATION

Fiber composites often consist of layers that are bonded together as part of the curing process. These layers may be readily identified as in the various layers of a prepreg laminate, or may be more indistinct as in layers of a braided composite. In any case, delamination is the separation of these layers. Delamination often leads to complete loss of function of the part. For example, if the part must carry bending loads, delamination usually leads to significant loss of bending stiffness and strength. Delamination can also lead to loss of load-carrying ability in compression, as the composite may buckle due to the loss of bending stiffness. As mentioned before, both strength and fracture mechanics principles may be used to analyze and design against delamination. These approaches are described in the following.

5.2.1 Strength Analysis

The basic idea in a strength analysis for delamination failure is to determine the interlaminar allowable properties from experimental tests and then compare these with the calculated interlaminar stresses. The interlaminar stresses may consist of both shear and normal stress. As described in Chapters 6 and 7 for plates and beams, respectively, shear stresses are associated with bending, much as is the case for isotropic beams. In situations in which the shear stresses are assumed to dominate, the strength analysis consists of comparing the calculated interlaminar shear stress with the allowable interlaminar shear stress.

Interlaminar shear allowables are often determined by means of the "short-beam shear test." As implied by the name, this test consists of a three-point bend loading of a short, thick, laminated specimen that has high shear stress relative to bending stress because of the aspect ratio. This test is routinely used for quality control purposes and can be considered to give an estimate of the allowable shear stresses. However, as discussed by Whitney [5.1], the test is difficult to analyze in detail because of the complexity of the stress field. Another test is the Iosepescu test [5.2, 5.3], already discussed in Chapter 4. Also as discussed in Chapter 4, other shear tests such as the rail shear can be employed to give shear allowables, but questions remain about the effects of end grips with these tests.

Example of interlaminar shear strength analysis.   Consider that a simply supported laminated composite beam is required to carry a distributed load. Among other design considerations, it is necessary to compare the calculated interlaminar shear stress with an appropriate allowable interlaminar shear strength. A schematic of the beam is shown in Figure 5.1.

Using equilibrium of the transverse forces shows that the maximum shear force is given by $V = qL/2$. It will be shown in Chapter 7 on analysis of composite beams that the shear-stress distribution of composite beams can differ from that in isotropic beams, de-

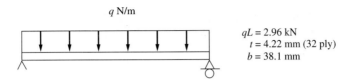

q N/m

$qL = 2.96$ kN
$t = 4.22$ mm (32 ply)
$b = 38.1$ mm

Figure 5.1   Interlaminar shear strength analysis for beam loading.

pending on the layup. However, for plies that are well distributed throughout the layup, this effect is in many cases not large. For the present, this difference is neglected and the usual isotropic-beam shear-stress formula $\tau = VQ/Ib$ is used, where V is the shear force, I is the area moment of inertia of the cross-section, and b is the thickness (width) of the beam at the location where the shear stress is being computed. Q is defined as the first moment of part of the cross-section, which is bounded by the plane at which the shear stress is desired (i.e., the distance from the neutral axis) and the outer surface of the beam. The maximum shear stress occurs at the beam midplane, and is given by $\tau = 1.5V/A$. Consider that the beam has a loading and dimensions as shown in Figure 5.1. The shear stress at the beam center line, adjacent to the support, is calculated to be $\tau = 13.8$ MPa (2000 psi). A typical interlaminar shear allowable value for an epoxy-matrix composite may be on the order of 48.3 MPa (7000 psi), giving a factor of safety of 3.5 for this illustration.

5.2.2 Fracture Mechanics Approach

An alternative viewpoint for assessing the reliability of laminates with respect to delamination is to adopt a fracture mechanics viewpoint. With this approach, the presence of an initial cracklike flaw is assumed, which in this case is an initial delamination. The question is then asked as to what loading is required to cause the flaw to propagate. The fracture mechanics approach to delamination is based on an assessment of the propagation of an existing delamination. In the usual case, in which the delamination is not actually present, the assessment relates to the question: "What if there were an initial delamination?" Obviously, the structure is usually not designed with an initial delamination. However, initial delaminations can arise from loadings such as accidental impact or from initial imperfections in the structure.

The propensity for a crack to propagate can be related to the energy release rate, a concept that dates back to Griffith and that has been developed for isotropic materials in an extensive literature. Perhaps because of the background and success of fracture mechanics with metals, many attempts have been made to apply similar principles to fiber composites. In general, these attempts were not always successful, because the very nature of fiber composites may violate certain assumptions inherent in the fracture mechanics literature for metals. For example, cracks normal to fibers may fail by splitting along the fibers, rather than propagating through them. The resulting description of the failure process thus must be quite different than with isotropic materials. However, it is generally agreed that delamination is a natural application of fracture mechanics to composites, as the delamination is constrained to propagate in a self-similar manner, thus facilitating the theoretical interpretation.

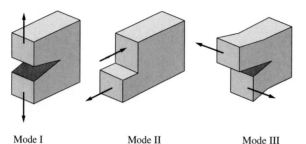

Mode I   Mode II   Mode III

Figure 5.2 Three crack-propagation modes.

As illustrated in Figure 5.2, a crack can be considered to propagate in three different modes. Mode I is the opening mode, and Modes II and III are shearing modes. Tests for allowable properties are usually interpreted in terms of critical energy-release rates in each of the three modes. Two of the more popular tests are described in what follows.

Double-cantilever-beam test.   The double-cantilever-beam (DCB) test is illustrated in Figure 5.3. The basic idea is that an initial flaw is caused to propagate under load and that the load can then be interpreted in terms of the opening-mode energy-release rate. Variations of the test sometimes employ geometries that are tapered in either the width or thickness to make the results independent of the size of the flaw. Although more complicated finite-element analysis is possible, the results are often determined in terms of simple-beam theory. This theory is illustrated in the following.

The basic idea to be developed is that energy is dissipated as "fracture energy" as the crack (delamination) propagates. This energy is sometimes called "surface energy," which is not precise, as the actual fracture energy can involve many dissipative mechanisms that are much larger than the actual surface energy. The energy balance can be written for a structure with a crack as

$$W = U + \Gamma \tag{5.1}$$

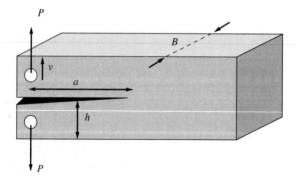

Figure 5.3 The double-cantilever-beam specimen for measuring opening-mode critical energy-release rate.

where W is the work due to externally applied loads, U is the strain energy in the body, and Γ is the fracture energy. Taking the rate of change of these quantities with respect to crack extension gives

$$\frac{dW}{da} = \frac{dU}{da} + \frac{d\Gamma}{da} = \frac{dU}{da} + BG \qquad (5.2)$$

where a is the length of the crack, B is the thickness of the cracked structure, and G is the fracture energy per unit length of the crack. Consider each of these quantities during an extension of the crack. For linear elastic materials, the energy is given by

$$U = (1/2)P\,\delta \qquad (5.3)$$

Also, the definition of compliance C of the structure is given by

$$\delta = CP \qquad (5.4)$$

where δ is the displacement at the point of the load. By substituting Eq. (5.4) into (5.3), the strain energy can be written as

$$U = (1/2)CP^2 \qquad (5.5)$$

and differentiating with respect to crack length gives

$$\frac{dU}{da} = CP\frac{dP}{da} + \frac{P^2}{2}\frac{dC}{da} \qquad (5.6)$$

If the crack extends under fixed-grip conditions,

$$\frac{dW}{da} = 0$$

and the load will decrease as

$$\frac{dP}{da} = \frac{-P}{C}\frac{dC}{da} \qquad (5.7)$$

If the load is constant, the work done during the crack extension will be

$$\frac{dW}{da} = P\frac{d\delta}{da} = P\left(C\frac{dP}{da} + P\frac{dC}{da}\right) \qquad (5.8)$$

Substituting either the fixed-grip or the constant-load expressions into the energy-rate balance, Eq. (5.2), gives

$$\frac{P^2}{2B}\frac{dC}{da} = G \qquad (5.9)$$

This general result can be applied to the double-cantilever-beam test. The strength-of-materials approach to the analysis of the specimen is illustrated. The idealization to be made is that each leg of the specimen can be idealized as a cantilever beam with length equal to the crack length. From symmetry, the displacement of each leg is one-half of the total displacement, and can be given as

$$\frac{\delta}{2} = \frac{Pa^3}{3EI} \qquad (5.10)$$

where E is the axial modulus, and I is the moment of inertia of each leg. From this, the compliance is given by

$$C = \frac{2a^3}{3EI}$$ (5.11)

Differentiating gives

$$\frac{dC}{da} = \frac{2a^2}{EI}$$ (5.12)

Substituting into Eq. (5.8) gives

$$G = \frac{P^2 a^2}{BEI}$$ (5.13)

The energy-release rate given by Eq. (5.13) for a load P that extends the crack can be considered to be a critical (or allowable) energy-release rate in the opening mode, Mode I. This critical energy-release rate is commonly called G_{Ic}. Values determined from the DCB test are commonly employed in fracture mechanics analysis.

An improvement to the analysis just given was suggested by Kanninen [5.4], who noted that the model of a cantilever overstates the amount of restraint at the base of each beam. Rather, the beams each rotate against the elastic support provided where they join together. Kanninen used a beam on an elastic foundation to account for this effect.

The end-notched flexure test.   The Mode II critical energy-release rate values can be determined by using the end-notched flexure (ENF) test illustrated in Figure 5.4. Because the delamination lies along the center line, which is the neutral axis of the uncracked specimen, the crack propagation is driven primarily by the shear stresses, and thus is primarily Mode II.

This specimen has been subject to both strength-of-materials and finite-element analysis [5.5]. The strength-of-materials approach is illustrated here. From Eq. (5.9), it can be seen that it is only necessary to derive the compliance of the beam as a function of the delamination length a. This can be easily done with a variety of ordinary beam techniques. The use of Castigliano's second theorem is illustrated here. By using the free-body diagram of Figure 5.5 and the expression for strain energy given by

$$U = \int_0^L \frac{M^2}{2EI} \, dx$$ (5.14)

the strain energy for the beam is given by

$$U = \int_0^L \frac{(Px/2)^2}{2EI} dx + \int_0^{L-a} \frac{[P(L-x)/2]^2}{2EI} dx + 2\int_{L-a}^L \frac{[P(L-x)/4]^2}{2EI/8} dx$$ (5.15)

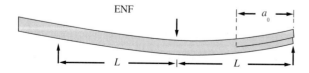

ENF

a_0

L L

Figure 5.4   End-notched flexure specimen for measuring shearing-mode critical energy-release rate.

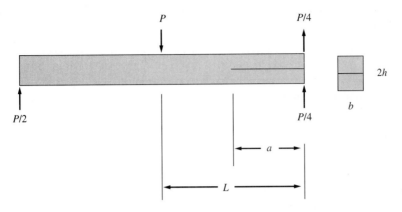

Figure 5.5   Free-body diagram for the end-notch flexure specimen.

The assumption has been made that the delaminated section of the beam acts as two independent beams, with each carrying half of the applied load. With this assumption, the EI of one of the delaminated beams is 1/8 of the EI of the intact beam. Then from Castigliano's second theorem,

$$\delta = \frac{\delta U}{\delta P} = \int_0^L \frac{Px^2}{4EI} dx + \int_0^{L-a} \frac{P(L-x)^2}{4EI} dx + \int_{L-a}^L \frac{P(L-x)^2}{EI} dx \qquad (5.16)$$

Carrying out the integrals gives

$$C = \frac{\delta}{P} = \frac{2L^3 + 3a^3}{12EI} = \frac{2L^3 + 3a^3}{8Ebh^3} \qquad (5.17)$$

where the dimensions of the intact beam are taken as b wide by $2h$ high. Differentiating with respect to a and substituting into Eq. (5.9) gives the usual expression for strain-energy-release rate for the ENF beam as

$$G = \frac{9P^2a^2}{16Eb^2h^3} \qquad (5.18)$$

The procedure in running the ENF test is to prepare the specimens with a preexisting end delamination, say, by inserting Teflon strips prior to lamination. The starter delamination may be combined with further delamination extension by fatigue cracking. The critical load for delamination extension is then taken from the deviation from the linearity of the load-deflection curve when tested in a stiff testing machine. The critical strain-energy-release rate is then calculated for this load value from Eq. (5.18).

The mixed-mode bending test.   The two tests described before are commonly used to determine Mode I and Mode II delamination-resistance properties. However, applications may produce loadings that apply both Modes I and II together. Thus, it is necessary to have a mixed-mode criterion that can predict delamination under combined loading, and, in turn, this criterion must be developed and verified for delamination under known conditions of combined Mode I and II loading. A test to accomplish this has been offered by Reeder and Crews [5.6] known as the mixed-mode bending (MMB) test. The test specimen is illustrated in Figure 5.6 and a free-body diagram of the loading is given in Figure 5.7.

The basic idea of the specimen is that it combines the loadings of the DCB specimen and the ENF specimen, depending on the position of the loading point. The energy-release rates can then be accomplished by using the formulas given previously, combined by super-position. By using the notation of Figure 5.7, the components of the applied force leading to Mode I and Mode II loadings are given by

$$P_I = \frac{3c - L}{4L}P \tag{5.19}$$

and

$$P_{II} = \frac{c + L}{L}P \tag{5.20}$$

Substituting the loads into the expressions for Mode I and Mode II loading developed before for the double-cantilever-beam and the end-notched flexure tests then gives the expression for energy-release rate in the mixed-mode bending specimen as

$$G_I = \frac{3a^2P^2}{4b^2h^3L^2E_{11}}(3c - L)^2 \tag{5.21}$$

and

$$G_{II} = \frac{9a^2P^2}{16b^2h^3L^2E_{11}}(c + L)^2 \tag{5.22}$$

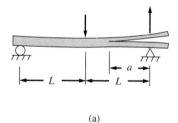

(a)

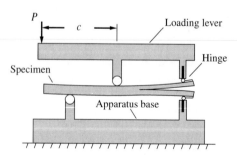

(b)

Figure 5.6   The mixed-mode bend specimen: (a) test specimen and loading, and (b) schematic diagram of apparatus.

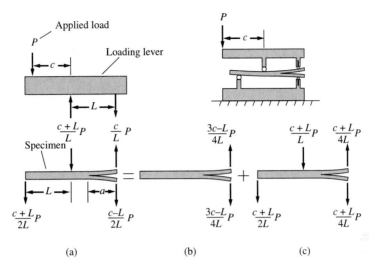

Figure 5.7   Free-body diagrams for the mixed-mode bend specimen: (a) MMB specimen loading, (b) Mode I loading, and (c) Mode II loading.

The ratio of the two loadings depends only on the geometry of the specimen and loading arm, and is given by

$$G_{\mathrm{I}}/G_{\mathrm{II}} = \frac{4}{3}\left[\frac{3c-L}{c+L}\right]^2 \qquad \text{for} \qquad c \geqslant \frac{L}{3} \tag{5.23}$$

where the restriction on length c is given to avoid contact between the two arms of the specimen not accounted for in the data reduction.

Reeder and Crews [5.6] compared the results given before for energy-release rates as determined by beam theory with finite-element results. They advocate the correction given by Kanninen [5.4] for the DCB analysis, which then gives

$$G_{\mathrm{I}} = \frac{12P_1^2}{b^2 h^3 E_{11}}\left(a^2 + \frac{2a}{\lambda} + \frac{1}{\lambda^2}\right) \tag{5.24}$$

where

$$\lambda = \left(\frac{3k}{b^2 h^3 E_{11}}\right)^{1/4} \qquad \text{and} \qquad k = \frac{2bE_{22}}{h}$$

Using this correction, the energy-release rates predicted by the beam formulas agree with the finite-element results within about 8%.

Test results were given by Reeder and Crews [5.6] for AS4/PEEK (APC2) thermoplastic resin. The results are shown in Figure 5.8 for pure Mode I and II loadings and three ratios of mixed-mode loading. Reeder and Crews noted that the calculation for the G_1 and G_2 components were sensitive to nonlinear geometric changes in the locations of the applied loadings with flexible specimens and offered a nonlinear large deflection analysis to account for this. They also redesigned the test apparatus to minimize these nonlinear effects. The test results shown indicate a strong interaction between the Mode I and II loadings, which can be described by the expression

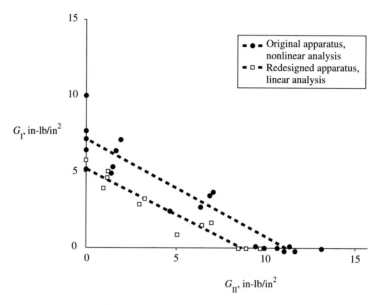

Figure 5.8   Delamination toughness results for AS4/PEEK (APC2), showing effects of mixed-mode loading. (*Source:* From [5.6].)

$$\frac{G_{\mathrm{I}}}{G_{\mathrm{I}c}} + \frac{G_{\mathrm{II}}}{G_{\mathrm{II}c}} = 1 \qquad (5.25)$$

Literature values for interlaminar fracture energy.   Some literature values for interlaminar fracture energies are given in Table 5.1. The differences in delamination between the various systems are quite interesting. The carbon/epoxy systems vary significantly from the earlier resin systems often described as "brittle," such as AS4/3501-6 and T300/5208, which were formulated primarily to provide good strength under hot and wet conditions. The new high-toughness epoxies and the thermoplastics display significant improvements in delamination resistance.

Application of fracture mechanics in design.   The fracture mechanics approach described before may be implemented in design with two general approaches. The first is simply to use the test results to rank candidate materials. The idea is that the energy-release rates are a good indication of the ability of the material system to resist delamination in service, and the fracture mechanics tests are used only to rate and rank alternative material systems.

The second approach in the use of the fracture mechanics principles is more analytical and requires that the structure being considered also be analyzed to determine the energy-release rates of the delaminations. These delaminations may be either real, perhaps from a damage incident, or else are hypothetical, perhaps representing a "worst-case" situation that could still pass inspection. These energy-release rates for the structure are often determined by means of finite-element analysis, using a variety of numerical techniques. One popular

Table 5.1   Typical Interlaminar Fracture Energy Values

| Material System | Fracture Energy | | Ref. |
	Mode I (kJ/m²)	Mode II (kJ/m²)	
AS4/3501-6 Carbon/epoxy	0.136	0.737	5.7, 5.8
AS4/3501-6 Carbon/epoxy	0.175		5.9
AS4/3501-6 Carbon/epoxy	0.137	1.292	5.10
AS4/Dow-Q6 Carbon/epoxy	0.848	2.84	5.10
AS4/PEEK (APC2)	1.23	2.54	5.5
IM7/8551-7 Carbon/epoxy	0.513	1.565	5.8
IM7/8551-7 Carbon/epoxy		1.87	5.7
IM7/X8553 Carbon/epoxy		1.64	5.7
T300/5208 Carbon/epoxy	0.088		5.11
T300/934 Carbon/epoxy	0.373		5.12
AS4/F185 Carbon/epoxy	1.88		5.11
AS4/205 Carbon/epoxy	2.05		5.11
Carbon/BP907 epoxy	0.285		5.13
Carbon/985 epoxy	0.130		5.13
Carbon/F263 epoxy	0.115		5.13
AS6/2220-3 Carbon/epoxy	0.212		5.14
AS6/5245 Carbon/epoxy	0.360		5.14
C-6000/F185	2.25		5.15
E-glass/epoxy	0.207		5.16
E-glass/epoxy	0.227		5.17
E glass/epoxy	0.525–1.02		5.18

technique is called the "modified virtual crack closure method" [5.19]. Although widely used, it was noted in [5.20] that care must be taken in the finite-element analysis to avoid nonphysical interpenetration of the crack surfaces with finite-element analysis of anisotropic materials.

5.3 EDGE EFFECTS IN LAMINATES

An interesting phenomenon exists at the edges of laminates loaded by in-plane loads that consists of extra interlaminar stresses not predicted by the usual lamination theory. These stresses can lead to delamination. An illustration of a uniaxial load and the free edges is shown in Figure 5.9. The stresses are affected by the stacking sequence of the lamination, that is, the ordering sequence of the various layers in the laminate. Various strategies can be employed to minimize the effects of these edge-effect stresses, including optimizing the stacking sequence, adding extra resin-rich thermoplastic interleaf layers to the laminate, adding doublers to the edges of the laminate, and using tougher resins that withstand these stresses.

The existence of these stresses can be seen by considering the state of stress at the free edge of the laminate. This is illustrated in what follows.

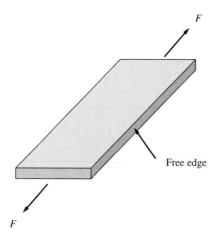

Free edge

Figure 5.9   Free edges in a laminate, which lead to localized interlaminar stresses not predicted by standard lamination theory.

5.3.1 v_{xy} Mismatch

Consider a $[0/90]_s$ laminate, stressed in the x direction, which is taken to be the fiber direction for the 0 ply. Lamination theory predicts that away from the edges of the laminate, there is a constant strain ϵ_x and a strain ϵ_y due to the Poisson effect. Now consider the stresses within the plies. If the 0 ply had no stress in the y direction, it would have a strain given by $\epsilon_y = -v_{12}\epsilon_x$. Similarly, the 90 ply would have a lateral strain $\epsilon_y = -v_{21}\epsilon_x$. However, these y-direction strains would be very different, because the Poisson ratios often vary by more than an order of magnitude. Because the lamination forces these strains to be the same, clearly the individual plies are not in a state of uniaxial stress. The 0 ply is under tension in the y direction, and the 90 ply is under compression to make the strains compatible. These transverse stresses are shown in Figure 5.10.

Now consider the situation near the edge of the laminate, as illustrated in Figure 5.11. In order for the element shown to be in equilibrium in the y direction, interlaminar shear stresses must exist, because the 0-ply tension does not exist at the free edge. Further, for the element to be in moment equilibrium, interlaminar tension σ_z must also exist.

The preceding analysis indicates that these interlaminar stresses must exist, but does not give their magnitude. A number of analytical and numerical schemes have been used to calculate these stresses [5.21]. In addition, it has been shown that a singularity exists at the edge, under the usual assumptions of perfectly layered geometries [5.22]. Thus, it is not

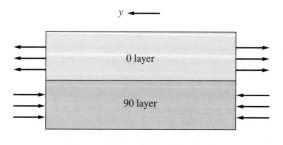

y

0 layer

90 layer

Figure 5.10   Transverse stresses predicted for $[0/90]_s$ laminate loaded in the x direction. Lateral stresses result from the differences in the Poisson ratio between the layers that occurs because of the orientation of each layer.

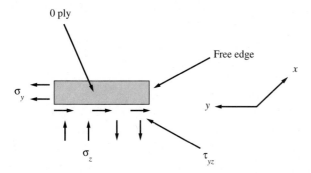

Figure 5.11 Free-edge stresses in a $[0/90]_s$ laminate.

necessarily meaningful to look at stress magnitudes, but rather a fracture mechanics approach may be useful.

5.3.2 Free-Edge Interlaminar Stresses in a $[\pm\theta]$ Laminate

A similar approach shows that free-edge stresses must also exist for more general angle-ply laminates. Consider the case of a general $[\pm\theta]$ laminate under loading in the x direction, as illustrated in Figure 5.12.

The in-plane shear stress τ_{xy} is related to the normal strains by

$$\tau_{xy} = \overline{Q}_{16}\epsilon_x + \overline{Q}_{26}\epsilon_y \tag{5.26}$$

It can be noted by referring to Eq. (2.30) that the $\overline{Q}$ terms are odd in θ, so that the sign of τ_{xy} changes from the $+\theta$ to the $-\theta$ plies. Further, the τ_{xy} shear stress must vanish at the free edge. A consideration of the equation of equilibrium in the x direction gives further insight into the interlaminar stresses. The equilibrium equation is

$$\frac{\partial\sigma_x}{\partial x} + \frac{\partial\tau_{xy}}{\partial y} + \frac{\partial\tau_{xz}}{\partial z} = 0 \tag{5.27}$$

Because in this case σ_x is assumed to be uniform in the x direction, this equation can be integrated with respect to z to give

$$\tau_{xz} = -\int_{-h/2}^{z} \frac{\partial\tau_{xy}}{\partial y}\,dz \tag{5.28}$$

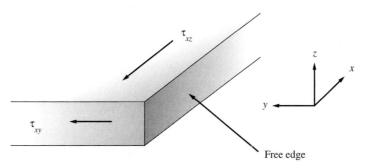

Figure 5.12 Loading of a $[\pm\theta]$ laminate leading to free-edge stresses. The figure shows one layer, with the τ_{xy} in-plane shear stress predicted by lamination theory. Interlaminar shear stress τ_{xz} is required to satisfy equilibrium.

Because τ_{xy} varies from zero at the free edge to the value given by Eq. (5.26) within the interior, shear stress τ_{xz} must exist within the vicinity of the free edge. Further, because changes in sign of τ_{xy} occur as the ply orientation changes sign, this shear stress must exist throughout the thickness of the laminate at the edge.

Stacking sequence.   An extensive literature exists on free-edge effects [5.23–5.37]. One of the practical results is that the stacking sequence can be selected to minimize the free-edge effects. For example, arranging the layers of a quasi-isotropic layup as [0/45/90/−45] is believed to give lower edge interlaminar stresses than a [0/±45/90] layup.

5.3.3 Edge-Delamination Test

An experimental test for edge-delamination resistance has been developed by O'Brien [5.33] that is often called the "edge-delamination test" (EDT). The test utilizes a laminated composite specimen loaded in tension that is designed to have strong edge effects. These edge effects are likely to lead to edge delamination in the specimen, as illustrated in Figure 5.13. The stiffness of the specimen decreases as a result of the delamination, which can be observed in the measured force-displacement response by a drop or change in slope. The specimen may also rupture at a decreased load level due to stress concentrations associated with edge delamination. The test can be used as a means of comparing the delamination resistance of different material systems, such as different matrix materials. Because the test measures a property that is desired in the final product, namely, resistance to edge delamination, it would seem to be useful for materials comparison and development.

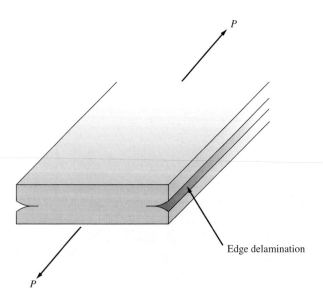

Figure 5.13   Edge delamination under tension loading.

It is also possible to relate the measured experimental test values to more fundamental fracture mechanics parameters by carrying out an analysis of the specimen. In general, this could be accomplished by using the finite-element techniques described earlier. A simplified strength-of-materials approach has also been presented by O'Brien [5.33] that gives insight into the data interpretation. This simplified approach is explained in the following.

Simplified analysis of the edge-delamination test.   As presented by O'Brien [5.33], an approximate analysis for the energy-release rate with delamination extension from the edge can be obtained by considering a delaminated and an undelaminated region, as shown in Figures 5.14 and 5.15. The stiffness of the undelaminated region is obtained by the axial-direction modulus, called E_{lam}, and the apparent effective (average) axial modulus of the delaminated region is called E^*. This latter effective modulus is to be calculated from a rule-of-mixtures approximation, using the calculated axial modulus for both parts of the delaminated region (the top and bottom portions in the figure). The relationship between compliance change and energy-release rates was given previously in Eq. (5.9) as

$$\frac{P^2}{2B}\frac{dC}{da} = G \tag{5.9}$$

where P is the load, B is the width of the crack (length L is the present case because the specimen is cracked along its entire length), C is the specimen compliance, and a is the crack length. At the time of delamination, the critical load for delamination establishes the critical delamination energy.

The compliances are calculated as follows. Assuming that all applied loads are uniaxial, the general expression for compliance is given as

$$C = \frac{L}{AE_t} \tag{5.29}$$

The effective modulus E_t of the entire specimen is obtained from

$$E_t = E_{lam}\left(\frac{w - a}{w}\right) + E^* \times \frac{a}{w} \tag{5.30}$$

where w is the entire width of the specimen, and a is the delamination length in the transverse direction. The change in the compliance with delamination region extension is then

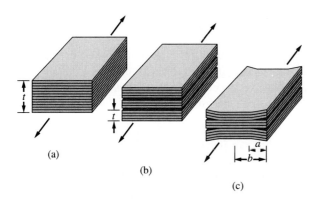

(a)

(b)

(c)

Figure 5.14   Edge delamination: (a) laminated, (b) totally delaminated, and (c) partially delaminated. Because of symmetry, edge delamination is expected in four locations.

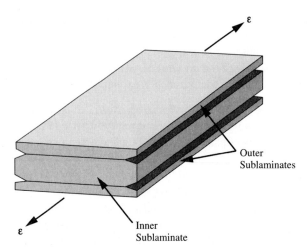

Figure 5.15   Edge-delamination specimen.

found by differentiating Eq. (5.29) with respect to a, the width of the delaminated region. This results in

$$\frac{dC}{da} = \frac{L}{Aw} \frac{E_{\text{lam}} - E^*}{E_t^2} \tag{5.31}$$

It is convenient to write the energy-release rate in terms of an applied axial strain using

$$\epsilon = \frac{P}{AE_t} \tag{5.32}$$

Substituting Eq. (5.32) into the energy-release-rate expression, Eq. (5.9), results in

$$G = \frac{\epsilon^2 t}{2} (E_{\text{lam}} - E^*) \tag{5.33}$$

Using the critical strain value for edge-delamination propagation gives an expression for the critical energy-release rate for edge delamination. That is,

$$G_c = \frac{\epsilon_c^2 t}{2} (E_{\text{lam}} - E^*) \tag{5.34}$$

This value of G_c is presumably a material property that reflects the delamination resistance of the materials being used.

O'Brien et al. [5.11, 5.33, 5.38] have used the preceding to calculate the apparent fracture energy for edge-delamination resistance. A typical layup used is $[\pm 30/\pm 30/90_{1.5}]_s$ and delamination is expected and observed to occur at the $-30/90$ interfaces. A typical example of the data reduction follows, using data from [5.33].

Example of edge-delamination-test data reduction.   The specimen and the expected location of the delaminations are illustrated in Figure 5.15. This figure differs from that given before in that two edge-delamination locations are expected on each side. The derivation given earlier can be repeated for this case, with the result that the thickness to be used in Eq. (5.34) is actually half the total thickness of the entire laminate. An alternative viewpoint is to use the quarter section shown in Figure 5.16, which uses two planes of symmetry. The result is the same for either viewpoint.

The effective modulus for the entire laminate and the two sublaminates can be obtained by calculating the A matrix for these three laminates, inverting, and then using the relationship

$$S_{avg} = tA^{-1}$$

and

$$E_x = 1/S_x$$

The entire layup is $[\pm30/\pm30/90_{1.5}]_s$ and the two sublaminates of the quarter section are $[\pm30]_s$ and $[90_{1.5}]$. If only the A matrix and its inverse are used in calculating the axial moduli, it does not matter if the sublaminates are symmetric or not. Using the material properties $E_{11} = 134$ GPa, $E_{22} = 10.2$ GPa, $G_{12} = 5.5$ GPa, and $v_{12} = 0.30$ gives the laminate moduli as follows:

$$[\pm30/\pm30/90_{1.5}]_s : E_x = 55.2 \text{ GPa}$$
$$[\pm30]_s : \qquad\quad E_x = 49.7 \text{ GPa}$$
$$[90_{1.5}] : \qquad\quad E_x = 10.2 \text{ GPa}$$

The expression for E^*, the average modulus of the delaminated region, is then given by the rule-of-mixtures expression

$$E^* = \frac{4(49.7) + 1.5(10.2)}{5.5} = 38.9 \text{ GPa}$$

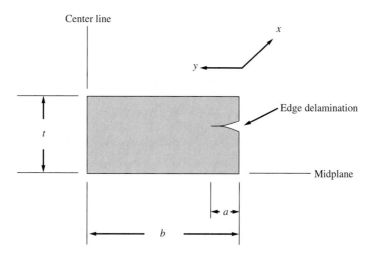

Figure 5.16   Quarter section used in analysis of the edge-delamination specimen.

Using a thickness t of 5.5 plies at 0.1320 mm/ply (the thickness of the quarter section of Figure 5.16, half of the total 11-ply layup of the specimen), and the critial strain value of 0.00347 measured by O'Brien [5.33], and substituting in Eq. (5.34) gives

$$G_c = \epsilon^2 \frac{t}{2}(E_{\text{lam}} - E^*) = (0.00347)^2 \frac{0.726 \text{ mm}}{2}(55.2 \text{ GPa} - 38.9 \text{ GPa}) = 0.0712 \text{ kN/m}^2$$

or $G_c = 0.071$ kJ/m². It should be noted that this value is just one-half that reported in [5.33, 5.38] using the same data.

   An additional complication with edge delamination is that it involves mixed Mode I and Mode II energy-release rates. O'Brien et al. [5.11] report finite-element calculations to determine the amount of each mode and also show that the apparent G_c for the tougher material systems with values in the range of 1 to 2 kJ/m² depends on the relative amounts of Mode I and Mode II, and thus on the layup considered.

5.4 MATRIX CRACKING

Matrix cracking is typically part of the failure process in fiber composites (see Figure 5.17). Matrix cracking often occurs in the off-axis plies, such as in 90° plies in a laminate that is loaded in the 0° direction. Matrix cracking can occur at strain levels well below ultimate failure of the laminate, perhaps on the order of half way to failure or less. It can occur in plies at transverse strain levels well below the failure strain of the matrix material alone, because of the stress and strain concentrations due to the more rigid fibers. As described in

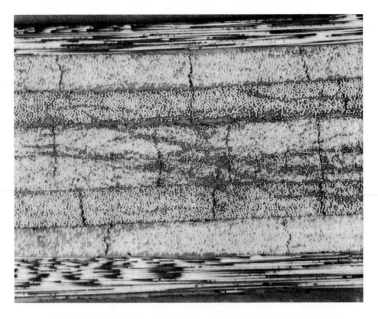

Figure 5.17 Typical matrix cracks in an AS4/3501-6 carbon/epoxy laminate. The photo was taken by edge replication while the specimen was under mechanical load.

Chapter 4, matrix microcracking may not lead directly to ultimate failure of the laminate. However the matrix cracks do have some effect on the laminate, and these effects must be examined if the entire failure process is to be understood. For example, matrix cracks have been observed to serve as initiation points for delaminations under repeated loading. Matrix cracks change the matrix-dominated stiffness properties of the laminate, and thus cause re-distribution of the stresses within the laminate. Matrix cracks also change the permeability of the material to moisture and can change apparent coefficients of thermal expansion. A recent review of the literature on matrix cracking has been given by Abrate [5.39].

5.4.1 Physical Description

A schematic of matrix cracks in off-axis plies is illustrated in Figure 5.18. Matrix cracks can be observed by x-ray and by examining the polished edges of specimens under load with a low-power optical microscope. The latter can be conveniently accomplished by using acetate replicates of the edge of the specimen [5.40]. The matrix-cracking process starts with isolated cracks, say, at transverse strain levels on the order of 0.5% strain. Increasing the applied strain causes more cracks to occur, until a more or less regular pattern is established prior to ultimate failure. This cracking pattern is sometimes called a "characteristic damage state" [5.41]. It is believed that the cracks start to appear at weak points and/or high-stress locations in the matrix, and thus occur at random locations. Once a microcrack is formed, it changes the local stress distribution within the ply, and in particular, it lowers the stress in the material in that same ply that is adjacent to the microcrack. Consider the matrix crack located in a ply that is normal to the principal loading direction, as illustrated in Figure 5.19. This ply is in transverse tension. The microcrack forms a free surface and thus relieves the stress in the matrix, neglecting for the moment the stresses around the tips of the crack. The stresses build back up in the ply by shear transfer from the adjacent 0 plies, until some distance away, the transverse stress has returned to its original value. Adjacent cracks form due to statistical variations in the matrix strength or distribution of flaws, but do not tend to occur close to the original crack because of the stress shielding. Higher transverse strain levels and/or repeated loads are thus required to produce cracks that are closer together. In this way, the observed crack density, expressed as the number of cracks per unit length in the loading direction, gradually increases with increasing applied load. These cracking patterns are easy to observe with low-power magnification and have been noted by many observers [5.42–5.48].

5.4.2 Prediction of Microcracking

The prediction of microcracking is often based on transverse strain, including both strains due to the mechanical load as well as residual thermal strains from cooldown from the cure

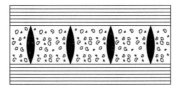

Figure 5.18   Matrix cracking in plies transverse to the loading direction.

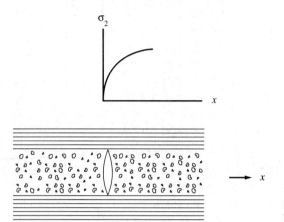

Figure 5.19 Stress shielding and stress buildup adjacent to a matrix crack.

temperature [5.44]. The crack patterns are often observed in laminate coupon specimens, and the values are then used directly to estimate cracking in structural components. The thickness of the transverse plies has interesting effects on the microcrack formation, however. It has been observed by a number of investigators that thicker transverse ply groups cause microcracking to occur at lower strain levels relative to thinner ply groups [5.42–5.47, 5.49]. This seems well established as an empirical fact, although apparently just how strong the effect is depends on the matrix properties and perhaps the moisture level in the matrix, with the more brittle resins showing a more pronounced thickness effect [5.50, 5.51]. The reason for the thickness effect is often explained on fracture mechanics grounds with energy-release rate arguments [5.43, 5.45, 5.49, 5.52]. If a strain criterion for crack formation is used, it must be considered to be an in situ critical value that depends on the thickness of the transverse ply groups.

Typical observed crack densities, expressed as the number of cracks per unit length in the loading direction, are shown in Figure 5.20, taken from [5.52]. Although results are often plotted as shown in the figure, an argument can be made for normalizing the crack densities by the ply group thickness. From the concepts of stress relief adjacent to a microcrack, it should be expected that the stress buildup adjacent to a microcrack would be at a distance that is normalized to the ply group thickness. Thus, if no other effects were present, the average distance between microcracks at a given loading level should scale as the ply group thickness. Further effects, such as thicker ply groups being weaker because of a statistical distribution of larger defects, would then modify this expected pattern.

5.4.3 Effects of Microcracks on Lamina Stiffness

The formation of microcracks lowers the effective matrix-dominated stiffness properties of the cracked ply group. Early attempts to incorporate these effects into laminate analysis used the so-called "ply discount method," in which the moduli E_{22} and G_{12} were set to zero once cracking had occurred. More recent investigations have used a variety of techniques to get more refined estimates of average reduced stiffness properties, which are smeared in a continuum sense over some suitable material distance. The basic idea of stress relief adja-

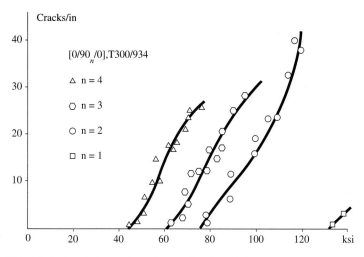

Figure 5.20   Typical result for crack density as a function of ply group thickness and stress level. (*Source:* From [5.52].)

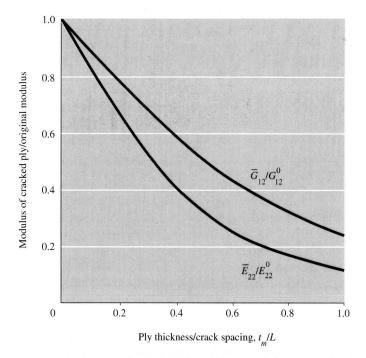

Figure 5.21   Predicted effect of matrix microcracking on matrix-dominated properties. (*Source:* From [5.55].)

cent to a microcrack lends itself to a shear lag analysis to determine the stress distributions, similar to that shown in Section 4.3.1 for stresses adjacent to a broken fiber. Accordingly, a number of investigators have used shear lag analysis to obtain the stress distributions, which are then integrated to get stiffness properties [5.42, 5.43, 5.53–5.55]. Typical results are shown in Figure 5.21, expressed as a function of the crack density. Other approaches have also been used to determine the changes in stiffness with the formation of matrix microcracks [5.56–5.61].

Models of progressive failure involving the elements described earlier have been developed by a number of investigators, including [5.54, 5.62–5.64]. The features of these models are criteria for initial formation of microcracks, analysis for stiffness reduction due to the microcracks and the resultant stress redistribution within the laminate, and criteria for further development of microcracks. A typical result is shown in Figure 5.22, taken from [5.62], in which the averaged stress–strain response for biaxial loading of a [±45] layup is plotted. The nonlinear response for this layup is dominated by the matrix crack formation and matrix nonlinear shear stiffness.

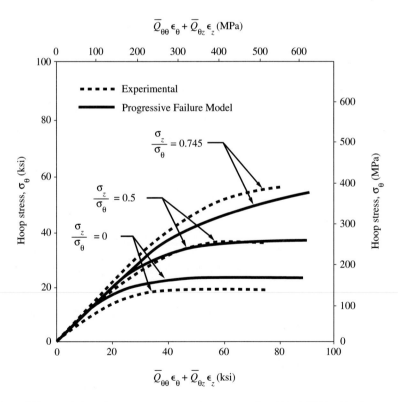

Figure 5.22 Prediction of nonlinear stress–strain response of [±45] AS4/3501-6 laminate under biaxial tension loading. (*Source:* From [5.62].)

5.4.4 Example of Shear Lag Analysis of Matrix Microcracks

As a specific example of the calculations involved, the shear lag analysis of [5.55] is given here. As illustrated in Figure 5.23, the shear lag equations are based on equilibrium of a material element in the ply containing the microcracks, and thus relating the change in normal stress in the ply to shear stress at the edge of the ply. Figure 5.23(b) shows the transverse normal tension loading, and Figure 5.23(c) shows in-plane shear loading. Only the transverse tension loading is given here, although the shear loading case is also given in [5.55].

Consideration of equilibrium for transverse tension loading gives

$$t_m \frac{\partial \sigma_x}{\partial x} + \tau_{zx} = 0 \tag{5.35}$$

where t_m is the half-thickness of the cracked ply, σ_x is the normal stress in the cracked ply, τ_{zx} is the shear stress at the interface with the adjacent constraining ply, and the x direction is local to the ply and is as shown in Figure 5.23(a). Substituting in terms of displacement derivatives gives

$$\frac{E_{22} t_m}{K G_{23}} \frac{d^2 u}{dx^2} - u_0 + u_f = 0 \tag{5.36}$$

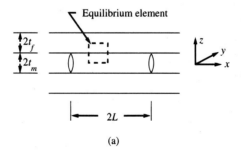

(a)

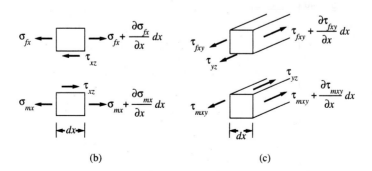

(b)   (c)

Figure 5.23 Equilibrium of (a) cracked ply and adjacent ply under (b) transverse tension loading and (c) shear loading.

where an average shear strain γ_{zx} in the ply is given by the relation

$$\gamma_{zx} \approx \frac{u_f - u_0}{t_m} \tag{5.37}$$

so that

$$K \approx \frac{1}{t_m} \tag{5.38}$$

The usual shear lag analysis ignores the variation in the strain of the adjacent plies in the vicinity of the microcrack. However, a similar shear lag analysis can be worked out for the adjacent plies using the equilibrium of the adjacent plies indicated in Figure 5.23. Equilibrium then gives for the adjacent ply

$$t_f \frac{\partial \sigma_f}{\partial x} + \tau_{zx} = 0 \tag{5.39}$$

and substituting in terms of displacements gives

$$\frac{E_f t_f}{K G_{23}} \frac{d^2 u_f}{dx^2} - u_f + u_0 = 0 \tag{5.40}$$

where E_f is the tensile modulus of the restraining ply in the coordinate direction local to the cracked ply.

This system of two differential equations can then be solved to give expressions for the stresses and displacements as

$$u_f = \frac{\epsilon_0}{\beta} \left[\beta x + \frac{E_{22} t_m}{E_f t_f} \left(\sinh \beta x + \tanh \beta L - \tanh \beta L \cosh \beta x \right) \right] \tag{5.41}$$

and

$$\frac{\sigma_m}{E_{22} \epsilon_0} = \tanh \beta L \sinh \beta x + 1 - \cosh \beta x \tag{5.42}$$

where

$$\beta^2 = K G_{23} \left(\frac{1}{E_f t_f} + \frac{1}{E_{22} t_m} \right) \tag{5.43}$$

The reduction in stiffness of the cracked ply can be obtained directly from the displacement solution by evaluating at a distance $x = L$ and comparing with the displacement corresponding to the uniform applied strain. The result is that the reduced stiffness is given by

$$\frac{\overline{E}_{22}}{E_{22}^0} = \frac{1 + (1/\alpha)}{1 + (\alpha/\beta L) \tanh \beta L} - \frac{1}{\alpha} \tag{5.44}$$

where

$$\alpha = \frac{E_{22} t_m}{E_f t_f} \tag{5.45}$$

The reduction in the transverse modulus predicted as a function of the crack spacing by the preceding expression is shown in Figure 5.21, along with a similar result for the reduction in the in-plane shear modulus.

5.4.5 Effects of Matrix Cracks on Ultimate Failure

As mentioned before, the formation of matrix cracks can have a number of effects on the macroscopic material properties such as stiffness and permeability, and can lead to delamination under fatigue loading. The question remains as to what are the effects of matrix cracks on ultimate strength under monotonic loading. Clearly, in some cases, such as the [±45] layup of Figure 5.22, the response and ultimate strength are strongly influenced by the matrix cracking, but this is hardly a practical layup, as it does not take advantage of the fibers. Failure in practical fiber-dominated layups and loadings is a complex subject, as discussed in Chapter 4. In Chapter 4, it was mentioned that the "Cook–Gordon" effect [5.65] is a mechanism that tends to relieve the stress-concentration effects of matrix cracks on the adjacent fibers through microdelaminations adjacent to the tips of the matrix cracks. It was also mentioned that several carbon-fiber/epoxy systems apparently differed significantly in the effect of fiber strength loss due to the matrix cracks. The discussion of ultimate laminate failure given in Chapter 4 indicates that matrix cracking does not directly coincide with ultimate failure, but that it can influence ultimate failure by an amount that depends on the details of the material system. Clearly, this is an area for further study.

5.5 DURABILITY: EFFECTS OF IMPACT DAMAGE AND FATIGUE

The question of the durability of fiber composites is important in establishing service life. Because of the relative newness of fiber composites, and particularly so in strength-critical applications, the question of durability is of significant interest. In general, fiber composites display a significant resistance to environmental attack, and are widely used in situations in which their corrosion resistance plays a vital role, as in the chemical processing industries. The carbon-fiber composites typically display excellent fatigue resistance. However, carbon-fiber composites with epoxy matrices display a sensitivity to impact damage that can lead to delaminations that propagate under fatigue loading.

5.5.1 Impact Damage

The susceptibility of carbon-fiber laminates to accidental impact damage is well known [5.66, 5.67] and must be accounted for in design. Impact damage takes the form of matrix cracking, splitting along fibers, delaminations, and fiber breakage [5.68]. Recognition of impact-damage resistance as a design goal has led to the development of new materials for matrices, such as thermoplastics and high-toughness epoxies. These higher-toughness matrices have demonstrated the ability to minimize the delamination accompanying impacts. Two recent commercial uses of carbon-fiber/toughened epoxy systems have highlighted this need for impact-damage resistance. One example is the compressor fan blade used in the GE 90 jet engine, where the Hercules IM7/8551-7 system is employed in a design that is driven in large part by resistance to damage from bird-strike impact. The second is the Boeing 777 commercial airliner that uses the Toray T800/3900-2 carbon-fiber/toughened epoxy system for the tail. Here the resistance to impact damage is a key element in permitting the use of strain allowables that more effectively utilized the high strain to failure carbon fiber.

The aerospace industry uses various tests to assess impact-damage resistance and impact-damage tolerance. One of these is the compression-after-impact test, in which a plate is subjected to central impact by a falling weight, and then tested in compression. The compression after impact then gives a measure of both the damage created and the effect of the damage on the compression strength. The values measured are primarily for ranking materials. More discussion of this test follows.

It is instructive to consider a simple example, that of central impact of a simply supported beam. Consider the beam specimen that is subjected to impact by a falling weight, as shown in Figure 5.24. Under certain conditions, the impact can be characterized as quasi-static, which permits a simple analysis procedure. In a quasi-static analysis, the actual impact is replaced by an equivalent statically applied force. The magnitude of the force is obtained by equating the energy of the impactor to the strain energy of the beam under static loading. Two conditions must apply for the quasi-static analysis to be applicable. The velocity of the impact must be much less than the stress-wave velocity for the material, otherwise stress waves and phenomena such as spallation are produced. The second condition is that the impacted specimen must deform in the lowest mode shape, which corresponds to the deflected shape under the equivalent static loading. The latter condition can be estimated on the basis of the ratio of the mass of the impactor to an "effective mass" for the target [5.69].

The "effective mass" is the mass that would be used in an equivalent lumped mass calculation of the natural frequency of the beam. Comparisons with dynamic calculations of the impact for plates and cylinders showed that the quasi-static calculation could be used with good accuracy if the impact mass was a factor of 10 higher than the equivalent mass of the target specimen. The ratio of the effective mass of the target to the total mass of the target depends on the boundary conditions of support, but varied from a few percent for impacted cylinders to 20 or 25% for plates, and 40 to 50% for beams.

The quasi-static analysis of the beam impact is as follows. The analysis uses isotropic-beam properties, but it is straightforward to change the derivation for the directional properties of fiber composites. The static deflection of the beam under a central load is given by

$$\delta = \frac{PL^3}{48EI} \tag{5.46}$$

The strain energy of the beam is given by $P\delta/2$, and equating the impact energy U to the strain energy of the beam gives

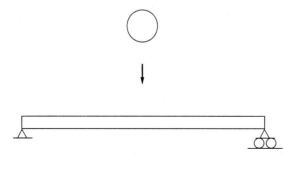

Figure 5.24 Drop-weight impact of a beam specimen.

$$\frac{P^2 L^3}{96 EI} = U \qquad (5.47)$$

or

$$P = \left(\frac{96 EIU}{L^3}\right)^{1/2} \qquad (5.48)$$

The quasi-static assumption then considers that this force applied statically has the same effect on the beam as the impact itself. Three values from this impact should be considered. The impact force produces a local Hertzian contact stress that may produce local damage. The stress or strain in the fibers of the laminated beam may lead to fiber breakage and matrix cracking. Finally, the shear stress may produce delaminations. The strain at the outer surface is calculated from the usual beam-bending formula as

$$\epsilon = \frac{Mc}{EI} = \frac{PLh/2}{Ebh^3/12} = 3\left(\frac{2U}{LEbh}\right)^{1/2} \qquad (5.49)$$

where b is the width and h is the height of the beam cross-section. The shear stress, using the isotropic-beam distribution, is given by

$$\tau = \frac{3V}{2A} = \frac{3P}{4A} = \left(\frac{3EhU}{64b}\right)^{1/2} \qquad (5.50)$$

This calculation is based on a linear stress–strain response, and so does not include effects of material damage. Obviously, much more detail could be added to the calculation. The preceding does show that the aspect ratio of the specimen does affect the relative values of shear stress and normal stress or strain, so that comparisons of impact damage in different material systems can be difficult to make unless standardized tests, with the same specimen geometry, are used.

There is a significant amount of literature concerning the impact problem. In general, much progress has been made in understanding the features of impact damage, but it is still difficult to relate the various studies to service-life predictions on actual structures. Investigators have established the basic parameters of impact and measured damage formation and strength reduction [5.66–5.68, 5.70–5.72]. Sun et al. [5.73–5.75] have shown how the Hertzian contact deformation could be incorporated into the impact problem by showing that the static indentation law is reasonably adequate in dynamic impact analysis. Dynamic analyses of cylinders [5.76] and plates [5.77] have been developed, in addition to finite-element analysis methods. Interesting studies of scaling have been reported, showing the effects of specimen size on impact-damage formation in beams [5.78], plates [5.79], and cylinders [5.80]. The results reported in [5.79, 5.80] demonstrate that delamination scales as predicted by fracture mechanics, and thus larger specimens show relatively larger delamination size than would be predicted based only on geometric scaling.

Compression after impact (CAI).   One test that is frequently used to assess the toughness of the matrix in combination with specific fiber systems is the compression-after-impact test, in which a standardized drop-weight impact is performed on a composite specimen, which is then subject to a compression test after the impact. The residual strength gives an indication of the working strength of the material system after accidental impact damage, and compression strength is sensitive to the damage. Table 5.2, taken from [5.81],

Table 5.2 Compression Strength After
6650 J/m (1500 ft-lb/ft) Impact

| | Compression Strength | |
Material	Mpa	ksi
AS4/BP907	275	40
AS4/3502	210	30.1
AS4/3501-6	165	24
T300/914	130	18.7
CHS/5245	175	25.3
C12/5245	225	32.2
AS4/5245	210	30.2
CHS/1504	180	26.1
T700/1504	215	30.9
C6/HST-7	270	39.3
AS4/2501	250	36
AS6/6376	260	38
AS4/8551	310	45
XASn/Peek APC-1	285	41.6
AS4/Peek APC-2	275	40

Source: From [5.81].
Tests were performed on a standard Boeing specimen. Impact values are normalized by dividing by the specimen thickness.

shows a comparison of strength after impact for a number of carbon-fiber and resin systems. The table gives the carbon-fiber designation followed by the commercial designation for the resin system. It can be seen that there are substantial differences between matrix systems. The last two entries in the table are thermoplastic resins, which, along with the toughened epoxies, show improved compression after impact strength.

5.5.2 Effects of Fatigue Loading

The fatigue resistance of composites is a complex issue. Fiber composites, and particularly the carbon-fiber composites, generally display excellent fatigue resistance, and have been used in fatigue-critical applications such as helicopter blades because of this. However, as is discussed in the following, fatigue resistance can depend on the layup, type of loading, and the presence of stress risers such as holes or impact damage. Reviews of fatigue in fiber composites have been given by Curtis [5.82] and in the text by Talreja [5.83].

Early work on unidirectional carbon-fiber composites under tension loadings displayed a high degree of resistance to fatigue [5.82–5.84]. A typical result is that shown in Figure 5.25, taken from [5.82]. The curve shows the excellent fatigue resistance of carbon-fiber composites. Glass fiber permits higher strain in the matrix because of the lower modulus and higher strain-to-failure fiber, and the somewhat poorer fatigue resistance is attributed to that fact. An additional factor with glass fiber is the susceptability of glass to stress corrosion with moisture. A comparison of fatigue results on a notched carbon-fiber composite with that for aluminum-lithium alloy is shown in Figure 5.26, taken from [5.82], again showing the superiority of the carbon-fiber composite.

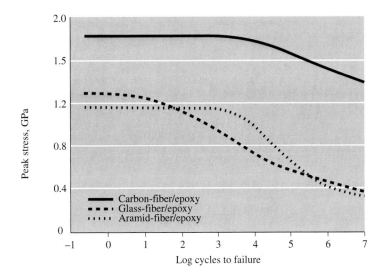

Figure 5.25 S-N fatigue data for unidirectional fiber-composite materials under tension fatigue loading. (*Source:* From [5.82].)

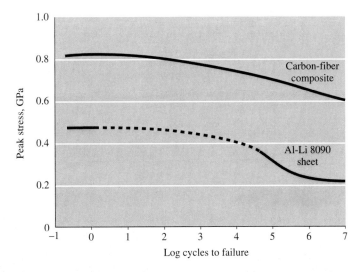

Figure 5.26 Comparison of the tensile fatigue behavior of notched carbon-fiber composite and an aluminum-lithium alloy. (*Source:* From [5.82].)

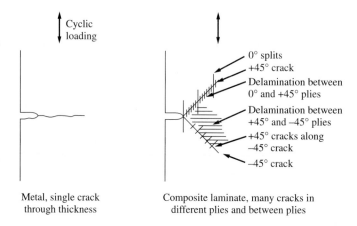

Figure 5.27 Typical damage zones at notches in fatigue loading of metals and fiber-composite materials. (*Source:* From [5.82].)

In situations in which the matrix is more highly loaded, such as in tests of laminates with off-axis fibers, specimens with holes or damage, and in compression loadings, the resistance to fatigue is typically not as good as it is in tension loadings of unidirectional composites. The failure mechanisms have been identified by a number of investigators to be quite different from the crack propagation usually observed in metals. As illustrated in Figure 5.27, taken from [5.82], the failure in composite laminates can consist of splits parallel to the fibers, matrix cracks, and delaminations. This damage tends to be more diffuse throughout the material. Because of the noted failure mechanisms and the role of the ma-

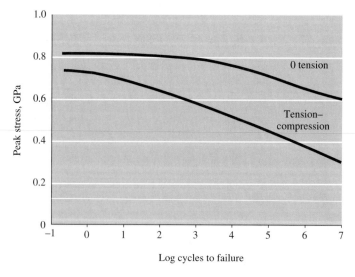

Figure 5.28 Comparison of tensile and reversed axial fatigue of $[\pm 45/0_2]$ laminates of carbon-fiber material. (*Source:* From [5.82].)

trix, fatigue involving notched specimens that tend to put higher stresses in the matrix show more effects of fatigue [5.85–5.87]. The same is true of compression loading, where again the matrix plays a more vital role in determining compressive strength. Figure 5.28, taken from [5.82], shows lower fatigue life for specimens loaded in reversed tension-compression as compared to zero to tension loading. It is believed that tension fatigue may propagate delaminations, which then become critical on the compression side of the loading in lowering the support that the matrix gives to the fiber. A similar result is shown in Figure 5.29, taken from [5.88], that shows that mixed tension-compression is more severe than tension loadings alone. The *R* ratio of that figure is the ratio of minimum to maximum applied stress.

The mechanisms of fatigue-damage generation have been studied by a number of investigators [5.89–5.91]. The damage noted typically consists of matrix cracks and delaminations, and reductions in stiffness are often used as an indicator of fatigue damage.

The combination of impact damage with subsequent fatigue loading provides an important test of the durability of composites. Figure 5.30 shows compression after impact, fatigue strength under compression loading after impact, and residual strength after 10^6 cycles of compression fatigue loading after impact for quasi-isotropic laminates of IM7/3501-6 carbon/epoxy [5.92]. This composite system is a high-strength carbon fiber with a standard (brittle) epoxy resin. The results show an unusual effect, in that the 10^6 cycles of compression loading after the impact actually improved the compressive strength of the specimens,

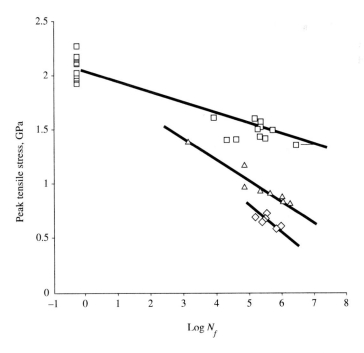

Figure 5.29 Effect of increasing the compressive component of cyclic stress on fatigue strength of XAS/914 unidirectional carbon/epoxy composites, with (☐) $R = 0.1$, (△) $R = -0.6$, and (◇) $R = -1.2$. (*Source:* From [5.88].)

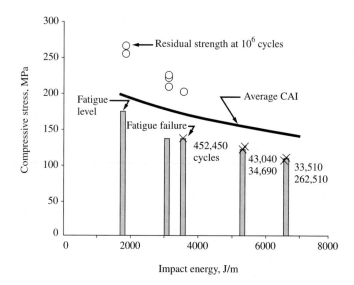

Figure 5.30 Residual strength at 10^6 cycles after impact and fatigue strength after impact for IM7/3501-6 carbon/epoxy quasi-isotropic laminates. (*Source:* From [5.92].)

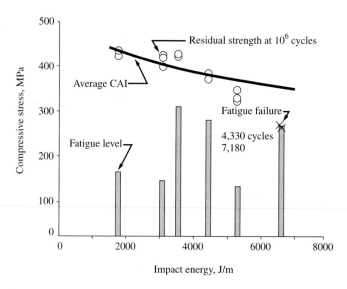

Figure 5.31 Residual strength at 10^6 cycles after impact and fatigue strength after impact for IM7/8551-7 carbon/epoxy quasi-isotropic laminates. (*Source:* From [5.92].)

relative to the compression-after-impact specimens without fatigue loading. This is a well-known phenomenon, related to the fact that the matrix damage created by the fatigue cycles tend to relieve the stress concentrations in the fibers, for the region adjacent to the impact-damage zone.

Questions have been raised about the role of the newer high-toughness resins related to fatigue after impact. Although the high-toughness resins show markedly increased resistance to impact damage, it was reported by Bakis et al. [5.93] and in [5.94] that the fatigue life of AS4/PEEK, a high-toughness thermoplastic resin, was inferior to that of more conventional brittle resins, based on residual strength normalized to initial strength. However, the test results shown in Figure 5.31 for an IM7/8551-7, taken from [5.92], show improved fatigue performance for this toughened resin system relative to the brittle 3501-6 resin system of Figure 5.30. The results show that compression after impact, residual strength after 10^6 cycles of compression loading after impact, and compression fatigue after impact all exhibit marked superiority of the toughened resin relative to the brittle resin.

5.6 CLOSURE

This chapter gave an overview of the factors affecting the useful life of fiber-composite materials and products, and in particular addressed the issues of delamination, matrix cracking and durability. These are difficult issues for any material, including composite materials. It is fair to say that the answers to many of these issues have not been fully reduced to engineering practice. However, at least preliminary assessments are being made. The principles of fracture mechanics have been applied to the problem of delamination, which, of course, is a unique and important problem for laminated composite materials. The mechanics of the formation of matrix cracks has been studied extensively, but the interaction of matrix cracks with the subsequent performance of the material has not beeen as well characterized. Accidental impact damage remains an issue of importance for fiber composites. The fatigue resistance of composites is generally very good, but assessment of fatigue life is complicated by the interaction with factors such as matrix cracking, delamination, and impact damage in general. Many of the durability issues appear to depend on an interaction between the matrix and fiber, and depend on the materials involved.

REFERENCES

5.1 Whitney, J. M., and C. E. Browning, "On Short-Beam Shear Tests for Composite Materials," *Exper. Mech.* 25 (1985): 294–300.

5.2 Iosipescu, N., "New Accurate Procedure for Single Shear Testing of Metals," *J. Mater.* 2 (1967): 537–566.

5.3 Walrath, D. E., and D. F. Adams, "The Iosipescu Shear Test as Applied to Composite Materials," *Exper. Mech.* 23 (1983): 105–110.

5.4 Kanninen, M. F., "An Augmented Double Cantilever Beam Model for Studying Crack Propagation and Arrest," *Int. J. Frac.* 9 (1973): 83–92.

5.5 Russell, A. J., and K. N. Street, "Moisture and Temperature Effects on the Mixed-Mode Delamination Fracture of Unidirectional Graphite/Epoxy," in *Delamination and Debonding of Materials*, ASTM STP 876, ed. W. S. Johnson (Philadelphia: American Society for Testing and Materials, 1985), pp. 349–370.

5.6 Reeder, J. R., and J. H. Crews, "Nonlinear Analysis and Redesign of the Mixed-Mode Bending Delamination Test," NASA Technical Memorandum 102777 (Hampton, VA: National Aeronautics and Space Administration, 1991).

5.7 Cairns, D. S., "Static and Dynamic Mode II Strain Energy Release Rates in Toughened Thermosetting Composite Laminates," *J. Composites Tech. Res.* 14 (1992): 37–42.

5.8 Long, B. J., and S. R. Swanson, "Ranking of Laminates for Edge Delamination Resistance," *Composites* 25 (1994): 183–188.

5.9 Wang, A. S. D., "An Overview of the Delamination Problem in Structural Composites," in *Interlaminar Fracture of Composites*, ed. E. A. Armanios (Aedermannsdorf, Switzerland: Trans Tech Publications, 1989), pp. 1–20.

5.10 Hibbs, M. F., and W. L. Bradley, "Correlations Between Micromechanical Failure Processes and the Delamination Toughness of Graphite/Epoxy Systems," in *Fractography of Modern Engineering Materials: Composites and Metals*, ASTM STP 948, eds. J. E. Masters and J. J. Au (Philadelphia: American Society for Testing and Materials, 1987), pp. 68–97.

5.11 O'Brien, T. K., et al., "A Simple Test for the Interlaminar Fracture Toughness of Composites," *SAMPE J.* 18 (1982): 8–15.

5.12 El-Zein, M. S., and K. L. Reifsnider, "Evaluation of G_{1c} of a DCB Specimen Using an Anisotropic Solution," *J. Comp. Tech. Res.* 10 (1988): 151–155.

5.13 Deary, P. E. et al., "Mode I Interlaminar Fracture Toughness of Composites Using Slender Double Cantilevered Beam Specimens," *J. Composite Mater.* 19 (1985): 154–177.

5.14 Shah, R. C., G. Miliziano, and A. V. Viswanathan, "Interlaminar Fracture Characteristics of Tougher Thermoset Materials," *J. Aircraft* 23 (1986): 599–605.

5.15 Hunston, D. L., "Composite Interlaminar Fracture: Effect of Matrix Fracture Energy," *Composites Tech. Rev.* 6 (1984): 176–180.

5.16 Hwang, W., and K. S. Han, "Interlaminar Fracture Behavior and Fiber Bridging of Glass-Epoxy Composite under Mode I Static and Cyclic Loadings," *J. Composite Mater.* 23 (1989): 396–430.

5.17 Benzeggagh, M. L., Y. Prel, and F. X. de Charentenay, "Experimental Analysis of Mode I Delamination Testing," in *Proceedings of the Fifth International Conference on Composite Materials*, eds. W. C. Harrigan, J. Strife, and A. K. Dhingra (Warrendale, PA: The Metallurgical Society, Inc., 1987), pp. 127–139.

5.18 Devitt, D. F., R. A. Schapery, and W. L. Bradley, "A Method for Determining the Mode I Delamination Fracture Toughness of Elastic and Viscoelastic Composite Materials," *J. Composite Mater.* 14 (1980): 270–285.

5.19 Rybicki, E. F., and M. F. Kanninen, "A Finite Element Calculation of Stress Intensity Factors by a Modified Crack Closure Integral," *Eng. Frac. Mech.* 9 (1977): 931–938.

5.20 Tian, Z., and S. R. Swanson, "Effect of Delamination Face Overlapping on Strain Energy Release Rate Calculations," *Composite Struct.* 21 (1992): 195–204.

5.21 Pipes, R. B., and N. J. Pagano, "Interlaminar Stresses in Composite Laminates Under Uniform Axial Extension," *J. Composite Mater.* 4 (1970): 538–548.

5.22 Wang, S. S., and I. Choi, "Boundary-Layer Effects in Composite Laminates: Part 1—Free-Edge Stress Singularities: Part 2—Free-Edge Stress Solutions and Characteristics," *J. Appl. Mech.* 49 (1982): 541–559.

5.23 Pagano, N. J., and R. B. Pipes, "The Influence of Stacking Sequence on Laminate Strength," *J. Composite Mater.* 5 (1971): 50–57.

5.24 Whitney, J. M., and C. E. Browning, "Free-Edge Delamination of Tensile Coupons," *J. Composite Mater.* 6 (1972): 300–303.

5.25 Crossman, F. W., "Analysis of Free Edge Induced Failure of Composite Laminates," in *Fracture of Composite Materials*, ed. G. C. Sih and V. P. Tamuzs (Alphenaanden Rijn, the Netherlands: Sijthoff and Noordhoff, 1979), pp. 291–302.

5.26 Wang, A. S. D., M. Slomiana, and R. B. Bucinell, "Delamination Crack Growth in Composite Laminates," in *Delamination and Debonding of Materials*, ASTM STP 876, ed. W. S. Johnson (Philadelphia: American Society for Testing and Materials, 1985), pp. 135–167.

5.27 Zhou, S. G., and C. T. Sun, "Failure Analysis of Composite Laminates with Free Edge," *J. Composites Tech. Res.* 12 (1990): 91–97.

5.28 Chan, W. S., and A. S. D. Wang, " Effects of a 90 Ply on Matrix Cracks and Edge Delamination in Composite Laminates," *Composites Sci. Tech.* 38 (1990): 143–157.

5.29 Browning, C. E., and H. S. Schwartz, "Delamination Resistant Composite Concepts," in *Composite Materials: Testing and Design (Seventh Conference)*, ASTM STP 893, ed. J. M. Whitney (Philadelphia: American Society for Testing and Materials, 1986), pp. 256–265.

5.30 Mignery, L. A., T. M. Tan, and C. T. Sun, "The Use of Stitching to Suppress Delamination in Laminated Composites," in *Delamination and Debonding*, ASTM STP 876, ed. W. S. Johnson (Philadelphia: American Society for Testing and Materials, 1985), pp. 371–385.

5.31 Howard, W. E., T. Gossard, and R. M. Jones, "Composite Laminate Free-Edge Reinforcement with U-Shaped Caps, Part I: Stress Analysis," *AIAA J.* 27 (1989): 610–623.

5.32 Herakovich, C. T., "On the Relationship Between Engineering Properties and Delamination of Composite Materials," *J. Composite Mater.* 15 (1981): 336–348.

5.33 O'Brien, T. K., "Characterization of Delamination Onset and Growth in a Composite Laminate," in *Damage in Composite Materials*, ASTM STP 775, ed. K. L. Reifsnider (Philadelphia: American Society for Testing and Materials, 1982), pp. 140–167.

5.34 Wang, A. S. D., "Fracture Analysis of Interlaminar Cracking," in *Interlaminar Response of Composite Materials*, ed. N. J. Pagano (Amsterdam: Elsevier, 1989), pp. 69–109.

5.35 Chang, C. C., R. S. Sandhu, R. L. Sierakowski, and W. E. Wolfe, "Continuous Strain Finite-Element Analysis of Free-Edge Effect in Laminated Composite Specimens," *J. Composite Tech. Res.* 10 (1988): 54–64.

5.36 Law, G. E., "A Mixed-Mode Fracture Analysis of $(\pm 25/90_n)_s$ Graphite/Epoxy Composite Laminates," in *Effect of Defects in Composite Materials*, ASTM STP 836 (Philadelphia: American Society for Testing and Materials, 1984), pp. 143–160.

5.37 Sun, C. T., and S. G. Zhou, "Failure of Quasi-Isotropic Laminates with Free Edges," *J. of Reinforced Plast. Composites* 7 (1988): 515–557.

5.38 O'Brien, T. K., et al., "Determination of Interlaminar Fracture Toughness and Fracture Mode Dependence of Composites Using the Edge Delamination Test," in *Proceedings of the International Conference on Testing, Evaluation, and Quality Control of Composites* (London: Butterworths, 1983), pp. 223–232.

√5.39 Abrate, S., "Matrix Cracking in Laminated Composites: A Review," *Composites Eng.* 1 (1991): 337–353.

5.40 Masters, J. E., "Surface Replication: A Reliable Method of Detecting Matrix Cracks in Composite Laminates," *Composites Tech. Rev.* 3 (1981): 35–36.

5.41 Masters, J. E., and K. L. Reifsnider, *An Investigation of Cumulative Damage Development in Quasi-Isotropic Graphite/Epoxy Laminates*, ASTM STP 775, ed. K. L. Reifsnider (Philadelphia: American Society for Testing and Materials, 1982), pp. 40–62.

5.42 Garrett, K. W., and J. E. Bailey, "Multiple Transverse Fracture in 90° Cross-Ply Laminates of a Glass Fibre-Reinforced Polyester," *J. Mater. Sci.* 12 (1977): 157–168.

5.43 Parvizi, A., K. W. Garrett, and J. E. Bailey, "Constrained Cracking in Glass Fibre-Reinforced Epoxy Cross-Ply Laminates," *J. Mater. Sci.* 13 (1978): 195–201.

5.44 Flaggs, D. L., and M. H. Kural, "Experimental Determination of the In Situ Transverse Lamina Strength in Graphite/Epoxy Laminates," *J. Composite Mater.* 16 (1982): 103–116.

5.45 Wang, A. S. D., "Growth Mechanisms of Transverse Cracks and Ply Delamination in Composite Laminates," in *Proceedings of the Third International Conference on Composite Materials: Advances in Composite Materials* (Paris, 1980), pp. 170–185.

5.46 Morley, J. G., and G. Pissinou, "Transverse Ply Cracking Strains in 90/90 and ($\pm\theta$/90) Laminates," *J. Mater. Sci.* 21 (1986): 4206–4214.

5.47 Flaggs, D. L., "Prediction of Tensile Matrix Failure in Composite Laminates," *J. Composite Mater.* 19 (1985): 29–50.

5.48 Daniel, I. M., and J. W. Lee, "Damage Development in Composite Laminates Under Monotonic Loading," *J. Composites Tech. Res.* 12 (1990): 98–102.

5.49 Crossman, F. W., and A. S. D. Wang, "The Dependence of Transverse Cracking and Delamination on Ply Thickness in Graphite/Epoxy Laminates," in *Damage in Composite Materials*, ASTM STP 775, ed. K. L. Reifsnider (Philadelphia: American Society for Testing and Materials, 1982), pp. 118–139.

5.50 Coxon, B., and L. Ilcewicz, "Process Related Changes in the Transverse Matrix Crack Resistance of High Performance Composites," in *Proceedings of the American Society for Composites, Fourth Technical Conference* (Lancaster, PA: Technomic Publishing, 1989), pp. 483–492.

5.51 Rothschilds, R. J., et al., "The Effect of Hygrothermal Histories on Matrix Cracking in Fiber Reinforced Laminates," *J. Eng. Mater. Tech.* 110 (1988): 158–168.

5.52 Wang, A. S. D., "Fracture Mechanics of Sublaminate Cracks in Composite Materials," *Composites Tech. Rev.* 6 (1984): 45–62.

5.53 Highsmith, A. L., and K. L. Reifsnider, "Stiffness-Reduction Mechanisms in Composite Laminates," in *Damage in Composite Materials*, ASTM STP 775, ed. K. L. Reifsnider (Philadelphia: American Society for Testing and Materials, 1982), pp. 103–117.

5.54 Laws, N., and G. J. Dvorak, "Progressive Transverse Cracking in Composite Laminates," *J. Composite Mater.* 22 (1988): 900–916.

5.55 Swanson, S. R., "On the Mechanics of Microcracking in Fiber Composite Laminates Under Combined Stress," *J. Eng. Mater. Tech.* 111 (1989): 145–149.

5.56 Hashin, Z., "Analysis of Cracked Laminates: A Variational Approach," *Mech. Mater.* 4 (1985): 121–136.

5.57 Hashin, Z., "Analysis of Stiffness Reduction of Cracked Cross-Ply Laminates," *Eng. Fract. Mech.* 25 (1986): 771–778.

5.58 Hashin, Z., "Analysis of Orthogonally Cracked Laminates Under Tension," *J. Appl. Mech.* 54 (1987): 872–879.

5.59 Nairn, J., "The Initiation of Microcracking in Cross-Ply Laminates: A Variational Mechanics Analysis," in *Proceedings of the American Society for Composites, Third Technical Conference* (Lancaster, PA: Technomic Publishing, 1988), pp. 472–481.

5.60 Nairn, J., "The Strain Energy Release Rate of Composite Microcracking: A Variational Approach," *J. Composite Mater.* 23 (1989): 1106–1129.

5.61 Nuismer, R. J., and S. C. Tan, "The Role of Matrix Cracking in the Continuum Constitutive Behavior of a Damaged Composite Ply," in *Proceedings of the IUTAM Symposium on the Mechanics of Composite Materials: Recent Advances* (New York: Pergamon Press, 1982), pp. 437–448.

5.62 Swanson, S. R., and A. P. Christoforou, "Progressive Failure in Carbon/Epoxy Laminates Under Biaxial Stress," *J. Eng. Mater. Tech.* 109 (1987): 12–16.

5.63 Tan, S. C., and R. J. Nuismer, "A Theory for Progressive Matrix Cracking in Composite Laminates," *J. Composite Mater.* 23 (1989): 1029–1047.

5.64 McCartney, L. N., "The Prediction of Cracking in Biaxially Loaded Cross-Ply Laminates Having Brittle Matrices," *Composites* 24 (1993): 84–92.

5.65 Cook, J., and J. E. Gordon, "A Mechanism for the Control of Crack Propagation in All-Brittle Systems," *Proc. Roy. Soc. London Ser. A* 282 (1964): 508–520.

5.66 Ross, C. A., and R. L. Sierakowski, "Studies on the Impact Resistance of Composite Plates," *Composites* 4 (1973): 157–161.

5.67 Starnes, J. H., M. D. Rhodes, and J. G. Williams, "Effect of Impact Damage and Holes on the Compressive Strength of a Graphite/Epoxy Laminate," in *Nondestructive Evaluation and Flaw Criticality for Composite Materials*, ASTM STP 696 (Philadelphia: American Society for Testing and Materials, 1979), pp. 145–171.

5.68 Boll, D. J., W. D. Bascom, J. C. Weidner, and J. C. Murri, "A Microscopy Study of Impact Damage of Epoxy-Matrix Carbon-Fiber Composites," *J. Mater. Sci.* 21 (1986): 2667–2677.

5.69 Swanson, S. R., "Limits of Quasi-Static Solutions in Impact of Composite Structures," *Composites Eng.* 2 (1992): 261–267.

5.70 Labor, J. D., "Impact Damage Effects on the Strength of Advanced Composites," in *Nondestructive Evaluation and Flaw Criticality for Composite Materials*, ASTM STP 696 (Philadelphia: American Society for Testing and Materials, 1979), pp. 172–184.

5.71 Caprino, G., "Residual Strength Prediction of Impacted CFRP Laminates," *J. Composite Mater.* 18 (1984): 508–518 .

5.72 Levin, K., "Effect of Low-Velocity Impact on Compression Strength of Quasi-Isotropic Laminate," in *Proceedings of the First Technical Conference of the American Society for Composites* (Lancaster, PA: Technomic Publishing, 1986), pp. 313–325.

5.73 Yang, S. H., and C. T. Sun, "Indentation Law for Composite Laminates," in *Composite Materials: Testing and Design (Sixth Conference)*, ASTM STP 787 (Philadelphia: American Society for Testing and Materials, 1982), pp. 425–449.

5.74 Sun, C. T., and J. K. Chen, "On the Impact of Initially Stressed Composite Laminates," *J. Composite Mater.* 19 (1985): 490–504.

5.75 Tan, T. M., and C. T. Sun, "Use of Statical Indentation Law in the Impact Analysis of Laminated Composite Plates," *J. Composite Mater.* 52 (1985): 6–12.

5.76 Christoforou, A. P., and S. R. Swanson, "Analysis of Simply-Supported Orthotropic Cylindrical Shells Subject to Lateral Impact Loads," *J. Appl. Mech.* 57 (1990): 376–382.

5.77 Qian, Y., and S. R. Swanson, "Experimental Measurement of Impact Response in Carbon/Epoxy Plates," *AIAA J.* 28 (1990): 1069–1074.

5.78 Morton, J., "Scaling of Impact-Loaded Carbon-Fiber Composites," *AIAA J.* 26 (1988): 989–994.

5.79 Qian, Y., S. R. Swanson, R. J. Nuismer, and R. B. Bucinell, "An Experimental Study of Scaling Rules for Impact Damage in Fiber Composites," *J. Composite Mater.* 24 (1990): 559–570.

5.80 Swanson, S. R., N. L. Smith, and Y. Qian, "Analytical and Experimental Strain Response in Impact of Composite Cylinders," *Composite Struct.* 18 (1991): 95–108.

5.81 Gosnell, R. B., "Thermoplastic Resins," in *Engineered Materials Handbook, Vol. 1, Composites* (Metals Park, OH: American Society for Metals, 1987), pp. 97–104.

5.82 Curtis, P. T., "The Fatigue of Organic Matrix Composite Materials," in *Advanced Composites*, ed. I. K. Partridge (London: Elsevier, 1989), pp. 331–367.

5.83 Talreja, R., *Fatigue of Composite Materials* (Lancaster, PA: Technomic Publishing, 1987).

5.84 Salkind, M. J., "Fatigue of Composites," in *Composite Materials: Testing and Design (Second Conference)*, ASTM STP 497 (Philadelphia: American Society for Testing and Materials, 1972), pp. 143–169.

5.85 Bakis, C. E., and W. W. Stinchcomb, "Response of Thick, Notched Laminates Subjected to Tension-Compression Cyclic Loads," in *Composite Materials: Fatigue and Fracture*, ASTM STP 907, ed. H. T. Hahn (Philadelphia: American Society for Testing and Materials, 1986), pp. 314–334.

5.86 Simonds, R. A., and W. W. Stinchcomb, "Response of Notched AS4/PEEK Laminates to Tension/Compression Loading," in *Advances in Thermoplastic Matrix Composite Materials*, ASTM STP 1044, ed. G. M. Newaz (Philadelphia: American Society for Testing and Materials, 1989), pp. 133–145.

5.87 Grimes, G. C., "Experimental Study of Compression-Compression Fatigue of Graphite/Epoxy Composites," in *Test Methods and Design Allowables for Fibrous Composites*, ASTM STP 734, ed. C. C. Chamis (Philadelphia: American Society for Testing and Materials, 1981), pp. 281–337.

5.88 Harris, B., et al., "Fatigue Behaviour of Carbon Fibre Reinforced Plastics," *Composites* 21 (1990): 232–242.

5.89 Reifsnider, K. L., and W. W. Stinchcomb, "A Critical-Element Model of the Residual Strength and Life of Fatigue-Loaded Composite Coupons," in *Composite Materials: Fatigue and Fracture*, ASTM STP 907, ed. H. T. Hahn (Philadelphia: American Society for Testing and Materials, 1986), pp. 298–313.

5.90 Highsmith, A. L., and K. L. Reifsnider, "Internal Load Distribution Effects During Fatigue Loading of Composite Laminates," in *Composite Materials: Fatigue and Fracture*, ASTM STP 907, ed. H. T. Hahn (Philadelphia: American Society for Testing and Materials, 1986), pp. 233–251.

5.91 Charewicz, A., and I. M. Daniel, "Damage Mechanisms and Accumulation in Graphite/Epoxy Laminates,"in *Composite Materials: Fatigue and Fracture*, ASTM STP 907, ed. H. T. Hahn (Philadelphia: American Society for Testing and Materials, 1986), pp. 274–297.

5.92 Swanson, S. R., D. S. Cairns, M. E. Guyll, and D. L. Johnson, "Compression Fatigue Response for Carbon Fiber with Conventional and Toughened Epoxy Matrices with Damage," *ASME J. Eng. Mater. Tech.* 115 (1993): 116–121.

5.93 Bakis, C. E., R. A. Simonds, L. W. Vick, and W. W. Stinchcomb, "Matrix Toughness, Long-Term Behavior, and Damage Tolerance of Notched Graphite Fiber-Reinforced Composite Materials," in *Composite Materials: Testing and Design (Ninth Conference)*, ASTM STP 1059, ed. S. P. Garbo (Philadelphia: American Society for Testing and Materials, 1990), pp. 349–370.

5.94 Henaff-Gardin, C., and M. C. Lafarie-Frenot, "Fatigue Behavior of Thermoset and Thermoplastic Cross-Ply Laminates," *Composites* 23 (1992): 109–116.

PROBLEMS

5.1. Calculate the maximum distributed load in the beam of Figure 5.1 as limited by the interlaminar shear strength, taking the interlaminar shear strength as being the same as the in-plane shear strength given in Chapter 4 for AS4/3501-6 carbon/epoxy. Use the isotropic-beam formulas for shear stress.

5.2. Show the steps in detail leading from Eqs. (5.1) to (5.9). These equations provide a general description of the relation of energy-release rates to loads and compliances in fracture mechanics analysis.

5.3. Show the steps in detail leading from Eqs. (5.10) to (5.13). These equations give the beam analysis of the double-cantilever-beam test for Mode I delamination.

5.4. Make a sketch of the specimen that could be used for a laboratory test for Mode I delamination energy-release rate, including your recommendation for layup, thickness, and dimensions.

5.5. Show how a DCB specimen with variable width could be used to minimize the influence of delamination length on the calculated energy-release rate (see Figure 5.32).

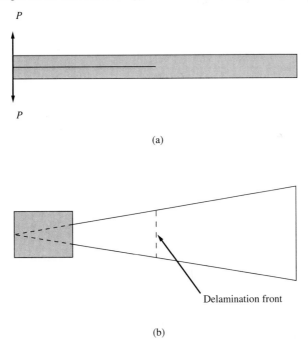

(a)

(b)

Figure 5.32   Possible width-tapered DCB specimen: (a) edge view, and (b) top view.

5.6. Show how a DCB specimen with variable thickness could be used to minimize the influence of delamination length on the calculated energy-release rate.

5.7. Carry out an analysis of the ENF (end-notched flexure) test for delamination resistance using a strength-of-materials approach to find the critical shearing-mode energy-release rate as a function of the load, properties, and geometry of the specimen.

5.8. Draw the free-body diagram for the mixed-mode bend specimen, and derive the relationships between the geometry and Mode I and II loadings.

5.9. Compare the experimental results shown in Figure 5.8 with expressions given in the literature for estimating delamination under mixed-mode loading with the following:

(a) $G_I + G_{II}$ = constant

(b) $G_I/G_{Ic} + G_{II}/G_{IIc} = 1$

(c) $(G_I/G_{Ic})^2 + (G_{II}/G_{IIc})^2 = 1$

5.10. Fit a function of your own choosing of the type shown in Problem 5.9 to the data of Figure 5.8.

5.11. Plot values of the delamination energy-release rate for composite systems from Table 5.1 and compare with the data given in Figure 5.8. Note particularly the differences between brittle epoxy systems like 3501-6 and 5208 and the newer high-toughness epoxies and thermoplastic resins.

5.12. Discuss how one could actually use the measured delamination energy-release rates in design.

5.13. Consider a [0/90]$_s$ laminate loaded by a uniaxial stress in the 0 direction (taken as the x direction). Indicate why transverse (σ_y) stresses exist within the interior of the laminate and what their sign will be in each ply.

5.14. Consider the problem of free-edge effects in a [0/90]$_s$ laminate loaded by a uniaxial stress in the 0° direction (taken as the x direction). Draw a free-body diagram of the 0° plies at an edge. Give reasons why each of the stress components that you identify must exist. Also indicate which of these stresses could cause delamination from the free edge.

5.15. Consider a [±θ]$_s$ laminate loaded by a uniaxial stress in the 0° direction (taken as the x direction). Indicate why in-plane shear stresses exist within the interior of the laminate and what their sign will be in each ply. Verify that these stresses are predicted by lamination theory by using a lamination computer program to calculate their value.

5.16. Consider the problem of free-edge effects in a [±θ]$_s$ laminate loaded by a uniaxial stress in the 0 direction (taken as the x direction). Draw a free-body diagram of one of the plies at an edge. Give reasons why each of the stress components that you identify must exist. Also indicate which of these stresses could cause delamination from the free edge.

5.17. Show in detail the steps leading from Eqs. (5.29) to (5.34) for the edge-delamination test. These equations give a strength-of-materials result for the edge-delamination energy-release rate.

5.18. Develop an expression for the energy-release rate for the specimen shown in Figure 5.15, the edge-delamination test specimen.

5.19. Replot the data of Figure 5.20 as crack density (cracks/in) versus the applied mechanical strain. Comment on the differences in this and the original figure. Note that plotting the crack density as a function of applied strain is quite different than plotting as a function of applied stress, due to the changes in the layup.

5.20. Estimate the cooldown strains for the specimens shown in Figure 5.20, and replot the data of the figure as crack density versus the total (thermal + mechanical) strain. The time history of the thermal strain is quite different than with the subsequent mechanical strain, and the question of how they should be combined has not been completely answered. One answer is just to add them together, as is asked for here.

5.21. Show in detail the steps leading from Eqs. (5.35) to (5.43). These equations give a simplified shear lag analysis that can be used to estimate stiffness changes with microcracking.

5.22. Show how Eq. (5.44) is obtained from Eq. (5.41). This equation is the final estimate of the effect of microcracking on the transverse tensile modulus of a cracked lamina.

5.23. Derive expressions for shear and normal stress for quasi-static impact at the end of a cantilever beam using the isotropic-beam formulas.

5.24. Give reasons why high-modulus fiber composites, such as carbon/epoxy, would be expected to show better fatigue properties than lower-modulus fiber composites, such as glass/epoxy.

5.25. Give reasons why compression fatigue would be expected to be more severe than tension fatigue in fiber composites.

5.26. Figure 5.24 shows that in some cases, the compressive strength after impact was actually improved by one million cycles of compression fatigue loading after the impact. Give a possible explanation for this.

5.27. Consider the edge-delamination test. Analyze the test using the simplified strength-of-materials technique of O'Brien and apply it to an AS4/3501-6 carbon/epoxy specimen with the layup $[\pm30/\pm30/90/\overline{90}]_s$, where delamination is expected between the two $-30°$ and $90°$ interfaces. (Note that the center line splits the center $90°$ ply.)

6

Introduction to the Analysis of Plates

6.1 INTRODUCTION

Plates are structural members with two dimensions much larger than the third, as a beam has one dimension that is much larger than the other two. The analysis of plates made of isotropic materials is a classical subject that has been well documented in the engineering literature [6.1–6.3]. Plates made of orthotropic materials have also been studied extensively. The results of these studies are well documented in the current literature [6.4–6.6] The objective at present is to briefly present the governing equations and classical solution techniques as an introduction to the subject.

6.2 EQUILIBRIUM EQUATIONS

The equilibrium equations of plates are, of course, the same independent of the type of material. They are often developed by integrating the usual equilibrium equations of elasticity. The equilibrium equations of elasticity without body forces can be written as

$$\frac{\partial \sigma_x}{\partial x} + \frac{\partial \tau_{xy}}{\partial y} + \frac{\partial \tau_{xz}}{\partial z} = 0 \tag{6.1}$$

$$\frac{\partial \sigma_y}{\partial y} + \frac{\partial \tau_{xy}}{\partial x} + \frac{\partial \tau_{yz}}{\partial z} = 0 \tag{6.2}$$

$$\frac{\partial \sigma_z}{\partial z} + \frac{\partial \tau_{xz}}{\partial x} + \frac{\partial \tau_{yz}}{\partial y} = 0 \tag{6.3}$$

The equations of equilibrium for in-plane loads can be obtained by integrating the first two equations through the thickness. Integrating the first equation results in

$$\int_{-h/2}^{h/2} \left(\frac{\partial \sigma_x}{\partial x} + \frac{\partial \tau_{xy}}{\partial y} + \frac{\partial \tau_{xz}}{\partial z} \right) dz = 0$$

165

or noting the definitions for stress resultants given in Chapter 3 as

$$\begin{Bmatrix} N_x \\ N_y \\ N_{xy} \end{Bmatrix} = \int_{-h/2}^{h/2} \begin{Bmatrix} \sigma_x \\ \sigma_y \\ \tau_{xy} \end{Bmatrix} dz \tag{3.7}$$

Substituting gives

$$\frac{\partial N_x}{\partial x} + \frac{\partial N_{xy}}{\partial y} + \tau_{1x} - \tau_{2x} = 0 \tag{6.4}$$

Similarly, by integrating Eq. (6.2) through the thickness,

$$\frac{\partial N_y}{\partial y} + \frac{\partial N_{xy}}{\partial x} + \tau_{1y} - \tau_{2y} = 0 \tag{6.5}$$

The shear terms in these equations represent possible shear loadings on the faces of the plate. The in-plane resultants are shown in Figure 6.1.

New definitions are needed for transverse shear resultants to integrate Eq. (6.3). Defining

$$Q_x \equiv \int_{-h/2}^{h/2} \tau_{xz} \, dz \tag{6.6}$$

$$Q_y \equiv \int_{-h/2}^{h/2} \tau_{yz} \, dz \tag{6.7}$$

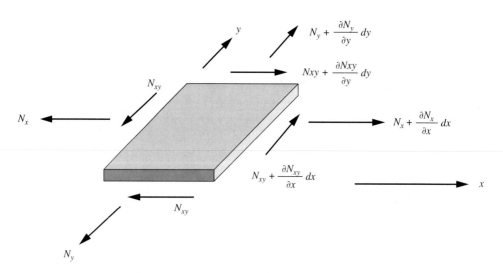

Figure 6.1 In-plane stress resultant terms for plate equilibrium.

With these definitions, the integration of Eq. (6.3) through the thickness is given as

$$\frac{\partial Q_x}{\partial x} + \frac{\partial Q_y}{\partial y} + p = 0 \tag{6.8}$$

where $p(x,y)$ is the pressure loading on the plate.

The moment equilibrium equations can be derived by multiplying Eqs. (6.1) and (6.2) through by z and then integrating through the thickness. Again, noting the definitions of moment resultants from Chapter 3, given as

$$\left\{ \begin{matrix} M_x \\ M_y \\ M_{xy} \end{matrix} \right\} = \int_{-h/2}^{h/2} \left\{ \begin{matrix} \sigma_x \\ \sigma_y \\ \tau_{xy} \end{matrix} \right\} z \, dz \tag{3.8}$$

results in

$$\frac{\partial M_x}{\partial x} + \frac{\partial M_{xy}}{\partial y} - Q_x + \frac{h}{2}(\tau_{1x} + \tau_{2x}) = 0 \tag{6.9}$$

and

$$\frac{\partial M_y}{\partial y} + \frac{\partial M_{xy}}{\partial x} - Q_y + \frac{h}{2}(\tau_{1y} + \tau_{2y}) = 0 \tag{6.10}$$

Equations (6.4) and (6.5) represent the equilibrium of in-plane stress resultants, Eq. (6.8) is the equilibrium of the transverse shear resultants, and Eqs. (6.9) and (6.10) represent moment equilibrium. The moment resultants are shown in Figure 6.2.

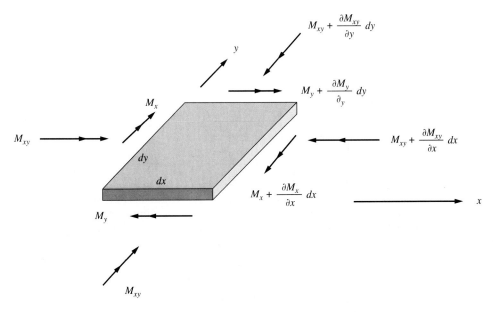

Figure 6.2   Moment resultants. Moments are shown by the double arrow according to the right-hand rule.

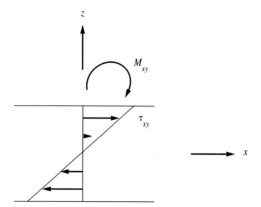

Figure 6.3   The moment resultant M_{xy} resulting from the distribution of the in-plane shear stress through the thickness.

The moment resultants M_{xy} result from the distribution of the in-plane shear stress through the thickness, and an example is illustrated in Figure 6.3.

Equations (6.9) and (6.10) can be combined with Eq. (6.6). Solving Eqs. (6.9) and (6.10) for the transverse shear resultants, taking derivatives with respect to x and y, and substituting into Eq. (6.8) gives

$$\frac{\partial^2 M_x}{\partial x^2} + 2\frac{\partial^2 M_{xy}}{\partial x\, \partial y} + \frac{\partial^2 M_y}{\partial y^2} = -p(x,y) \tag{6.11}$$

To proceed further, it is necessary to express Eq. (6.11) in terms of displacements. The usual Kirchhoff theory, without transverse shear deformation, is developed first. For symmetric layups, it was shown in Chapter 3 that the B matrix vanishes and the stress resultants and moment results are uncoupled. In the following, this assumption is made. Thus, the moments can be related to the plate curvatures through the D matrix. This relationship was given previously as

$$\begin{Bmatrix} M_x \\ M_y \\ M_{xy} \end{Bmatrix} = \begin{bmatrix} D_{11} & D_{12} & D_{16} \\ D_{12} & D_{22} & D_{26} \\ D_{16} & D_{26} & D_{66} \end{bmatrix} \begin{Bmatrix} \kappa_x \\ \kappa_y \\ \kappa_{xy} \end{Bmatrix} \tag{6.12}$$

If the further assumption is made that the D_{16} and D_{26} terms vanish, considerable simplification results. It was mentioned in Chapter 3 that this happens approximately if the layup is balanced, and the more dispersed the plies, the closer the approximation. For the present, it is assumed that these terms vanish. Substituting Eq. (6.12) into (6.11) and using the definitions of the curvature terms given in Chapter 3 results in

$$D_{11}\frac{\partial^4 w}{\partial x^4} + 2(D_{12} + 2D_{66})\frac{\partial^4 w}{\partial x^2\, \partial y^2} + D_{22}\frac{\partial^4 w}{\partial y^4} = p(x,y) \tag{6.13}$$

This is the governing differential equation for bending of orthotropic plates in rectangular coordinates. This equation can be solved analytically for certain boundary conditions. For more general cases, approximate techniques such as energy principles can be employed.

6.3 NAVIER SOLUTION FOR SIMPLY SUPPORTED RECTANGULAR PLATES

The boundary conditions for simply supported edges are that the displacement and normal moment both vanish on the boundary. This can be stated as

$$w = 0 \tag{6.14}$$

$$M_n = 0 \tag{6.15}$$

Thus, from Eq. (6.12), it follows that the normal curvature also vanishes, as the twisting curvature vanishes along a simply supported edge. Thus, Eq. (6.15) can be expressed as

$$\frac{\partial^2 w}{\partial n^2} = 0 \tag{6.16}$$

The governing differential equation, Eq. (6.13), with the boundary conditions, Eqs. (6.14) and (6.16), can be solved by using a Fourier-series expansion. The pressure load is expanded in a Fourier series, and then displacement w is taken in the form of a Fourier series with unknown coefficients. That is, express the load as

$$p(x,y) = \sum_{m=1}^{\infty} \sum_{n=1}^{\infty} B_{mn} \sin \frac{m\pi x}{a} \sin \frac{n\pi y}{b} \tag{6.17}$$

where a and b are the dimensions of the plate in the x and y directions, as shown in Figure 6.4. Coefficients B_{mn} can be determined for any given pressure distribution, as shown in the example to follow. The solution for w then can be obtained by expanding w in a Fourier series as

$$w(x,y) = \sum_{m=1}^{\infty} \sum_{n=1}^{\infty} A_{mn} \sin \frac{m\pi x}{a} \sin \frac{n\pi y}{b} \tag{6.18}$$

where now the coefficients are undetermined. It should be pointed out that this expansion for w satisfies the boundary conditions on all edges of the plate. Substituting Eq. (6.18) into

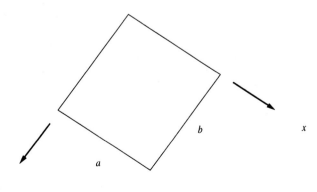

Figure 6.4   Coordinate system and dimensions of a rectangular plate.

the governing differential equation, Eq. (6.13), permits solving coefficients A_{mn}. Carrying out this substitution and equating term by term gives

$$A_{mn} = \frac{B_{mn}}{E_{mn}} \tag{6.19}$$

where

$$E_{mn} = D_{11}\left(\frac{m\pi}{a}\right)^4 + 2(D_{12} + 2D_{66})\left(\frac{m\pi}{a}\right)^2\left(\frac{n\pi}{b}\right)^2 + D_{22}\left(\frac{n\pi}{b}\right)^4 \tag{6.20}$$

Because the B_{mn} are known from the pressure distribution, coefficients A_{mn} can be determined. This gives a complete solution for the displacements, and thus for all of the variables of the problem. The strains and stresses in all the plies can be determined from the displacements, using equations given previously in Chapter 3. Thus, the curvatures are first found by differentiating the solution for w using Eq. (3.6). The strain distribution then can be found for any position z from Eq. (3.4), noting that the center-line strains are zero. The strains are thus known in all the plies in terms of the global x,y coordinate system. These strains then can be rotated into the fiber directions for the particular ply, and, finally, the stresses in the ply can be obtained by multiplying the ply strains by the ply stress–strain relationship using Eq. (2.14). Thus, the ply stresses and strains are completely determined.

EXAMPLE 6.1 Pressure loading of a simply supported plate using the Navier solution

Consider the problem of a fiber-composite plate with simply supported edges loaded by a constant pressure to be obtained using the Navier solution. The general procedure to be followed is to expand the pressure distribution in a Fourier series, as given in Eq. (6.17), then solve for the displacement coefficients from Eqs. (6.19) and (6.20), and then finally the stresses throughout the plate can be obtained from the displacements. Consider a constant pressure over the surface of the plate. Because the solution is linear in the pressure, a value of unity is used. Coefficients B_{mn} of the pressure distribution are obtained by multiplying Eq. (6.17) by a sine term in each of the x and y directions, and integrating over the plate as

$$\int_0^b\int_0^a p(x,y)\sin\frac{K\pi x}{a}\sin\frac{L\pi x}{b}\,dx\,dy$$

$$= \int_0^b\int_0^a\left(\sum_n\sum_m B_{mn}\sin\frac{m\pi x}{a}\sin\frac{n\pi y}{b}\sin\frac{K\pi x}{a}\sin\frac{L\pi y}{b}\right)dx\,dy$$

The right-hand side is simplified by using the orthogonality of trigonometric functions, which is expressed in this case as

$$\int_0^q \sin\frac{m\pi t}{q}\sin\frac{n\pi t}{q}\,dt = \left\{\begin{array}{ll} 0, & m \ne n \\ q/2, & m = n \end{array}\right\}$$

where m and n are integers. The left-hand side is easily integrated for a constant pressure $p = p_0$. Carrying out the operations gives

$$\frac{4abp_0}{\pi^2 KL} = B_{KL}\frac{a}{2}\frac{b}{2}\quad K = 1, 3, 5, \ldots; L = 1, 3, 5, \ldots$$

or

$$B_{KL} = \frac{16p_0}{\pi^2 KL}\quad K = 1, 3, 5, \ldots; L = 1, 3, 5, \ldots$$

Substituting in Eqs. (6.19) and (6.20) gives coefficients A_{mn} of the displacement terms, and substituting into Eq. (6.18) gives the displacements at any position in the plate. The strains then can be obtained from the displacements using the usual relations of lamination theory. From Eq. (3.4), the strains are given as

$$\{\epsilon\} = \{\epsilon^0\} + z\{\kappa\} \tag{3.4}$$

and the center-line strains vanish for the present case of a symmetric laminate (thus, $B = 0$) and no in-plane loads. The curvatures and thus the strains are obtained from the preceding displacement solution using Eq. (3.6):

$$\begin{Bmatrix} \kappa_x \\ \kappa_y \\ \kappa_{xy} \end{Bmatrix} = \begin{Bmatrix} -\dfrac{\partial^2 w}{\partial x^2} \\ -\dfrac{\partial^2 w}{\partial y^2} \\ -2\dfrac{\partial^2 w}{\partial x\, \partial y} \end{Bmatrix} \tag{3.6}$$

The strains are then resolved into fiber directions using Eq. (3.30):

$$\begin{Bmatrix} \epsilon_1 \\ \epsilon_2 \\ \gamma_{12} \end{Bmatrix} = [R][T][R^{-1}] \begin{Bmatrix} \epsilon_x \\ \epsilon_y \\ \gamma_{xy} \end{Bmatrix} \tag{3.30}$$

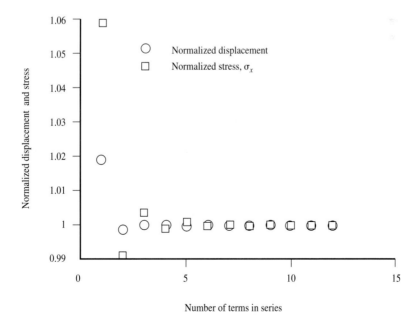

Figure 6.5   Convergence of the simply supported plate solution with the number of nonzero terms in each direction.

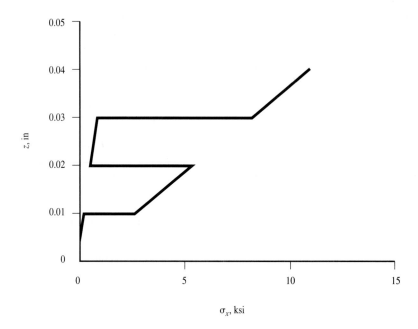

Figure 6.6 Variation of σ_x through half of the plate thickness for pressure loading of a simply supported laminated plate.

and the fiber-direction stresses are given by Eq. (3.30) as

$$\begin{Bmatrix} \sigma_1 \\ \sigma_2 \\ \tau_{12} \end{Bmatrix} = [Q] \begin{Bmatrix} \epsilon_1 \\ \epsilon_2 \\ \gamma_{12} \end{Bmatrix} \qquad (3.30)$$

This computation has been carried out for a carbon/epoxy laminate with a $[0_2/90_2/0_2/90_2]_s$ layup of AS4/3501-6.

The results are shown in Figures 6.5 and 6.6. Figure 6.5 shows the convergence with the number of nonzero (odd) terms in each direction, for both displacement and stress at the position $x = a/2$ and $y = b/2$. The results show that the displacement solution converges more quickly than the stress solution, but that both converge very quickly. A plot of the stress σ_x, again at the location $x = a/2$ and $y = b/2$ is shown in Figure 6.6, plotted through half of the thickness. The jumps in the stress are, of course, due to the orientation of the different ply groups. The solution for a different value of constant pressure can be obtained by multiplying the present results for unit pressure by the desired pressure loading. ∎

6.4 RECOVERY OF INTERLAMINAR SHEAR STRESSES

The interlaminar shear stresses τ_{xz} and τ_{yz} can be determined from the previous solution given by use of the equilibrium equations [6.7]. This procedure is very much like that used to determine the shear distribution in the usual strength-of-materials beam theory, where equilibrium considerations are employed in conjunction with the solution for the in-plane normal stress. In the present case, equilibrium equations, Eqs. (6.1) and (6.2), are solved for the interlaminar shear stresses by integrating through the thickness from a location of interest to the outer (shear-stress-free) surface. The result is

$$\tau_{xz}(x,y,\xi) = \int_{\xi}^{h/2} \left(\frac{\partial \sigma_x}{\partial x} + \frac{\partial \tau_{xy}}{\partial y} + F_x \right) dz \tag{6.21}$$

$$\tau_{yz}(x,y,\xi) = \int_{\xi}^{h/2} \left(\frac{\partial \sigma_y}{\partial y} + \frac{\partial \tau_{xy}}{\partial x} + F_y \right) dz \tag{6.22}$$

Because the in-plane stresses have already been solved, these expressions can be readily integrated. To carry out these integrals, follow the usual procedures of lamination theory in interchanging the order of differentiation and integration and breaking the integrals into a sum of integrals over each ply. The stress–strain law for an individual ply is written as usual as

$$\{\sigma\} = \overline{Q}\{\epsilon\} = \overline{Q}\{\epsilon_0\} + z\overline{Q}\{\kappa\} \tag{6.23}$$

This then permits the integrals of the stresses to be related to the center-line strains and curvatures as

$$\int_{\xi}^{h/2} \{\sigma\} \, dz = \widetilde{A}\{\epsilon_0\} + \widetilde{B}\{\kappa\} \tag{6.24}$$

and the constants are the same as usually defined in lamination theory except that the integrations are only carried out over part of the thickness of the laminate, as indicated. Thus, the interlaminar shear stresses can be easily evaluated as a postprocessing step after the in-plane solution is obtained. Similar procedures have been used previously in finite-element analysis [6.8].

6.5 SHEAR-DEFORMABLE THEORY

The classical plate equations discussed thus far include the transverse shear forces in the equilibrium equations, but neglect any deformations associated with the transverse shear. However, it is possible to include this shear deformation in an approximate manner, with the resulting theory being called "shear-deformable plate theory." It has been shown that shear deformations are much more important in composite material plates because of the much lower transverse shear stiffnesses relative to homogeneous materials. The shear deformation becomes relatively more important in thicker plates.

    The equations for shear-deformable plate theory are developed in what follows.

6.5.1 Plate Deformations

Displacement u in the x direction can be related to the center-line displacement u_0 and the transverse displacement of the plate center-line w, as shown in Figure 6.7. The new feature

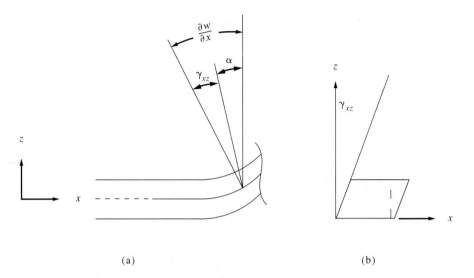

(a)   (b)

Figure 6.7   Shear deformation in a plate showing (a) the relationship of the normal to the center line, shear angle, and deformation of the plate; and (b) the average shear angle γ_{xz}.

here is that the plate deformation now includes a transverse shear. The in-plane displacements thus can be expressed as

$$u = u_0 + z\alpha$$
$$v = v_0 + z\beta \tag{6.25}$$

where

$$\alpha = \gamma_{xz} - \frac{\partial w}{\partial x}$$
$$\beta = \gamma_{yz} - \frac{\partial w}{\partial y} \tag{6.26}$$

Note that these equations reduce to those given previously for classical theory if the transverse shear deformations are taken as zero.

6.5.2 *ABD* Relationships

The usual *ABD* relationships are unchanged, and are given as usual as

$$\begin{Bmatrix} N \\ M \end{Bmatrix} = \begin{bmatrix} A & B \\ B & D \end{bmatrix} \begin{Bmatrix} \epsilon_0 \\ \kappa \end{Bmatrix} \tag{6.27}$$

where

$$\kappa_x = \frac{\partial \alpha}{\partial x} \qquad \kappa_y = \frac{\partial \beta}{\partial y} \qquad \kappa_{xy} = \frac{\partial \alpha}{\partial y} + \frac{\partial \beta}{\partial x} \tag{6.28}$$

We also need relationships involving the transverse shear resultants. These can be developed as follows. The transverse shear stress–strain relationships can be expressed in fiber-direction coordinates as

$$\begin{Bmatrix} \tau_{23} \\ \tau_{13} \end{Bmatrix} = \begin{bmatrix} G_{23} & 0 \\ 0 & G_{13} \end{bmatrix} \begin{Bmatrix} \gamma_{23} \\ \gamma_{13} \end{Bmatrix} \tag{6.29}$$

These shear stresses can be related to transverse shear stresses in general x,y,z coordinates by

$$\begin{Bmatrix} \tau_{23} \\ \tau_{13} \end{Bmatrix} = \begin{bmatrix} \cos\theta & -\sin\theta \\ \sin\theta & \cos\theta \end{bmatrix} \begin{Bmatrix} \tau_{yz} \\ \tau_{xz} \end{Bmatrix} \tag{6.30}$$

where θ is the angle of rotation in the x,y plane. The reader is urged to verify the preceding by considering a general 3-D transformation of stress components, and noting that the 3 direction always coincides with the z direction and is thus normal to the x,y plane. The transformation for strain components is the same if tensor components are used.

Using the preceding, it is easy to show that the relationship between transverse shear stress and strain in x,y coordinates is given by

$$\begin{Bmatrix} \tau_{yz} \\ \tau_{xz} \end{Bmatrix} = \begin{bmatrix} c^2 G_{23} + s^2 G_{13} & cs(G_{13} - G_{23}) \\ cs(G_{13} - G_{23}) & c^2 G_{13} + s^2 G_{23} \end{bmatrix} \begin{Bmatrix} \gamma_{yz} \\ \gamma_{xz} \end{Bmatrix} \tag{6.31}$$

where $s = \sin\theta$ and $c = \cos\theta$. The shear stresses then can be integrated through the thickness to get the transverse shear resultants:

$$\begin{Bmatrix} Q_y \\ Q_x \end{Bmatrix} = \begin{Bmatrix} \int_{-h/2}^{h/2} \tau_{yz}\, dz \\ \int_{-h/2}^{h/2} \tau_{xz}\, dz \end{Bmatrix} = k \begin{bmatrix} A_{44} & A_{45} \\ A_{45} & A_{55} \end{bmatrix} \begin{Bmatrix} \gamma_{yz} \\ \gamma_{xz} \end{Bmatrix} \tag{6.32}$$

It is usual to incorporate a shear-correction factor k to account for the fact that shear strains are actually nonuniform through the thickness, rather than having a constant value as is assumed here. Further discussion of the shear-correction factor will be given subsequently.

6.5.3 Plate Equilibrium

The plate equilibrium equations are unchanged. Remember that they were derived by using the equilibrium equations of elasticity and then integrating through the thickness. Two additional moment equilibrium equations were obtained by first multiplying the x- and y-direction equations through by z and then integrating through the thickness. The z-direction equation and the two moment equations are repeated as

$$\frac{\partial M_x}{\partial x} + \frac{\partial M_{xy}}{\partial y} - Q_x = 0$$

$$\frac{\partial M_y}{\partial y} + \frac{\partial M_{xy}}{\partial x} - Q_y = 0 \tag{6.33}$$

$$\frac{\partial Q_x}{\partial x} + \frac{\partial Q_y}{\partial y} + p(x,y) = 0$$

In the previous classical theory, we combined these three equations into one by eliminating the transverse shear resultants. It is now more convenient to deal with the three equations without combining them.

6.5.4 Substitution of Displacements into Plate Equilibrium

The *ABD* relationships are now used to substitute for moment and shear resultants in terms of the derivatives of the displacement variables α, β, and w. We consider only orthotropic symmetric plates, so that the *B* matrix vanishes and $D_{16} = D_{26} = 0$. Note that the shear strains are eliminated by using Eqs. (6.26). The three equations then become

$$D_{11}\frac{\partial^2\alpha}{\partial x^2} + (D_{12} + D_{66})\frac{\partial^2\beta}{\partial x\,\partial y} + D_{66}\frac{\partial^2\alpha}{\partial y^2} - A_{55}\left(\alpha + \frac{\partial w}{\partial x}\right) = 0$$

$$D_{22}\frac{\partial^2\beta}{\partial y^2} + (D_{12} + D_{66})\frac{\partial^2\alpha}{\partial x\,\partial y} + D_{66}\frac{\partial^2\beta}{\partial x^2} - A_{44}\left(\beta + \frac{\partial w}{\partial y}\right) = 0 \qquad (6.34)$$

$$A_{55}\left(\frac{\partial\alpha}{\partial x} + \frac{\partial^2 w}{\partial x^2}\right) + A_{44}\left(\frac{\partial\beta}{\partial y} + \frac{\partial^2 w}{\partial y^2}\right) + p(x,y) = 0$$

6.5.5 Solution for Simply Supported Rectangular Plates

The solution to the preceding governing equations for simply supported boundary conditions can be found by assuming a solution of the form

$$w(x,y) = \sum_{m=1}^{\infty}\sum_{n=1}^{\infty} C_{mn}\sin\frac{m\pi x}{a}\sin\frac{n\pi y}{b}$$

$$\alpha(x,y) = \sum_{m=1}^{\infty}\sum_{n=1}^{\infty} A_{mn}\cos\frac{m\pi x}{a}\sin\frac{n\pi y}{b} \qquad (6.35)$$

$$\beta(x,y) = \sum_{m=1}^{\infty}\sum_{n=1}^{\infty} B_{mn}\sin\frac{m\pi x}{a}\cos\frac{n\pi y}{b}$$

with the distributed surface normal traction $p(x,y)$ expressed as

$$p(x,y) = \sum_{m=1}^{\infty}\sum_{n=1}^{\infty} q_{mn}\sin\frac{m\pi x}{a}\sin\frac{n\pi y}{b} \qquad (6.36)$$

It can be seen that this solution satisfies the boundary conditions of simple support for a rectangular plate of lengths a and b in the x and y directions. These boundary conditions are as usual zero transverse displacement and zero normal moment on each of the four edges. Substituting into the three governing equations gives a solution for a particular mn term as

$$\begin{bmatrix} L_{11} & L_{12} & L_{13} \\ L_{12} & L_{22} & L_{23} \\ L_{13} & L_{23} & L_{33} \end{bmatrix} \begin{Bmatrix} A_{mn} \\ B_{mn} \\ C_{mn} \end{Bmatrix} = \begin{Bmatrix} 0 \\ 0 \\ q_{mn} \end{Bmatrix} \qquad (6.37)$$

where

$$L_{11} = D_{11}\lambda_m^2 + D_{66}\lambda_n^2 + A_{55}$$
$$L_{12} = (D_{12} + D_{66})\lambda_m\lambda_n$$

$$L_{13} = A_{55}\lambda_m \tag{6.38}$$
$$L_{22} = D_{22}\lambda_n^2 + D_{66}\lambda_m^2 + A_{44}$$
$$L_{23} = A_{44}\lambda_n$$
$$L_{33} = A_{44}\lambda_n^2 + A_{55}\lambda_m^2$$

and we have used

$$\lambda_m = \frac{m\pi}{a} \qquad \lambda_n = \frac{n\pi}{b} \tag{6.39}$$

These equations can be solved by Cramer's rule to give

$$A_{mn} = q_{mn}\frac{L_{12}L_{23} - L_{22}L_{13}}{\det}$$

$$B_{mn} = q_{mn}\frac{L_{12}L_{13} - L_{11}L_{23}}{\det} \tag{6.40}$$

$$C_{mn} = q_{mn}\frac{L_{11}L_{22} - L_{12}L_{12}}{\det}$$

where det is the determinant of coefficient matrix L.

Solving for the As, Bs, and Cs from Eq. (6.40) gives the complete solution to the problem. From these, the curvatures and thus the strains at any point can be calculated. Stresses then can be calculated by transforming the strains at a particular location into fiber-direction coordinates and then multiplying by the ply elasticity constants.

6.5.6 Transverse Shear-Correction Factor

A correction factor k was used in the relationship between the transverse shear resultant and the average shear strain to account in some way for shear strain varying through the thickness. In composite materials, the shear stress and thus shear strain vary through the thickness in a complicated way. However, in isotropic materials, it is easy to develop a correction factor according to various strategies. It is customary to use these isotropic shear-correction factors in composite plate analysis, although further investigation in this area might be fruitful.

A common strategy to determine k is to equate the strain energy in the plate analysis using a constant average shear strain (through the thickness) with the strain energy that follows from the parabolic shear distribution of isotropic materials. This latter distribution should be familiar from one-dimensional beam analysis.

The shear-strain energy density is given for one direction of the plate by

$$U = \frac{Q_y\gamma_{yz}}{2} = \frac{Q_y^2}{2kA_{44}} \tag{6.41}$$

where the relationship

$$Q_y = kA_{44}\gamma_{yz} \tag{6.42}$$

has been used to eliminate the average shear strain.

From elementary beam analysis, the shear-stress distribution through the thickness (in present notation) is given by

$$\tau = \frac{3Q}{2h}\left[1 - \left(\frac{2z}{h}\right)^2\right] \tag{6.43}$$

and the strain-energy density is obtained by integrating the shear stress through the thickness as

$$U = \int_{-h/2}^{h/2} \frac{\tau^2}{2G}\,dz = \frac{3Q^2}{5Gh} \tag{6.44}$$

Taking $A_{44} = Gh$ and equating the strain energies give

$$k = 5/6 \tag{6.45}$$

This value is commonly used in shear-deformable theory. A further discussion of shear-correction factors has been given by Whitney [6.9].

6.6 NATURAL FREQUENCIES AND BUCKLING LOADS FOR PLATES

The governing differential equation for plates can be used to find both natural frequencies and bifurcation buckling loads. The governing differential equation was given previously as

$$D_{11}\frac{\partial^2 w}{\partial x^4} + 2(D_{12} + 2D_{66})\frac{\partial^4 w}{\partial x^2 \partial y^2} + D_{22}\frac{\partial^4 w}{\partial y^4} = p(x,y) \tag{6.13}$$

Consider the problem of vibration. By writing a force balance for a differential element of the plate, and including acceleration terms, the right-hand side of Eq. (6.13) can be replaced by

$$\text{rhs} = p(x,y,t) - \rho_a \frac{d^2 w(x,y,t)}{dt^2} \tag{6.46}$$

where ρ_a is the mass per unit area of the plate. For free vibrations, the pressure loading is set to zero. The natural frequencies can be obtained for the simply supported plate by assuming a solution of the form

$$w(x,y,t) = \sum_n \sum_m A_{mn} \sin\frac{m\pi x}{a} \sin\frac{n\pi y}{b} \cos\omega_{mn}t \tag{6.47}$$

Substituting in the governing differential equation and equating term by term gives the expression for the natural frequencies as

$$\omega_{mn} = \frac{\pi^2}{\sqrt{\rho_a}}\left[D_{11}\left(\frac{m}{a}\right)^4 + 2(D_{12} + 2D_{66})\left(\frac{m}{a}\right)^2\left(\frac{n}{b}\right)^2 + D_{22}\left(\frac{n}{b}\right)^4\right]^{1/2} \tag{6.48}$$

The lowest or fundamental natural frequency is given by $n = m = 1$. The order of higher natural frequencies must be investigated by calculating for a number of m and n values.

It is also possible to use Eq. (6.13) to calculate the values of in-plane loads that cause bifurcation buckling of plates. The physical phenomenon of instability is similar to that studied in introductory texts for beam-columns, but is complicated by the two-dimensional nature of plates, as well as by the orthotropic properties of fiber-composite materials. The problem can be approached by considering the possibility of equilibrium states other than that of no transverse deflection. It will be seen that the in-plane loads must achieve critical values for the plate to be in equilibrium at other than the perfectly straight (no-transverse-deflection) position. These critical loads are called buckling loads, or the bifurcation or bifurcation buckling loads.

The approach to be followed is to consider that the plate is loaded by a set of in-plane loads N_x, N_{xy}, and N_y. A force balance in the z direction, taking into account the deflected shape of the plate, gives a set of forces that is in the direction of the pressure load of Eq. (6.13), and thus can be substituted for the pressure loading in the right-hand side of Eq. (6.13). This gives an equivalent right-hand side of Eq. (6.13) as

$$\text{rhs} = N_x \frac{\partial^2 w}{\partial x^2} + 2N_{xy} \frac{\partial^2 w}{\partial x\, \partial y} + N_y \frac{\partial^2 w}{\partial y^2} \tag{6.49}$$

A solution to Eq. (6.13) with the rhs term of Eq. (6.49) can be obtained for a plate with simply supported edges and N_x and N_y loading by assuming a solution in the form

$$w(x,y) = \sum_n \sum_m A_{mn} \sin \frac{m\pi x}{a} \sin \frac{n\pi y}{b} \tag{6.50}$$

Substituting in Eq. (6.13) and using the right-hand side of Eq. (6.49) gives

$$N_x\left(\frac{m}{a}\right)^2 + N_y\left(\frac{n}{b}\right)^2 = -\pi^2\left[D_{11}\left(\frac{m}{a}\right)^4 + 2(D_{12} + 2D_{66})\left(\frac{m}{a}\right)^2\left(\frac{n}{b}\right)^2 + D_{22}\left(\frac{n}{b}\right)^4\right] \tag{6.51}$$

It can be seen that at least one of the in-plane loads must be compressive, as of course would be expected. Also a variety of buckling loads are predicted, varying with the m and n values. Because usually only the lowest buckling load is of interest, this load must be obtained by calculating a variety of loads and selecting the lowest one. It is also possible to obtain an idea of the approximate values for m and n at the lowest load by considering m and n to be continuous variables, and thus differentiating to obtain the minimum as with an ordinary function. This gives a noninteger value for m and n, but selecting integer values that bracket this solution should give the minimum buckling load.

EXAMPLE 6.2   Plate buckling under N_x loading

Consider the problem of calculating the critical buckling load for a plate with simply supported edges under N_x loading. Assume that the plate has the same layup and dimensions as used in the previous example for pressure loading. The properties are for a carbon/epoxy laminate with a $[0_2/90_2/0_2/90_2]_s$ layup of AS4/3501-6, with properties of $E_1 = 127$ GPa (18.4 Msi), $E_2 = 11.0$ GPa (1.60 Msi), $G_{12} = 6.55$ GPa (0.95 Msi), and $v_{12} = 0.28$. A ply thickness of 0.127 mm (0.00500 in) was used, although the standard ply thickness is slightly higher than this. The dimensions of the plate were taken as $a = b = 254$ mm (10 in), with a total thickness of 2.032 mm (0.080 in). The plate bending stiffness coefficients are $D_{11} = 63.9$ N-m (564.9 in-lb), $D_{12} = 2.18$ N-m (19.25 in-lb), $D_{22} = 33.3$ N-m (294.3 in-lb), and $D_{66} = 4.58$ N-m (40.53 in-lb). Rearranging Eq. (6.51) for $N_y = 0$ gives

$$N_x = -\pi^2\left[D_{11}\left(\frac{m}{a}\right)^2 + 2(D_{12} + 2D_{66})\left(\frac{n}{b}\right)^2 + D_{22}\left(\frac{n}{b}\right)^4\left(\frac{a}{m}\right)^2\right]$$

It can be seen by inspection that because n only appears in the numerator, the value $n = 1$ gives the lowest critical load. However, because m appears in both the numerator and the denominator, the value of m to use is problem-dependent and must be established by calculating for the range of possible values. In the preceding problem, calculating for a range of m values shows that $m = 1$ gives the lowest critical load, with a value of $N_x = 18.33$ kN/m (104.6 lb/in). However, a plate with $b = 127$ mm (5 in) has the lowest load for $m = 2$ with $N_x = 73.3$ kN/m (418.4 lb/in), and a plate with $b = 63.5$ mm (2.5 in) has the lowest load for $m = 3$ with $N_x = 288$ kN/m

(1645 lb/in). It can be seen that the value of m for the critical load must be established by calculation. It can also be seen that, unlike the behavior of simple columns, the width has a strong effect on the load per unit width because of the effect of the boundary conditions on the $y = 0$ and $y = b$ edges.   ∎

6.7 PLATES WITH ONLY TWO SIMPLY SUPPORTED EDGES

The classical Navier solution is only applicable to situations in which all four edges of the plate are simply supported. This restriction on the boundary conditions can be relaxed to consider situations in which two opposite edges are simply supported and the other two edges may have other boundary conditions. The solution technique is called the "single series" approach, or the "Levy" solution [6.1]. The essential ideas are as follows.

Several slightly different but similar approaches are possible. Consider at first that the transverse pressure load has been expanded in a double Fourier series as given by Eq. (6.17). Consider a plate that is simply supported along $y = 0$ and $y = b$. Then assume a deflection in the form of

$$w(x,y) = \sum_{n=1}^{N} \phi_n(x) \sin \frac{n\pi y}{b} + \sum_{n=1}^{N} \sum_{m=1}^{M} A_{mn} \sin \frac{m\pi x}{a} \sin \frac{n\pi y}{b} \tag{6.52}$$

where the $\phi_n(x)$ functions are at present unknown. The second (double) series is the solution already obtained in Eqs. (6.18) to (6.20). This part of the solution solves the governing differential equation and fits the boundary conditions of simple support, but not the new boundary conditions at $x = 0$ and $x = a$ that are not those of simple support. Substituting this equation into the governing differential equation, Eq. (6.13), gives the homogeneous equation:

$$D_{11}\phi_n^{iv}(x) - 2(D_{12} + 2D_{66})\left(\frac{n\pi}{b}\right)^2 \phi_n''(x) + D_{22}\left(\frac{n\pi}{b}\right)^4 \phi_n(x) = 0 \tag{6.53}$$

To solve this equation, let

$$\phi_n(x) = \exp \frac{n\pi\lambda x}{b} \tag{6.54}$$

which results in the equation

$$D_{11}\lambda^4 - 2D_3\lambda^2 + D_{22} = 0 \tag{6.55}$$

where $D_3 = D_{12} + 2D_{66}$, with a solution

$$\lambda^2 = \frac{1}{D_{11}}[D_3 \pm (D_3^2 - D_{11}D_{22})^{1/2}] \tag{6.56}$$

The solution has three different forms, depending on the values of the plate stiffness constants. These cases are as follows.

Case 1. Roots Are Real and Unequal. The roots of Eq. (6.56) are then

$$\lambda = \pm\lambda_1, \pm\lambda_2 \tag{6.57}$$

and the solution is

$$\phi_n(x) = A_n \cosh \frac{n\pi\lambda_1 x}{b} + B_n \sinh \frac{n\pi\lambda_1 x}{b} + C_n \cosh \frac{n\pi\lambda_2 x}{b} + D_n \sinh \frac{n\pi\lambda_2 x}{b} \qquad (6.58)$$

Case 2. Roots Are Real and Equal. In this case, the solution is given by

$$\phi_n(x) = (A_n + B_n x) \cosh \frac{n\pi\lambda_1 x}{b} + (C_n + D_n x) \sinh \frac{n\pi\lambda_1 x}{b} \qquad (6.59)$$

Case 3. Roots Are Complex. In this case, let

$$\lambda_1 = \pm \left\{ \frac{1}{2} \left[\left(\frac{D_{22}}{D_{11}} \right)^{1/2} + \frac{D_3}{D_{11}} \right] \right\}^{1/2}$$

and

$$\lambda_2 = \pm \left\{ \frac{1}{2} \left[\left(\frac{D_{22}}{D_{11}} \right)^{1/2} - \frac{D_3}{D_{11}} \right] \right\}^{1/2} \qquad (6.60)$$

The solution is then given by

$$\phi_n(x) = \left(A_n \cos \frac{n\pi\lambda_2 x}{b} + B_n \sin \frac{n\pi\lambda_2 x}{b} \right) \cosh \frac{n\pi\lambda_1 x}{b}$$
$$+ \left(C_n \cos \frac{n\pi\lambda_2 x}{b} + D_n \sin \frac{n\pi\lambda_2 x}{b} \right) \sinh \frac{n\pi\lambda_1 x}{b} \qquad (6.61)$$

For all three cases, the four remaining constants are matched to the two boundary conditions at each of the $x = 0$ and $x = a$ edges.

In the example given previously for the Navier solution, the values used were $D_{11} = 63.9$ N-m (564.9 in-lb), $D_{12} = 2.18$ N-m (19.25 in-lb), $D_{22} = 33.3$ N-m (294.3 in-lb), and $D_{66} = 4.58$ N-m (40.53 in-lb). Substituting in Eq. (6.56) shows that there are complex roots, with values from Eq. (6.60) of $\lambda_1 = \pm 0.6706$ and $\lambda_2 = \pm 0.5216$, so that the solution is of the form of Eq. (6.61) of Case 3. Here the 1 direction is aligned with the x axis, and the edges at $y = 0$ and $y = b$ were simply supported. If, instead, the other two edges were simply supported, it would just amount to reversing the values of D_{11} and D_{22}. This would change the values of the roots, but they would still be in Case 3. An isotropic plate would give Case 2, that of repeated roots. Thus, a quasi-isotropic laminate with well-dispersed plies (so that the D matrix has similar behavior to the A matrix) would also be in Case 2.

Two common boundary conditions in addition to simply supported are free and clamped. The conditions on w for these are as follows.

Free.   The boundary condition on a free edge is given as (using an x edge, for example)

$$M_x = 0 \qquad \text{and} \qquad Q_x + \frac{\partial M_{xy}}{\partial y} = 0$$

which can be shown to be equivalent to

$$D_{11} \frac{\partial^2 w}{\partial x^2} + D_{12} \frac{\partial^2 w}{\partial y^2} = 0$$

and

$$D_{11} \frac{\partial^3 w}{\partial x^3} + (D_{12} + 4D_{66}) \frac{\partial^3 w}{\partial x \, \partial y^2} = 0 \qquad (6.62)$$

Clamped

$$w = 0 \quad \text{and} \quad \frac{dw}{dn} = 0 \tag{6.63}$$

As a specific example, consider that the plate is clamped on the edges $x = 0$ and $x = a$, and that the roots are complex, as in Case 3. The constants in Eq. (6.61) are determined from the boundary conditions at $x = 0$ and $x = a$. Using the first of the conditions in Eq. (6.63) gives

$$w(0,y) = 0 = \sum_n A_n \sin \frac{n\pi y}{b} \tag{6.64}$$

from which it is seen that

$$A_n = 0 \tag{6.65}$$

for all values of n. Similarly, the displacement condition at $x = a$ gives

$$B_n \sin (\alpha_{2n} a) \cosh (\alpha_{1n} a) + C_n \cos (\alpha_{2n} a) \sinh (\alpha_{1n} a) \tag{6.66}$$

$$+ \, D_n \sin (\alpha_{2n} a) \sinh (\alpha_{1n} a) = 0$$

where $\alpha_{1n} = n\pi\lambda_1/b$ and $\alpha_{2n} = n\pi\lambda_2/b$. Taking the derivative of Eq. (6.52) after substituting Eq. (6.61), and evaluating at $x = 0$ and $x = a$ gives the remaining two equations as

$$\alpha_{2n} B_n + \alpha_{1n} C_n = -R_n \tag{6.67}$$

$$B_n E_n + C_n F_n + D_n G_n = R_n \tag{6.68}$$

where

$$R_n = \sum_m A_{mn} \frac{m\pi}{a} \tag{6.69}$$

and

$$E_n = \alpha_{2n} \cos (\alpha_{2n} a) \cosh (\alpha_{1n} a) + \alpha_{1n} \sin (\alpha_{2n} a) \sinh (\alpha_{1n} a) \tag{6.70}$$

$$F_n = -\alpha_{2n} \sin (\alpha_{2n} a) \sinh (\alpha_{1n} a) + \alpha_{1n} \cos (\alpha_{2n} a) \cosh (\alpha_{1n} a) \tag{6.71}$$

$$G_n = \alpha_{2n} \cos (\alpha_{2n} a) \sinh (\alpha_{1n} a) + \alpha_{1n} \sin (\alpha_{2n} a) \cosh (\alpha_{1n} a) \tag{6.72}$$

These last four equations can be easily solved for the four coefficients of Eq. (6.61). Substituting into Eq. (6.52) then gives the displacement solution, and, by differentiating twice, the curvatures. Strains and stresses throughout the plate then can be solved by the usual procedures, as shown in the previous example.

For some problems, the pressure-distribution loading on the plate may be a function of one coordinate only, or can be taken as one function only as, for example, if the pressure is constant over the entire surface of the plate. In this case, the pressure distribution can be expressed as

$$p(x,y) = \sum_n B_{0n} \sin \frac{n\pi y}{b} \tag{6.73}$$

For this case, the assumed displacement can be taken as the single series part of Eq. (6.52), that is, assume

$$w(x,y) = \sum_{n=1}^{N} \phi_n(x) \sin \frac{n\pi y}{b} \tag{6.74}$$

Similar procedures to those described lead to the solution.

6.8. ENERGY METHODS FOR APPROXIMATE SOLUTIONS OF MECHANICS PROBLEMS FOR FIBER-COMPOSITE MATERIALS

There are a number of practical situations in which exact solutions to mechanics problems involving anisotropic materials are not available. It is very useful to consider approximate solutions, and energy methods are a principal method of obtaining these approximate solutions. Of the several energy theorems that are available, the theorem of minimum potential energy, used in the form of the Rayleigh–Ritz technique, is perhaps the most widely used and is particularly attractive for problems in anisotropic media. The theorem of minimum potential energy is described as follows.

6.8.1 Theorem of Minimum Potential Energy

Potential energy is defined as follows:

$$\pi_p = U + \Omega \tag{6.75}$$

where U is the strain energy, and Ω is the potential energy of the loads, given by

$$\Omega = -\sum F_i \delta_i - \int_V X_i u_i \, dV - \int_{S_\sigma} T_i u_i \, dS \tag{6.76}$$

where F_i are concentrated loads, X_i are body forces, and T_i are surface tractions, which are defined over that portion of the surface that is stress-prescribed.

The theorem states: "Among all admissible displacement fields of an elastic body, the actual configuration (that satisfies static equilibrium) makes the potential energy stationary with respect to small admissible variations of displacement."

A useful procedure that is based on the preceding is to assume displacement fields with unknown parameters and then minimize the potential energy with respect to these unknown parameters. This is often called the Ritz procedure, or the Rayleigh–Ritz procedure. The finite-element method for structural problems is almost always based on this procedure. The assumed displacement fields must satisfy the displacement boundary conditions.

6.8.2 Strain Energy for Fiber-Composite Plates

The first task is to obtain an expression for strain energy in terms of the *ABD* matrices of classical lamination theory. The strain energy can be written as

$$U = \frac{1}{2} \int_V \{\epsilon\}^T \{\sigma\} \, dV = \frac{1}{2} \int_A \left[\sum_k \int_{h_{k-1}}^{h_k} \{\epsilon\}^T [Q]_k \{\epsilon\} \, dz \right] dA \tag{6.77}$$

Carrying out the integral through the thickness, and using the usual A, B, and D definitions gives

$$U = \frac{1}{2} \int_A (\epsilon_0^T A \epsilon_0 + 2\epsilon_0^T B \kappa + \kappa^T D \kappa) \, dA \tag{6.78}$$

This expression for the strain energy then can be substituted into Eqs. (6.75) and (6.76).

6.8.3 Illustration of the Ritz Procedure for a Cantilever-Beam Problem

Consider the problem of a cantilever beam loaded by a concentrated force at the end. This problem is not special to fiber composites, but illustrates the techniques to be employed. For this one-dimensional problem, the potential energy can be written as

$$\pi_p = \frac{1}{2} \int_0^a EI(w'')^2 dx - Pw(a) \tag{6.79}$$

Select a series representation for the transverse displacement $w(x)$ with unknown coefficients as

$$w(x) = \sum_m A_m (1 - \cos \lambda_m x) \tag{6.80}$$

The displacement assumption must satisfy the displacement boundary conditions, which in this case are $w(0) = 0$ and $w'(0) = 0$. In addition, experience shows that convergence is faster if the displacements also satisfy the stress boundary conditions, or, in this case, $w''(a) = 0$. The essential displacement conditions are satisfied by Eq. (6.80) and the later condition can be accomplished if

$$\lambda_m = \frac{m\pi}{2a} \quad m = 1, 3, 5, \ldots \tag{6.81}$$

Substituting Eq. (6.80) into (6.79), taking the derivative with respect to A_k and setting equal to zero, and using orthogonality gives

$$A_k = \frac{Pa^3 2^5}{EI\pi^4 k^4} \tag{6.82}$$

Evaluating the preceding shows that convergence is very rapidly achieved for displacements. Using only one term gives a 1.5% error, and four terms reduces the error to 0.03%. The displacement solution would also be used to obtain the strains and stresses. In the present case, the moment calculated from the displacements can be compared to the moment obtained from equilibrium, because this happens to be a statically determinate problem. The convergence is much slower, with an eight-term series giving a 2.5% error. However, acceptable accuracy can be easily achieved.

6.9 USE OF BEAM FUNCTIONS IN RITZ SOLUTIONS FOR ANISOTROPIC PLATES

The Ritz method calls for assumed displacement fields with unknown coefficients that meet the displacement boundary conditions. Although not necessary, convergence is faster if the displacement functions also match the stress boundary conditions. Convergence is aided by selecting a series that has the property of completeness, that is, that the actual displacements can be represented by the assumed displacements if enough terms are taken. Several possibilities are available for these assumed displacement functions, such as trigonometric functions or polynomial functions. In this section, the use of so-called "beam functions" is illustrated. Beam functions are simply the mode shapes of beams vibrating at their natural frequencies. The actual physical basis of these functions is not important here, but rather their mathematical properties. These properties are that the functions automatically satisfy the boundary conditions of interest and form a complete series.

Beam functions have been widely used in the analysis of fiber-composite plates. However, there are two features of their use that cause some practical difficulties. The first is that whereas the functions themselves are orthogonal, not all combinations of derivatives are orthogonal. Thus, a system of equations must be solved to determine the unknown coefficients in the Ritz solution. The second problem is that a number of products of trigonometric and hyperbolic functions must be integrated, and all combinations of interest either must be programmed or evaluated numerically. Despite these difficulties, implementation is straightforward.

The assumed displacement functions for plates use a product of beam functions as

$$w(x,y) = \sum_n \sum_m A_{mn}\phi_m(x)\phi_n(y) \tag{6.83}$$

Beam functions are tabulated and can be just employed as mathematical functions, but it is instructive to see how they are derived. The equation for a beam under free vibration is

$$EI\frac{d^4w}{dx^4} = -\rho\frac{d^2w}{dt^2} \tag{6.84}$$

Assuming that the response varies sinusoidally in time as

$$w = \phi(x)\sin\omega t \tag{6.85}$$

gives

$$EI\phi^{iv} = \rho\omega^2\phi \tag{6.86}$$

with a solution

$$\phi_m(x) = A\sin\frac{\lambda_m x}{L} + B\cos\frac{\lambda_m x}{L} + C\sinh\frac{\lambda_m x}{L} + D\cosh\frac{\lambda_m x}{L} \tag{6.87}$$

where the constants are to be fitted to the boundary conditions. As an example, consider the case of a clamped-clamped beam. At the clamped end, the function and first derivative are zero. The boundary conditions at $x = 0$ give

$$B + D = 0 \quad \text{and} \quad A + C = 0 \tag{6.88}$$

and at $x = L$, the remaining conditions give (combined with the preceding)

$$\begin{bmatrix} (\sin\lambda_m - \sinh\lambda_m) & (\cos\lambda_m - \cosh\lambda_m) \\ (\cos\lambda_m - \cosh\lambda_m) & -(\sin\lambda_m + \sinh\lambda_m) \end{bmatrix}\begin{Bmatrix} A \\ B \end{Bmatrix} = \begin{Bmatrix} 0 \\ 0 \end{Bmatrix} \tag{6.89}$$

Setting the determinant of the coefficient matrix to zero (because the equations are homogeneous) gives

$$\cos\lambda_m\cosh\lambda_m = 1 \tag{6.90}$$

which gives the values for λ_m. These roots must be found numerically by a root-finding program. Equation (6.89) can be used to eliminate one of the constants, leaving one constant that is undetermined. The final expression is then given by

$$\phi_m(x) = (\cosh\lambda_m x/L - \cos\lambda_m x/L) - C_1(\sinh\lambda_m x/L - \sin\lambda_m x/L) \tag{6.91}$$

Table 6.1 Listing of Beam Functions

Type	Boundary Conditions	Frequency Equation	Eigenfunction $X_m(x)$	Roots of Frequency Equation λ_m
Clamped-clamped	$X(0) = X'(0) = 0$ $X(l) = X'(l) = 0$	$\cos \lambda \cosh \lambda = 1$	$J\left(\dfrac{\lambda_m x}{l}\right) - \dfrac{J(\lambda_m)}{H(\lambda_m)} H\left(\dfrac{\lambda_m x}{l}\right)$	$\lambda_1 = 4.7300$ $\lambda_2 = 7.8532$ $\lambda_3 = 10.9956$ $\lambda_4 = 14.1372$
Clamped-hinged	$X(0) = X'(0) = 0$ $X(l) = X''(0) = 0$	$\tan \lambda = \tanh \lambda$	$J\left(\dfrac{\lambda_m x}{l}\right) - \dfrac{J(\lambda_m)}{H(\lambda_m)} H\left(\dfrac{\lambda_m x}{l}\right)$	$\lambda_1 = 3.9266$ $\lambda_2 = 7.0686$ $\lambda_3 = 10.2102$ $\lambda_4 = 13.3518$
Clamped-free	$X(0) = X'(0) = 0$ $X''(l) = X'''(l) = 0$	$\cos \lambda \cosh \lambda = -1$	$J\left(\dfrac{\lambda_m x}{l}\right) - \dfrac{G(\lambda_m)}{F(\lambda_m)} H\left(\dfrac{\lambda_m x}{l}\right)$	$\lambda_1 = 1.8751$ $\lambda_2 = 4.6941$ $\lambda_3 = 7.8548$ $\lambda_4 = 10.9955$
Hinged-hinged	$X(0) = X''(0) = 0$ $X(l) = X''(l) = 0$	$\sin \lambda = 0$	$\sin \dfrac{m \pi x}{l}$	$\lambda_m = mx$
Free-free	$X''(0) = X'''(0) = 0$ $X''(l) = X'''(l) = 0$	$\cos \lambda \cosh \lambda = 1$	$G\left(\dfrac{\lambda_m x}{l}\right) - \dfrac{J(\lambda_m)}{H(\lambda_m)} F\left(\dfrac{\lambda_m x}{l}\right)$	Same as for clamped-clamped beam
Free-hinged	$X''(0) = X'''(0) = 0$ $X(l) = X''(l) = 0$	$\tan \lambda = \tanh \lambda$	$G\left(\dfrac{\lambda_m x}{l}\right) - \dfrac{G(\lambda_m)}{F(\lambda_m)} F\left(\dfrac{\lambda_m x}{l}\right)$	Same as for clamped-hinged beam

Natural frequencies and mode shapes for uniform beams: $v(x,t) = X_m(x) \sin w_m t$

Frequency: $\omega_m = \dfrac{\lambda_m^2}{l^2} \sqrt{\dfrac{EI}{\overline{m}}}$

where EI is the bending stiffness, $\overline{m}$ is the mass/unit length, and l is the length of beam.

Notation used:

$F(u) = \sinh u + \sin u$
$G(u) = \cosh u + \cos u$
$H(u) = \sinh u - \sin u$
$J(u) = \cosh u - \cos u$

where $u = \lambda_m x/l$, or $u = \lambda_m$.

where

$$C_1 = \frac{\cosh \lambda_m - \cos \lambda_m}{\sinh \lambda_m - \sin \lambda_m} \qquad (6.92)$$

The solutions for other boundary conditions are found in the same way.

The beam functions have some orthogonality properties. It can be shown that

$$\int_0^L \phi_m(x)\phi_n(x)\, dx = 0 \qquad \text{unless } m = n \qquad (6.93)$$

that is, the functions are orthogonal. Similarly, it can be shown that

$$\int_0^L \phi_m''(x)\phi_n''(x)\, dx = 0 \qquad \text{unless } m = n \tag{6.94}$$

and

$$\int_0^L \phi_m^{iv}(x)\phi_n(x)\, dx = 0 \qquad \text{unless } m = n \tag{6.95}$$

Unfortunately, other combinations of derivatives do not display orthogonality. Thus, the equation involved in the Ritz procedure, obtained by minimizing the potential energy with respect to the unknown coefficients, involves more than one coefficient. Thus, a system of equations must be solved to determine these coefficients.

Table 6.1 gives a listing of beam functions, along with some values for the roots.

6.10 CLOSURE

This chapter has presented an overview of the governing equations for orthotropic plates under various loads, including the equations that include transverse shear deformation. The analysis of composite plates has been well reported in the literature, and other results and descriptions of methods of solution can be found in the literature for those needing a more extensive coverage.

REFERENCES

6.1 Timoshenko, S., and S. Woinowsky-Krieger, *Theory of Plates and Shells*, 2d ed (New York: McGraw-Hill, 1959).

6.2 Gould, P. L., *Analysis of Shells and Plates* (New York: Springer-Verlag, 1988).

6.3 Vinson, J. R., *Structural Mechanics: The Behavior of Plates and Shells* (New York: Wiley, 1974).

6.4 Lekhnitskii, S. G., *Anisotropic Plates* (New York: Gordon and Breach, 1968).

6.5 Whitney, J. M., *Structural Analysis of Laminated Anisotropic Plates* (Lancaster, Pennsylvania: Technomic Publishing, 1987).

6.6 Vinson, J. R., and R. L. Sierakowski, *The Behavior of Structures Composed of Composite Materials* (Dordrecht: Martinus Nijhoff, 1987).

6.7 Pagano, N. J., "Exact Solutions for Composite Laminates in Cylindrical Bending," *J. Composite Mater.* 3 (1969): 398–411.

6.8 Engblom, J. J., and O. O. Ochoa, "Through-the-Thickness Stress Predictions for Laminated Plates of Advanced Composite Materials," *Int. J. Numer. Meth. Eng.* 21 (1985): 1759–1776.

6.9 Whitney, J. M., "Shear Correction Factors for Orthotropic Laminates Under Static Loading," *J. Appl. Mech.* 40 (1973): 302–304.

PROBLEMS

6.1. Show in detail the steps leading from Eqs. (6.1) to (6.13).

6.2. Show that Eq. (6.18) satisfies the governing equation and boundary conditions for a simply supported rectangular plate.

6.3. Consider the example problem given in the text of pressure loading a simply supported plate. The 0° plies are in the x direction. Answer the following, and compare with the answers given in the text.

(a) Calculate the displacement at the center of the plate for various numbers of terms.

(b) Calculate the stress σ_x at the top and bottom surfaces at the center of the plate, normalized by the applied pressure, for various number of terms.

(c) Plot the stress σ_x at the top surface of the plate at $x = a/2$, $b/2 < y < b$. Do this only for a number of terms that you feel comfortable with, from the results of part (b).

6.4. Draw a sketch indicating the relationship between β, dw/dy, and γ_{yz} for shear-deformable plate theory.

6.5. Draw a diagram showing the vector forces on the surface of an element resulting from τ_{xz} and τ_{yz}. From this, derive the transformation equation, Eq. (6.30).

6.6. Substitute Eqs. (6.29) and (6.30) to derive Eq. (6.31). Also give a specific definition for A_{44} and A_{55} of Eq. (6.32).

6.7. Substitute Eqs. (6.35) and (6.36) into Eq. (6.34) and verify that the result is indeed Eqs. (6.37) and (6.38).

6.8. Give expressions that indicate how you would calculate stresses in the plies of a plate using shear-deformable plate theory, assuming that you have calculated w, α, and β.

6.9. Consider the problem of buckling of a plate that is simply supported on all four edges and loaded by a stress resultant N_x.

(a) Give the governing differential equation that is to be solved for the buckling problem.

(b) Give the appropriate displacement assumptions that will satisfy the boundary conditions.

(c) Derive an expression for the critical load by substituting b into a.

(d) Carry out the analysis for the material properties given in Example 6.2 for $a = 250$ mm (10 in), and $b = 50$, 150, and 250 mm (2, 6, and 10 in).

6.10. Compute answers for the cantilever-beam problem loaded by a uniformly distributed load using the Ritz procedure. Compare the maximum deflection determined by the energy method with the usual beam-theory "exact" solution. Also compare the moment computed from the displacements with the exact moment. Give the percent error in both peak displacement and peak moment as a function of the number of terms in the displacement series.

6.11. Derive an expression for potential energy of a plate. Use the classical lamination theory that neglects transverse deformation, considers only isothermal conditions, and considers only symmetric laminates for simplicity. Write the potential energy as a matrix expression in terms of the D matrix, the curvatures, transverse deflection w, and normal pressure loading.

6.12. Derive in full detail the expression for the strain energy of a nonsymmetric plate in terms of the A, B, and D matrices and the center-line strains and curvatures.

6.13. Develop the equations to be used in solving for the displacements and stresses in a symmetric orthotropic plate under uniform normal pressure loading, with clamped boundary conditions on all four edges.

6.14. Sketch the solution process involved in using the potential energy theorem to solve plate buckling problems for more general boundary conditions than the simply supported case that we treated previously using classical techniques.

6.15. Consider a carbon/epoxy plate with a $[45_2/0_2]_s$ layup that measures 25 by 200 mm (1 by 8 in) and is loaded as a cantilever beam with a concentrated load at the end. Work out "beam-type" expressions for the deflection and the twist as a function of position measured from the clamped end.

6.16. Consider the problem of pressure loading of a plate with pinned edges, solved previously with the Navier solution, but now add the D_{16} and D_{26} terms.
(a) Derive the governing differential equation, that is, add the coupling terms.
(b) The displacement assumption used for the Navier solution satisfied the boundary conditions and also satisfied the governing differential equation. Can the new equation of part (a) still be solved by this assumption? Why or why not?

6.17. Consider the problem of obtaining an approximate solution to Problem 6.16, the simply supported, transversely loaded plate with D_{16} and D_{26} coupling.
(a) Write an expression for the strain energy, including the coupling terms.
(b) Can the displacement assumption of the Navier solution be used with the Ritz procedure to get an approximate solution for the coupled problem? Show why or why not, but do not carry out the steps to get a solution.

6.18. Consider the problem of obtaining an approximate solution to the problem of a transversely loaded plate with clamped boundary conditions on all four edges with D_{16} and D_{26} coupling. Could the "beam functions" be used as a displacement assumption in the Ritz procedure to include the coupling terms? Show why or why not, but do not carry out the steps to get a solution.

7

Analysis of Laminated Beams

7.1 INTRODUCTION

Fiber composites are often used in the form of beam structures, because beams are common in applications. The analysis of beams follows the basic fundamentals as usually presented in strength-of-materials texts for isotropic materials, but involves important differences. The formulas that are developed here for stiffness and stress distributions are of quite different forms for composites than for isotropic beams. Fiber-composite beams are constructed by various methods, including lamination, use of fiber preforms with resin injection, pultrusion, and even filament winding. Lamination theory can be used as a basis for the analysis procedures for all of these types of beams.

An important issue in beam theory for laminated beams is that whereas the slender shape of a beam is sufficient to ensure uniaxial stress for isotropic beams, that is not the case for many practical fiber-composite laminated beams. The difficulty is that the width of individual ply groups is typically not small with respect to the ply group thickness, as illustrated in Figure 7.1. Thus, the individual ply groups are in a condition of biaxial stress. It is straightforward to take account of these effects by including elements of classical lamination theory along with suitable "beam-type" assumptions, however, and this is demonstrated in the following. The refinement of transverse shear deformation in the beam can be readily included.

A number of interesting topics dealing with laminated beams such as shear center and bending–twisting coupling have been reported in the literature [7.1, 7.2]. These topics are not discussed further here. Rather the emphasis is placed on the implications of lamination on the basic ideas of determining stiffness and stress distributions in beams.

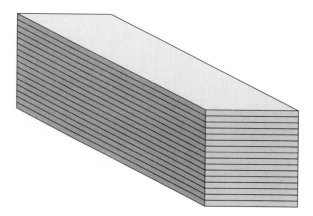

Figure 7.1 A laminated beam showing that the aspect ratio of individual plies can be much different than the aspect ratio of the overall beam cross-section.

7.2 BEAM ANALYSIS FUNDAMENTALS

The basic ideas of beam analysis as applied to isotropic beams serve as the foundation for laminated beams as well. These ideas can be listed as follows:

1. Moment loading is one-dimensional.
2. Axial force is zero.
3. Axial strain distributions are determined by plane sections remaining plane. Transverse shear deformations with constant shear angle across the cross-section can be included for a more refined theory.

The essential feature that must be added to this list when considering laminated beams is that the stress distribution within the individual plies is two-dimensional, not uni-axial. This affects the stiffness of the beam and is particularly significant in calculating stress distributions within the beam. It is straightforward to include these effects in a consistent theory for laminated beams, as is illustrated in the following.

The basic procedure to be followed is to first use the lamination theory relationships as developed in Chapter 3 to calculate an effective EI product for the laminated beam. The maximum moment and curvature are then found using usual procedures for statically determinate or indeterminate beams. The two-dimensional strain distributions are then obtained, and strain and stress distributions are calculated for the individual plies using lamination theory. The sign conventions to be used in the following are shown in Figure 7.2. Sign conventions used in beam analysis vary in different references. However, the conventions to be followed here have been selected to be compatible with lamination theory—which is, of course, essential for composite beams—and also are consistent with the usual theory of laminated plates as outlined in Chapter 6.

The deflection equation for the beam with this sign convention becomes

$$EI \frac{d^2w}{dx^2} = -M_{\text{beam}} \tag{7.1}$$

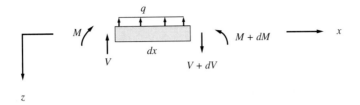

Figure 7.2 Sign conventions used for beam analysis.

The symbol used for curvature in Chapters 3 and 6 has been defined as

$$\kappa_x = -\frac{\partial^2 w}{\partial x^2} \tag{7.2}$$

so that the moment-curvature relation becomes

$$EI\kappa_x = M_{\text{beam}} \tag{7.3}$$

As will be explained fully, the moment for beams is defined for the entire width of the beam, and the moments used in lamination theory (and plate theory) are defined on a per unit width basis. When there is a chance to confuse these two definitions, the notation is explicit. Other beam sign conventions that follow from Figure 7.2 are

$$\frac{dM}{dx} = V \quad \text{and} \quad \frac{dV}{dx} = q \tag{7.4}$$

It should be noted that perhaps the most familiar result of conventional isotropic beam theory, the formula for stress distribution throughout the cross-section, given by

$$\sigma = \frac{Mz}{I}$$

does not hold for composite beams. The reason is simply that the formula is based on uniformly varying stress distributions, whereas the stresses in composite beams can be very nonuniform because of the changes in material properties from layer to layer. Similar situations occur in reinforced-concrete beams and other areas often encountered in introductions to strength of materials.

In the following, expressions for stiffness and stress distributions are developed for rectangular beams, followed by a discussion of these topics for I-beams.

7.3 SYMMETRIC RECTANGULAR BEAMS

Consider the beam with rectangular cross-section shown in Figure 7.3. Beams are often constructed with a symmetric shape and layup, and this case is considered first because it is the most common. Rectangular beams that are not symmetric about a midplane tend to show distortion with thermal effects, much like a bimetallic strip, and thus distort with temperature changes, such as when cooled from an elevated temperature cure to ambient temperature. Thus, symmetric shapes are usually used to avoid this problem. For simplicity, only a balanced layup is considered, so that twisting effects can be ignored. It may be recalled that a balanced layup ensures that the A_{16} and A_{26} terms vanish, and D_{16} and D_{26} ap-

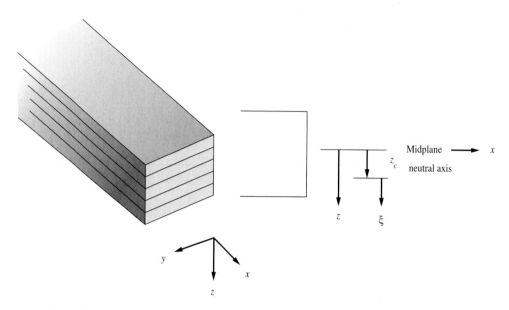

Figure 7.3 A rectangular laminated beam with laminations parallel to the neutral axis and notation for position in the cross-section.

proximately vanish when the plies are either well dispersed or are composed entirely of $0°$ and $90°$ layups. In the following, it is assumed that A_{16}, A_{26}, D_{16}, and D_{26} all vanish.

The beam to be discussed is subjected to loads transverse to the plies (in the z direction), so that the plies are parallel to the neutral axis of the beam, as illustrated in Figure 7.3. This loading direction is typical of many composite beams, but loading in a direction parallel to the plies is discussed in a later section dealing with laminated I-beams.

As with isotropic beams, in composite beams the strain distribution is taken to be linear. However, because the fibers in general have different orientations in the different plies or layers, the stiffnesses are quite different and the stress distributions do not follow the linearly varying strain distributions, but have discontinuous jumps in stress from one layer to the next. Thus, elements of lamination theory must be combined with beam theory.

The usual starting point of beam theory for rectangular composite beams is the relationship developed previously in Eq. (3.16a):

$$\begin{Bmatrix} M_x \\ M_y \\ M_{xy} \end{Bmatrix} = [D] \begin{Bmatrix} \kappa_x \\ \kappa_y \\ \kappa_{xy} \end{Bmatrix} \tag{3.16a}$$

It should be noted that the moment resultants in this equation are on a unit width basis, and must be multiplied by the width of the beam to get the total moment used in beam theory.

Two cases must now be distinguished, which can be referred to as narrow beams and wide beams, with the latter acting essentially as plates. Wide and narrow refer to the aspect ratio of the cross-section, that is, the ratio of the cross-section width to height. The differ-

Narrow-beam   Wide-beam
cross-section   cross-section

Figure 7.4 Illustration of anticlastic effect in narrow and wide beams showing the distortion of the cross-section.

ence between these two cases lies in the "anticlastic" effect, which refers to the transverse distortion of the beam. Consider an isotropic beam for simplicity, and in particular consider the transverse shape caused by the Poisson effect. The axial strain distributions give rise to a distortion of the cross-section in the transverse direction because of the Poisson effect. An illustration of this distortion is given in Figure 7.4. A wide beam, acting essentially as a plate, does not show this effect except at the outer edges of the cross-section, as illustrated also in the figure.

The two cases can be described mathematically by setting the transverse moment $M_y = 0$ for the narrow-beam case, and the transverse curvature $\kappa_y = 0$ for the wide-beam case. The moment-curvature relations can thus be written as follows.

Narrow beams

$$M_y = M_{xy} = 0$$

$$\begin{Bmatrix} \kappa_x \\ \kappa_y \\ \kappa_{xy} \end{Bmatrix} = [D^{-1}] \begin{Bmatrix} M_x \\ 0 \\ 0 \end{Bmatrix} = \begin{bmatrix} D_{11}^{-1} & D_{12}^{-1} & 0 \\ D_{21}^{-1} & D_{22}^{-1} & 0 \\ 0 & 0 & D_{33}^{-1} \end{bmatrix} \begin{Bmatrix} M_x \\ 0 \\ 0 \end{Bmatrix} \tag{7.5}$$

and the overall moment-curvature relationship for the beam can be written as

$$M_{\text{beam}} = bM_x = \frac{b}{D_{11}^{-1}} \kappa_x = \overline{EI}\kappa_x \tag{7.6}$$

so that for the narrow beam,

$$\overline{EI} = \frac{b}{D_{11}^{-1}} \tag{7.7}$$

and the effective EI for the beam is related to the reciprocal of the inverse bending stiffness from lamination theory. Here b is defined as the width of the cross-section.

Wide beams

$$\kappa_y = \kappa_{xy} = 0$$

$$\begin{Bmatrix} M_x \\ M_y \\ 0 \end{Bmatrix} = [D] \begin{Bmatrix} \kappa_x \\ 0 \\ 0 \end{Bmatrix} = \begin{bmatrix} D_{11} & D_{12} & 0 \\ D_{21} & D_{22} & 0 \\ 0 & 0 & D_{33} \end{bmatrix} \begin{Bmatrix} \kappa_x \\ 0 \\ 0 \end{Bmatrix} \tag{7.8}$$

and the overall moment-curvature relationship for the beam can be written as

$$M_{\text{beam}} = bM_x = bD_{11}\kappa_x = \overline{EI}\kappa_x \tag{7.9}$$

so that for the wide beam,

$$\overline{EI} = bD_{11} \tag{7.10}$$

where again b is the width of the cross-section of the beam, and the effective EI for the beam is related to the bending stiffness from lamination theory. The relationships given are also used in the following to obtain the stress distributions within the plies or layers of the beam.

The effective EI now can be used to solve for the deflection in fiber-composite beams using the same procedures as in the usual isotropic beam theory. For example, deflections can be obtained from tables developed for isotropic beams, or by using integration of the differential equation, noting again that

$$\kappa_x = -\frac{d^2 w}{dx^2} \tag{7.11}$$

The locations of the maximum moment are found from equilibrium, as usual for isotropic beams. The reactions in statically indeterminate beams are also obtained using procedures similar to those for isotropic beams using the effective EI, as required. Once the maximum moment is obtained, the stresses in the various plies or layers can be obtained by the relationships that follow.

The curvature in the x direction and the strain in the x direction are calculated from

$$\kappa_x = \frac{M_{\text{beam}}}{EI} \tag{7.12}$$

and

$$\epsilon_x = z\kappa_x \tag{7.13}$$

The transverse strain can be calculated from the preceding equations, again distinguishing between the narrow and wide beams.

Narrow beams

$$\kappa_y = D_{21}^{-1}M_x = \frac{D_{21}^{-1}}{D_{11}^{-1}}\kappa_x \tag{7.14}$$

and

$$\epsilon_y = z\kappa_y \tag{7.15}$$

Wide beams

$$\epsilon_y = 0 = \kappa_y \tag{7.16}$$

The strains then must be transformed into the fiber directions for the plies of interest, using the usual relations of Chapter 2, given as

$$\begin{Bmatrix} \epsilon_1 \\ \epsilon_2 \\ \gamma_{12} \end{Bmatrix} = [R][T][R^{-1}]\begin{Bmatrix} \epsilon_x \\ \epsilon_y \\ 0 \end{Bmatrix} \tag{2.23a}$$

and the fiber-direction stresses in the ply of interest are obtained from the lamina stress–strain law, given in Eq. (2.14) as

$$\left\{ \begin{array}{c} \sigma_1 \\ \sigma_2 \\ \tau_{12} \end{array} \right\} = [Q] \left\{ \begin{array}{c} \epsilon_1 \\ \epsilon_2 \\ \gamma_{12} \end{array} \right\} \tag{2.14}$$

The use of these relationships is illustrated in the following examples.

EXAMPLE 7.1   Stresses in a rectangular beam

The laminated composite beam to be considered is made of 24 plies of AS4/3501-6 carbon/epoxy, with a $[0_4/45_4/-45_4]$s layup. In practice, the plies are likely to be more interspersed, but this layup is used for illustration. The beam is simply supported at the ends and subject to a uniformly distributed load q, as shown in Figure 7.5. The desired answers are the deflection at the midpoint and the stresses in the individual plies. The data for the problem are summarized as follows:

Length $L = 254$ mm (10 in)

Width $b = 12.7$ mm (0.5 in)

Thickness $t = 3.150$ mm (0.124 in)

Distributed loading $q = 380$ N/m (2.17 lb/in)

Solution: The width-to-thickness aspect ratio of this beam is probably intermediate between the narrow and wide cases discussed before. Both assumptions are used to illustrate the difference. The general procedure for both is to first calculate an effective EI for the beam, calculate the curvature from the maximum moment, use the curvature to find the strain distribution through the thickness, and then use the stress–strain law and the transformation equations to find the stresses in the individual plies. The effective EI is also used to find the deflection.

The moment and shear diagrams are found from statics using the same procedures as for isotropic beams. The result is that the moment is maximum at the center, with a value given by $M_x = qL^2/8$. Also from the usual strength-of-materials formulas for beam deflections,

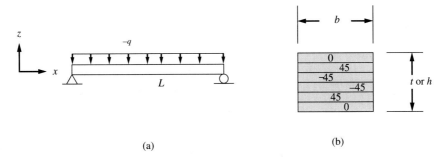

(a)   (b)

Figure 7.5   For Example 7.1, (a) laminated beam and loading (q is positive upward) and (b) cross-section showing the ply groups (not to scale).

the maximum deflection is at the center of the beam and is given by $\delta = 5qL^4/384EI$. The next step is to find an effective EI for the composite beam, using the D and D^{-1} matrices defined in Eq. (3.19) as

$$D_{ij} = \sum_{k=1}^{N} (\overline{Q}_{ij})_k \frac{h_k^3 - h_{k-1}^3}{3} \tag{3.19}$$

This computation and others can be carried out using the accompanying software, or other equivalent software. The result for the present layup is

$$D = \begin{bmatrix} 272 & 29.2 & 17.2 \\ 29.2 & 54.4 & 17.2 \\ 17.2 & 17.2 & 38.3 \end{bmatrix} \text{N-m} = \begin{bmatrix} 2410 & 258.3 & 152.2 \\ 258.3 & 481.7 & 152.2 \\ 152.2 & 152.2 & 339.1 \end{bmatrix} \text{lb-in}$$

and

$$D^{-1} = \begin{bmatrix} 3.93 & -1.805 & .952 \\ -1.805 & 22.3 & 9.18 \\ .952 & 9.18 & 30.7 \end{bmatrix} 10^{-3} \text{ (N-m)}^{-1} = \begin{bmatrix} 4.436 & -2.039 & -1.076 \\ -2.039 & 25.23 & -10.37 \\ -1.076 & -10.37 & 34.63 \end{bmatrix} 10^{-4} \text{ (lb-in)}^{-1}$$

Effective EI for narrow beams.   The effective EI for narrow beams is taken from Eq. (7.7) and uses the D^{-1} matrix. The result is

$$EI_{\text{eff,narrow}} = 3.23 \text{ N-m}^2 \text{ (1127 lb-in}^2)$$

Effective EI for wide beams.   The effective EI for wide beams is taken from Eq. (7.10) and uses the D matrix. The result is

$$EI_{\text{eff,wide}} = 3.46 \text{ N-m}^2 \text{ (1205 lb-in}^2)$$

The difference between the two estimates of the beam stiffness differ by about 7%. The difference in stiffness between the two cases is a familiar result for isotropic materials (see, e.g., [7.3]), and results there from replacing E in beam theory with $E/(1-\nu^2)$ in plate theory. The maximum deflection is then obtained by using this effective EI in isotropic beam formulas, obtaining the following:

Narrow beam:

$$\sigma = 6.38 \text{ mm (0.251 in)}$$

Wide beam:

$$\sigma = 5.97 \text{ mm (0.235 in)}$$

Stresses in the plies.   The values for stresses in the plies are then related to the moment by first calculating the curvature, from this finding the strain distribution in the beam, and finally obtaining the stresses in the individual plies from the strains.

The maximum curvature in the axial direction is found from Eq. (7.12). The axial strain is then obtained from Eq. (7.13) using the z (distance from the midplane) values of interest. The transverse strain is found from Eq. (7.14) and (7.15) for narrow beams, and Eq. (7.16) for wide beams. By taking the in-plane shear strain in the axial and transverse beam coordinates to be 0, the strain distribution through the cross-section of the beam is determined. The strains in the direction of the fibers for the plies are then found from Eq. (2.23a) and the stresses in the fiber coordinates from Eq. (2.14). The results follow for locations at the farthest distance away from the center line for each of the three-ply groups.

Narrow-beam assumption:

Ply Group	z mm (in)	ϵ_x %	ϵ_y %	σ_1 MPa (ksi)	σ_2 MPa (ksi)	τ_{12} MPa (ksi)
45	0.528 (0.0208)	0.050	−0.0230	17.7 (2.57)	1.92 (0.279)	4.78 (0.694)
−45	1.057 (0.0416)	0.1	−0.0460	35.4 (5.13)	3.85 (0.558)	−9.58(−1.39)
0	1.585 (0.0624)	0.150	−0.0690	190 (27.5)	−2.99 (−0.434)	0 (0)

Wide-beam assumption:

Ply Group	z mm (in)	ϵ_x %	ϵ_y %	σ_1 MPa (ksi)	σ_2 MPa (ksi)	τ_{12} MPa (ksi)
45	0.528 (0.0208)	0.047	0	30.6 (4.44)	3.32 (0.482)	3.06 (0.444)
−45	1.057 (0.0416)	0.094	0	61.2 (8.88)	6.65 (0.965)	−6.13 (−0.889)
0	1.585 (0.0624)	0.140	0	179 (26.0)	4.36 (0.633)	0 (0)

It is important to note that the stress distribution is very nonuniform across the cross-section, because of the change in stiffness properties with the different angular orientation of the plies. A plot of the axial stress for the wide-beam assumption is shown in Figure 7.6. In general, the isotropic beam formula for stress does not give acceptable accuracy. In the present case, the prediction of the maximum stress is low by about 60%.   ■

Another important application area lies in the use of composite sandwich beams. Sandwich construction using either honeycomb or foam cores have significant advantages in bending situations. All of the theory illustrated before can be easily applied to sandwich beams. The following example gives some details.

EXAMPLE 7.2   Stresses in a rectangular sandwich composite beam

A laminated composite sandwich beam to be considered is made of 24 plies of AS4/3501-6 carbon/epoxy, with two layers of $[0_2/45_2/-45_2]s$ layup bonded to a 6.35-mm (0.25-in) core. The beam is simply supported at the ends and subject to a uniformly distributed load q, as shown in Figure 7.7. The desired answers are the deflection at the midpoint and the stresses in the individual plies. The data for the problem are summarized as follows:

Length L = 508 mm (20 in)

Width b = 50.8 mm (2.0 in)

Sandwich core thickness = 6.35 mm (0.25 in)

Total thickness = 9.52 mm (0.3748 in)

Distributed loading q = 1401 N/m (8.0 lb/in)

Solution: The width-to-thickness aspect ratio of this beam makes it not obviously narrow or wide, and it is probably intermediate between the narrow- and wide-beam assumptions discussed earlier. As in the previous example, the moment and shear diagrams are found from statics to get the maximum moment at the center, given by $M_x = qL^2/8$ and the maximum deflection at the center of the beam given by $\delta = 5qL^4/384EI$. The next step is

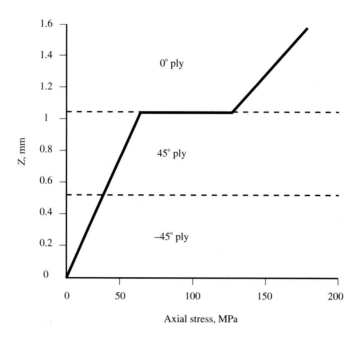

Figure 7.6   For Example 7.1, plot of axial stress in $[0/\pm45]_s$ laminated beam across the beam cross-section showing nonuniform axial stress.

to find an effective EI for the composite beam using the D and D^{-1} matrices defined in Eq. (3.19), as

$$D_{ij} = \sum_{k=1}^{N} (\overline{Q}_{ij})_k \frac{h_k^3 - h_{k-1}^3}{3} \qquad (3.19)$$

This computation and others can be carried out using the software available on the web (see Appendix), or other equivalent software. For practical purposes, the stiffness of the sandwich core itself does not add a significant amount to the overall beam stiffness, but just changes the location of the composite skins. Thus, it is not necessary to have precise values for the core moduli. Any low values of modulus work, although using 0 often gives numeri-

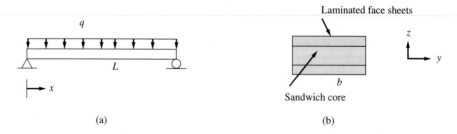

Figure 7.7   Sandwich beam with laminated face sheets.

cal problems, depending on the software employed. In the present case, a foam core is being considered, which is taken as an isotropic material with tensile modulus $E = 1000$ psi, shear modulus $G = 417$ psi, and Poisson ratio of 0.2. If the computer program available for use with this text is employed, these values can be used with the "user-supplied-material" option. The result for the D matrix is

$$D = \begin{bmatrix} 3620 & 1047 & 4.30 \\ 1047 & 1620 & 4.30 \\ 4.30 & 4.30 & 1220 \end{bmatrix} \text{N-m} = \begin{bmatrix} 32010 & 9271 & 38.05 \\ 9271 & 14360 & 38.05 \\ 38.05 & 38.05 & 10800 \end{bmatrix} \text{lb-in}$$

The effective EI for narrow and wide beams is taken from Eqs. (7.7) and (7.10) using the D^{-1} matrix and the D matrix, respectively. The result is

$$EI_{\text{eff,narrow}} = 149.4 \text{ N-m}^2 \ (52{,}060 \text{ lb-in}^2)$$

$$EI_{\text{eff,wide}} = 183.7 \text{ N-m}^2 \ (64{,}030 \text{ lb-in}^2)$$

It can be noted by comparing this result with that given in the previous example that the sandwich construction gives a significant improvement in stiffness. The beams illustrated in these two examples have the same amount of composite material and would weigh nearly the same per unit surface area, because the lightweight core adds little to the overall weight. It is also interesting to note that the two estimates for the beam stiffness differ significantly, with the narrow-beam assumption giving a 19% lower estimate. If closer bounds to the stiffness are important, finite-element or other numerical schemes with three-dimensional elasticity theory must be employed to give more accurate answers.

The maximum deflection is then obtained by using the effective EI in the isotropic beam formula, obtaining the following:

Narrow beam:
$$\sigma = 8.13 \text{ mm (0.320 in)}$$

Wide beam:
$$\sigma = 6.60 \text{ mm (0.260 in)}$$

Stresses in the plies.   The values for stresses in the plies are then related to the moment by use of the same procedures involved in the preceding example, that is, by first calculating the curvature and then finding the strain distribution in the beam, and finally obtaining the stresses in the individual plies from the strains.

The maximum curvature in the axial direction is found from Eq. (7.12). The axial strain is then obtained from Eq. (7.13) using the z (distance from the midplane) values of interest. The transverse strain is found from Eq. (7.14) and (7.15) for narrow beams, and Eq. (7.16) for wide beams. By taking the in-plane shear strain in the axial and transverse beam coordinates to be 0, the strain distribution through the cross-section of the beam is determined. The strains in the direction of the fibers for the plies are then found from Eq. (2.23a) and the stresses in the fiber coordinates from Eq. (2.14). The results follow for locations at the farthest distance away from the center line for each of outer three-ply groups, and the axial stress is shown plotted in Figure 7.8 for the wide-beam assumption. ∎

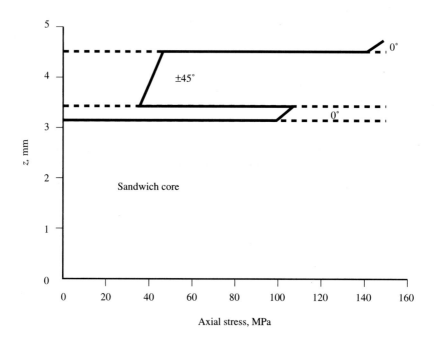

Figure 7.8 Axial stress in a sandwich beam under bending load with two $[0_2/45_2/-45_2]$s face sheets. The plies have different axial stiffness because of the fiber orientations, and carry different axial loads.

Narrow-beam assumption:

Ply Group	z mm (in)	ϵ_x %	ϵ_y %	σ_1 MPa (ksi)	σ_2 MPa (ksi)	τ_{12} MPa (ksi)
−45	4.23 (0.1666)	0.128	−0.083	29.7 (4.31)	3.23 (0.468)	13.8 (2.00)
45	4.50 (0.1770)	0.136	−0.088	31.6 (4.58)	3.43 (0.497)	−14.7 (−2.13)
0	4.76 (0.1874)	0.144	−0.093	181.3 (26.3)	−5.84 (−0.847)	0 (0)

Wide-beam assumption:

Ply Group	z mm (in)	ϵ_x %	ϵ_y %	σ_1 MPa (ksi)	σ_2 MPa (ksi)	τ_{12} MPa (ksi)
−45	4.23 (0.1666)	0.104	0	68.1 (9.88)	7.38 (1.07)	6.82 (0.989)
45	4.50 (0.1770)	0.111	0	72.4 (10.5)	7.86 (1.14)	−7.24 (−1.05)
0	4.76 (0.1874)	0.117	0	150 (21.7)	3.64 (0.528)	0 (0)

7.4 NONSYMMETRIC RECTANGULAR BEAMS

Laminated beams are usually made with a symmetric layup, because cooldown of nonsymmetric beams from an elevated cure temperature results in warping. For thin beams, this warping can be pronounced and can make the beam unacceptable. There are special situations when nonsymmetric beams are used, however, and a theory for these cases is developed here. For example, the lamination may be accomplished with room-temperature-cure adhesives, and so if the part is always used at room temperature, there will be no thermal distortion. Another case could involve sandwich beams that have face sheets of unequal thickness that are symmetric by themselves, and are cured to the core in a secondary bonding operation.

For nonsymmetric beams, the neutral axis does not lie at the geometric center line. A coordinate system is illustrated in Figure 7.3, with z denoting the position with respect to the center line, and ξ measured from the neutral axis. The z value at the neutral axis is denoted by z_c. Again the cases of narrow beams and wide beams are distinguished.

7.4.1 Narrow Nonsymmetric Beams

Consider the usual *ABD* relationship given in Chapter 3 as

$$\begin{Bmatrix} N \\ M \end{Bmatrix} = \begin{bmatrix} A & B \\ B & D \end{bmatrix} \begin{Bmatrix} \epsilon_0 \\ \kappa \end{Bmatrix} \tag{3.16}$$

with the inverse given by

$$\begin{Bmatrix} \epsilon_0 \\ \kappa \end{Bmatrix} = \begin{bmatrix} A & B \\ B & D \end{bmatrix}^{-1} \begin{Bmatrix} N \\ M \end{Bmatrix} \equiv [F] \begin{Bmatrix} N \\ M \end{Bmatrix} \tag{3.29}$$

Because the beam is unsymmetric, the *B* matrix does not vanish and the entire 6-by-6 *ABD* matrix must be inverted. For notational purposes, the inverse of the *ABD* matrix is called *F*, as shown in Eq. (3.29). The basic assumptions for all beams is that N_x, N_y, and N_{xy} all vanish, that is, there are no axial or twisting forces. Additionally, M_{xy} is taken as 0, and the γ^0_{xy} and κ_{xy} terms are neglected. Finally, for narrow beams, the transverse moment M_y is taken as zero. Substituting these assumptions into Eq. (3.29) gives

$$\begin{Bmatrix} \epsilon_x^0 \\ \epsilon_y^0 \\ \gamma_{xy}^0 \\ \kappa_x \\ \kappa_y \\ \kappa_{xy} \end{Bmatrix} = \begin{bmatrix} F_{11} & F_{12} & F_{13} & F_{14} & F_{15} & F_{16} \\ F_{21} & F_{22} & F_{23} & F_{24} & F_{25} & F_{26} \\ F_{31} & F_{32} & F_{33} & F_{34} & F_{35} & F_{36} \\ F_{41} & F_{42} & F_{43} & F_{44} & F_{45} & F_{46} \\ F_{51} & F_{52} & F_{53} & F_{54} & F_{55} & F_{56} \\ F_{61} & F_{62} & F_{63} & F_{64} & F_{65} & F_{66} \end{bmatrix} \begin{Bmatrix} 0 \\ 0 \\ 0 \\ M_x \\ 0 \\ 0 \end{Bmatrix} \tag{7.17}$$

Multiplying out the preceding gives the necessary relationships for the beam analysis as

$$\begin{aligned} \epsilon_x^0 &= F_{14}M_x & \kappa_x &= F_{44}M_x \\ \epsilon_y^0 &= F_{24}M_x & \kappa_y &= F_{54}M_x \end{aligned} \tag{7.18}$$

The strain distributions are given by

$$\begin{aligned} \epsilon_x &= \epsilon_x^0 + z\kappa_x = \xi\kappa_x \\ \epsilon_y &= \epsilon_y^0 + z\kappa_y = \xi\kappa_y \end{aligned} \tag{7.19}$$

The relationship between the coordinates is

$$\xi = z - z_c \tag{7.20}$$

Combining Eqs. (7.19) and (7.20) and using $\epsilon_x = 0$ at the neutral axis gives

$$0 = +\epsilon_x^0 + z_c \kappa_x = F_{14} M_x + z_c F_{44} M_x \tag{7.21}$$

and the location of the neutral axis is thus defined with respect to the midplane as

$$z_c = -F_{14}/F_{44} \tag{7.22}$$

The relationship between the moment and the curvature then can be expressed as

$$M_{\text{beam}} = b M_x = b(1/F_{44}) \kappa_x \tag{7.23}$$

so that

$$EI_{\text{eff}} = b(1/F_{44}) \tag{7.24}$$

where again b is the width of the beam. The preceding equation defines the effective EI stiffness for the unsymmetric beam. The general procedure in solving beam problems with an unsymmetric rectangular cross-section is to calculate the maximum moment using standard beam procedures, then calculate the curvature corresponding to this moment using the effective EI, find the strain distributions from Eq. (7.19), transform the strains into fiber-direction coordinates at locations of interest, and calculate stresses from the ply stress–strain relations. It should be emphasized again that the full 6-by-6 ABD matrix must be inverted to get the F matrix, as the B matrix is nonzero for nonsymmetric beams.

7.4.2 Wide Nonsymmetric Beams

The basic assumptions for all beams is that N_x, N_y, and N_{xy} all vanish, that is, there are no axial or twisting forces. Additionally, M_{xy} is taken as 0, and the γ_{xy}^0 and κ_{xy} terms are neglected. Finally, for wide beams, the transverse curvature κ_y is taken as zero. Substituting these assumptions into Eq. (3.19) gives

$$\begin{Bmatrix} \epsilon_x^0 \\ \epsilon_y^0 \\ \gamma_{xy}^0 \\ \kappa_x \\ 0 \\ \kappa_{xy} \end{Bmatrix} = \begin{bmatrix} F_{11} & F_{12} & F_{13} & F_{14} & F_{15} & F_{16} \\ F_{21} & F_{22} & F_{23} & F_{24} & F_{25} & F_{26} \\ F_{31} & F_{32} & F_{33} & F_{34} & F_{35} & F_{36} \\ F_{41} & F_{42} & F_{43} & F_{44} & F_{45} & F_{46} \\ F_{51} & F_{52} & F_{53} & F_{54} & F_{55} & F_{56} \\ F_{61} & F_{62} & F_{63} & F_{64} & F_{65} & F_{66} \end{bmatrix} \begin{Bmatrix} 0 \\ 0 \\ 0 \\ M_x \\ M_y \\ 0 \end{Bmatrix} \tag{7.25}$$

Multiplying out the preceding gives two sets of equations:

$$\begin{Bmatrix} \epsilon_x^0 \\ \epsilon_y^0 \end{Bmatrix} = \begin{bmatrix} F_{14} & F_{15} \\ F_{24} & F_{25} \end{bmatrix} \begin{Bmatrix} M_x \\ M_y \end{Bmatrix} \tag{7.26}$$

and

$$\begin{Bmatrix} \kappa_x \\ 0 \end{Bmatrix} = \begin{bmatrix} F_{44} & F_{45} \\ F_{54} & F_{55} \end{bmatrix} \begin{Bmatrix} M_x \\ M_y \end{Bmatrix} \tag{7.27}$$

Inverting the preceding gives

$$\epsilon_x^0 = \frac{F_{14} F_{55} - F_{15} F_{54}}{F_{44} F_{55} - F_{45} F_{54}} \kappa_x \tag{7.28}$$

and

$$\epsilon_y^0 = \frac{F_{24}F_{55} - F_{25}F_{54}}{F_{44}F_{55} - F_{45}F_{54}} \kappa_x \qquad (7.29)$$

The strain distributions again are given by

$$\epsilon_x = \epsilon_x^0 + z\kappa_x = \xi\kappa_x$$
$$\epsilon_y = \epsilon_y^0 + z\kappa_y = \xi\kappa_y \qquad (7.19)$$

and the relationship between the coordinates is

$$\xi = z - z_c \qquad (7.20)$$

Combining Eqs. (7.19) and (7.20) and using $\epsilon_x = 0$ at the neutral axis gives the location of the neutral axis with respect to the midplane as

$$z_c = -\frac{F_{14}F_{55} - F_{15}F_{54}}{F_{44}F_{55} - F_{45}F_{54}} \qquad (7.30)$$

The relationship between the moment and the curvature can be expressed as

$$M_{\text{beam}} = bM_x = b\frac{F_{55}}{F_{44}F_{55} - F_{45}F_{54}}\kappa_x \qquad (7.31)$$

so that

$$EI_{\text{eff}} = b\frac{F_{55}}{F_{44}F_{55} - F_{45}F_{54}} \qquad (7.32)$$

where again b is the width of the beam. The preceding equation defines the effective EI stiffness for the wide unsymmetric beam. As in the preceding, the general procedure in solving beam problems with an unsymmetric rectangular cross-section is to calculate the maximum moment using standard beam procedures, then calculate the curvature corresponding to this moment using the effective EI, find the strain distributions from Eq. (7.19), transform the strains into fiber-direction coordinates at locations of interest, and calculate stresses from the ply stress–strain relations. It should be emphasized again that the full 6-by-6 ABD matrix must be inverted to get the F matrix, as the B matrix is nonzero for nonsymmetric beams.

7.4.3 Symmetric or Unsymmetric Sandwich Beams with Thin Face Sheets

Another special case of unsymmetric beams is that of sandwich beams with thin face sheets. This is a very practically important case as the composite face sheets are often thin in comparison with the thickness of the sandwich core. Because of this thinness, the bending stiffness of each face sheet about its own axis is neglected in comparison with the stiffness about the overall sandwich beam axis. Thus, the properties of each face sheet are completely described by the A and the A^{-1} matrix. In many cases, both face sheets have the same thickness and layup, making the overall beam symmetric and thus ensuring freedom from thermal warping effects. However, there may be some cases in which it is desirable to make the face sheets of different thickness. For example, if the sandwich beam were loaded so that one side is always the compression side, it could be advantageous to make the face sheet on that side thicker, because fiber composites are often weaker in compression rela-tive to tension. If the face sheets were cured separately (and each individually had a sym-metric layup), and the core and face sheets then are secondary bonded together at room tem-perature, the thermal warping is eliminated. The theory is quite straightforward, so that it will be shown for the case of different face-sheet properties and/or thicknesses and the overall symmetric case reduced from that.

The sandwich beam and the coordinate system to be used is shown in Figure 7.9. The location of the neutral axis, located with a coordinate z_c, as shown in the figure, is obtained by setting the net axial force to zero. It is also assumed that the transverse strain in each face sheet is determined from the condition that the transverse force in each sheet individually is taken as zero. Note that the transverse strain in the two sheets then can be unequal. This dif-ference in transverse strain is assumed to be accommodated by the sandwich core, which has a lower shear stiffness.

The strains in either sheet are related to the stress resultant for that sheet by the A^{-1} matrix:

$$\left\{\begin{array}{c} \epsilon_x^0 \\ \epsilon_y^0 \end{array}\right\} = \begin{bmatrix} A_{11}^{-1} & A_{12}^{-1} \\ A_{21}^{-1} & A_{22}^{-1} \end{bmatrix} \left\{\begin{array}{c} N_x \\ 0 \end{array}\right\} \tag{7.33}$$

The strains in the top and bottom face sheets are given by

$$\epsilon_{x_t}^0 = -\left(\frac{h}{2} - z_c\right)\kappa_x \quad \text{and} \quad \epsilon_{x_b}^0 = \left(\frac{h}{2} + z_c\right)\kappa_x \tag{7.34}$$

The transverse strain in either face sheet is given from Eq. (7.33) as

$$\epsilon_y^0 = \frac{A_{21}^{-1}}{A_{11}^{-1}} \epsilon_x^0 \tag{7.35}$$

The location of the neutral axis is determined by the condition that the total axial force is zero. Thus,

$$N_{x_t} + N_{x_b} = 0 \tag{7.36}$$

where the subscripts t and b stand for top and bottom, respectively. Substituting gives

$$z_c = \frac{h}{2}\left(\frac{1 - R}{1 + R}\right) \tag{7.37}$$

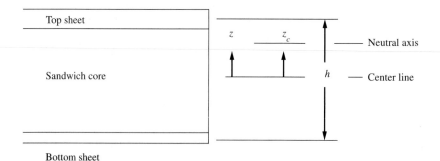

Figure 7.9   A sandwich beam with thin face sheets. z is measured from the geometric center line, and the position of the neutral axis is denoted by z_c.

where

$$R \equiv \frac{A_{11t}^{-1}}{A_{11b}^{-1}}$$

Taking moments about the neutral axis and using the preceding gives

$$M_{\text{beam}} = b\left[N_{x_b}\left(\frac{h}{2} + z_c\right) - N_{x_t}\left(\frac{h}{2} - z_c\right)\right]$$

or

$$M_{\text{beam}} = b\left[\frac{(h/2 + z_c)^2}{A_{11b}^{-1}} + \frac{(h/2 - z_c)^2}{A_{11t}^{-1}}\right]\kappa_x \tag{7.38}$$

Thus, the effective EI is given by

$$EI_{\text{eff}} = b\left[\frac{(h/2 + z_c)^2}{A_{11b}^{-1}} + \frac{(h/2 - z_c)^2}{A_{11t}^{-1}}\right] \tag{7.39}$$

For symmetric sandwich beams with thin faces, this reduces to

$$EI_{\text{eff}} = \frac{bh^2}{2A_{11}^{-1}} \tag{7.40}$$

where the A matrix is computed for each face sheet separately. The solution to practical problems with sandwich beams with thin face sheets then proceeds as in the examples treated previously. Solutions for deflection just involve replacing the EI of isotropic beam theory with the effective EI given previously. To find the stresses in the face sheets, the overall beam curvature is found from Eq. (7.3). The axial strains are then calulated in the face sheets from Eq. (7.34) and the transverse strains from Eq. (7.35). These strains are then transformed into the fiber-direction coordinates, and the stresses in the individual plies are calculated from the ply stress–strain law.

EXAMPLE 7.3   Stresses in a sandwich beam with thin composite face sheets

The problem to be considered is to find the maximum deflection and ply-direction stresses for a sandwich beam with relatively thin composite face sheets, as shown in Figure 7.10. The laminated composite beam to be considered is made of two face sheets, each composed of 12 plies

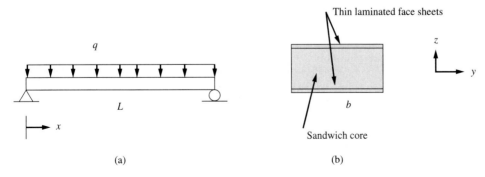

Figure 7.10   Sandwich beam with thin laminated face sheets: (a) loading and (b) cross-section.

of AS4/3501-6 carbon/epoxy, with a $[0_2/45_2/-45_2]_s$ layup. The data for the problem are summarized as follows:

Length $L = 508$ mm (20 in)

Width $b = 50.8$ mm (2.0 in)

Sandwich core thickness = 12.7 mm (0.5 in)

Thickness of each face sheet = 1.588 mm (0.0624 in)

Distributed loading $q = 1401$ N/m (8.0 lb/in)

Solution: The effective EI for the beam is calculated from Eq. (7.40), using the A^{-1} matrix for each face sheet individually. This value for EI is substituted into the usual strength-of-materials formula for deflection given as $\delta = 5qL^4/384EI$. By using the maximum moment as $M_{beam} = qL^2/8$, the maximum curvature is found from Eq. (7.12). The axial strain (taken as constant over the face sheet) is found from Eq. (7.34), taking $z_c = 0$ for the present case of a sandwich beam with overall symmetry. The transverse strain is then found from Eq. (7.35). Finally, the stresses in each ply are calculated from the strains by first transforming the strains into the ply directions and then using the ply stress–strain law. The results from these computations are as follows:

$$EI_{eff} = 146.1 \text{ N-m}^2 \, (50{,}900 \text{ lb-in}^2)$$

$$\delta = 2.565 \text{ mm } (0.1010 \text{ in})$$

The stresses in the ply groups on the tension side are as follows:

Ply Group	ϵ_x	ϵ_y	σ_1 MPa (ksi)	σ_2 MPa (ksi)	τ_{12} MPa (ksi)
45	6.817E − 4	− 4.41E − 4	15.8 (2.29)	1.71 (0.248)	7.35 (1.07)
−45	6.817E − 4	− 4.41E − 4	15.8 (2.29)	1.71 (0.248)	−7.35 (−1.07)
0	6.817E − 4	− 4.41E − 4	85.7 (12.4)	−2.77 (−0.402)	0 (0)

The EI stiffness value given before differs from that calculated using the narrow-beam estimate by 2.2%. It is likely that the accuracy of the wide-beam estimate would not be as good because of the shear deformation in the relatively thick sandwich core. Shear-deformable plate theory could be used to get improved estimates for intermediate cases. ∎

7.5 LAMINATED I-BEAM

Structural shapes such as I-beams can be made from fiber composites. The methods of construction can include pultrusion, dry fiber preforms made from textile composites such as braids, and prepreg layup. The general geometry of the I-beam considered is shown in Figure 7.11. The case to be considered is that of a laminated I-beam, but beams made from fiber preforms can be analyzed using similar techniques. Several features about the I-beam geometry and layup should be noted. The plies in the shear web are oriented normal to the neutral axis, and the plies in the flanges are parallel to the neutral axis, as illustrated in Figures 7.11 and 7.12. The shear web likely contains a layup with angle plies, such as ±45, for example, to resist the shear loading.

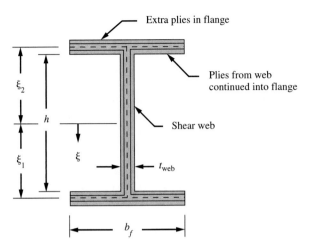

Figure 7.11 Cross-section of laminated I-beam. The beam shown has overall symmetry, but the flanges do not necessarily have symmetric layups about a local flange midplane.

A standard construction technique is to continue these plies into the flange and then add additional reinforcement to the flange. If one considers the flange alone, there is some motivation for making the flange itself unsymmetric. The case shown in Figure 7.11 illustrates this, where additional plies, say, at $0°$, have been added to the outer surface of the flange to increase both strength and stiffness. Although thermal distortion causes deformation in an unsymmetric flange, it is limited by the web. The overall beam may or may not be symmetric. If one side of the beam is known to always be in compression, the flange on that side may have material added to resist flange buckling and compensate for the generally lower compression strength of some fiber composites. Again, thermal distortion of the unsymmetric beam is limited by the web. In addition to the plies shown, there may be additional filler material in the vicinity of the junction of the flange and web. This can be easily included in the analysis but will not be shown here. For simplicity, we simply consider the web and two flanges each to be rectangular in section and the overall beam to be symmetric about the center line. The dimensions $\xi_1 = \xi_2$ are measured from the overall midplane to the center line of each flange.

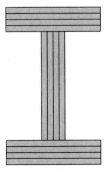

Figure 7.12 Orientation of plies in the cross-section of laminated I-beam. Many fabrication techniques give this ply orientation. The plies in the web may have a right-angle bend and continue into the flange.

The analysis of a beam such as the I-beam considered here can be based on the *ABD* relationships for the individual pieces of the cross-section taken separately, that is, in this case, for the web and the two flanges. The lamination constants should be computed as usual about a midplane of the individual piece, with the lamination direction for the individual piece parallel to the midplane of that piece. This location of local axes for computing the *A*, *B*, and *D* matrices for each of the three parts is illustrated in Figure 7.13.

The basic principles to be used are that the moment is found by integrating the axial stress times a moment arm over the entire area, and that the axial strain varies linearly with distance from the neutral axis. These principles are applied to the web and flanges as follows.

Web.   The plies in the web lie parallel to the vertical axis of the web. Note that because the bending moment carried in the web is not transverse to these plies as in the usual lamination theory developed previously, the *D* matrix has nothing to do with the bending stiffness of the web. However, it is straightforward to develop a new expression for the bending properties, because the properties in the web do not vary with position away from the neutral axis. Note that the axial stress in the web is just the in-plane stress resultant N_x divided by the thickness of the web, and the normal stress resultant in the web is related to the strains by

$$\epsilon_x^0 = A_{11(\text{web})}^{-1} N_x \qquad (7.41)$$

where the superscript on strain indicates the center line of the web (the *z* axis), not the overall center line of the entire I-beam. The axial strain distribution in the web is given by

$$\epsilon_x^0 = \xi \kappa_x \qquad (7.42)$$

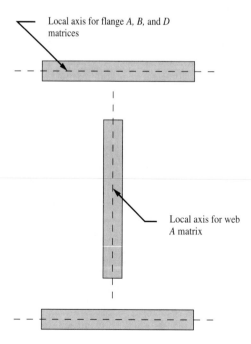

Local axis for flange *A*, *B*, and *D* matrices

Local axis for web *A* matrix

Figure 7.13   The local axes used for separate flange and web *A*, *B*, *D* matrices.

Thus, the normal force distribution is given by

$$N_{x(\text{web})} = [1/A^{-1}_{11(\text{web})}]\xi\kappa_x \tag{7.43}$$

The moment due to the stress distribution in the web then can be obtained from

$$M_{\text{web}} = \int_{-h/2}^{h/2} N_x \xi \, d\xi = \int_{-h/2}^{h/2} (1/A^{-1}_{11})\xi^2 \kappa_x d\xi \tag{7.44}$$

$$M_{\text{web}} = h^3/(12A^{-1}_{11})\kappa_x \tag{7.45}$$

This result is combined with the moment in the flanges. Again note that the A and A^{-1} matrix here are computed for the web alone, and are taken about an axis parallel to the web (a vertical axis in Figure 7.13).

Flanges.   Each flange is considered as a symmetric or nonsymmetric plate loaded by N_x and M_x, and with the axial strain distribution consistent with plane sections remaining plane for the entire cross-section. The analysis for the bottom flange is illustrated. We distinguish four separate cases, which are narrow symmetric flanges, wide symmetric flanges, narrow nonsymmetric flanges, and wide nonsymmetric flanges. As mentioned earlier, the flanges may be either symmetric or nonsymmetric. The difference between narrow and wide flanges involves the "anti-clastic" effect that distinguishes beam bending from plate bending. The usual beam theory assumes that there is no moment in the transverse direction of the flanges. This follows because there is no moment at the outside edge of the flange, and because the flange is assumed to be relatively narrow, the internal moment in the transverse direction is also taken to be zero. That is, if M_x is the primary moment applied to the beam, M_y is taken to be zero in the flanges. However, if the flange is wide, there can be a buildup of the transverse moment M_y within the flange. Then the appropriate assumption is that the transverse curvature of the flange is zero. In the following, these four cases are treated.

7.5.1 Symmetric Narrow Flanges

The lateral stress resultant N_y is assumed to be zero for all of the cases considered. In addition, bending moment M_y is taken as zero for narrow flanges. Here, the terms N_x, N_y, M_x, and M_y refer to in-plane stress resultants and moments for the flange taken alone. The local strains and curvatures in the flanges then can be related to the N_x and M_x loadings by the relations

$$\begin{Bmatrix} \epsilon_x^0 \\ \epsilon_y^0 \\ \gamma_{xy}^0 \end{Bmatrix} = [A^{-1}] \begin{Bmatrix} N_x \\ 0 \\ 0 \end{Bmatrix} \qquad \begin{Bmatrix} \kappa_x \\ \kappa_y \\ \kappa_{xy} \end{Bmatrix} = [D^{-1}] \begin{Bmatrix} M_x \\ 0 \\ 0 \end{Bmatrix} \tag{7.46}$$

From the preceding, the relations for N_x and M_x can be obtained as

$$N_x = \frac{1}{A^{-1}_{11}}\epsilon_x^0 = \frac{\xi_1}{A^{-1}_{11}}\kappa_x \qquad \text{and} \qquad M_x = \frac{1}{D^{-1}_{11}}\kappa_x \tag{7.47}$$

The relation between the center-line strain of the flange and the curvature of the beam follows from the assumption of plane sections remaining plane for the entire beam. Note that the stress and moment resultants of Eq. (7.47) are given on a per-unit-width basis, and thus must be multiplied by the width of the flange. The moment in the flange is thus given by

$$M_{\text{flange}} = b_f (N_x \xi_1 + M_x) = b_f \left(\frac{\xi_1^2}{A_{11}^{-1}} + \frac{1}{D_{11}^{-1}} \right) \kappa_x \tag{7.48}$$

where it should be noted that the properties are those of the flange, that is, one of the flanges. The total moment for the beam then can be obtained by summing the moments for the web and two flanges:

$$M_{\text{beam}} = M_{\text{web}} + 2M_{\text{flange}} = EI_{\text{eff}} \kappa_x \tag{7.49}$$

and the effective EI is an overall effective stiffness for the beam given by

$$EI_{\text{eff}} = \frac{h^3}{12 A_{11,\text{web}}^{-1}} + 2b_f \left(\frac{\xi_1^2}{A_{11,\text{flange}}^{-1}} + \frac{1}{D_{11,\text{flange}}^{-1}} \right) \tag{7.50}$$

Once the effective stiffness of the beam has been calculated from Eq. (7.50), the solution to beam problems can be carried out. The moment distributions are calculated just as in the usual strength-of-materials approach for statically determinant or indeterminant beams. Deflections can be calculated by using the usual techniques, such as integration of the differential equation for deflection given before, noting the definition of κ_x given previously.

The stress distributions in the beam can be calculated from the strain distributions. The axial strain distribution in the entire beam is given by

$$\epsilon_x = \xi \kappa_x \tag{7.51}$$

which applies to both the web and the flange. It is slightly more convenient to use the equivalent expression for the strain in the flange given by

$$\epsilon_x = \epsilon_x^0 + z \kappa_x = (\xi_1 + z) \kappa_x \tag{7.52}$$

where z is a local coordinate through the thickness of the flange. The strain in the y direction and the shear strain in the flange can be obtained from Eq. (7.46) as

$$\epsilon_y = \epsilon_y^0 + z \kappa_y = \left[\frac{A_{21}^{-1}}{A_{11}^{-1}} \xi_1 + z \frac{D_{21}^{-1}}{D_{11}^{-1}} \right] \kappa_x \tag{7.53}$$

where again the properties are those of the flange, and the shear strain in the flange will be zero if the flange layup is balanced. Thus, the strain distribution in the flange is known from the curvature. From this, the stresses are obtained as usual. That is, each ply is examined, and the strains in the x,y overall directions are rotated into the fiber directions. The stresses can then be calculated from the lamina properties, using the lamina stress–strain relationships.

7.5.2 Symmetric Wide Flanges

This case is very similar to that given before, but although in all cases N_y is taken as zero, for the wide-flange case, moment M_y is not zero, but rather the transverse curvature κ_y of the flange is taken as zero. Again, N_x and N_y refer to the in-plane resultants, and M_x and M_y refer to the moment resultants for the flange alone. Also M_{xy} is neglected. The equations are thus

$$
\begin{Bmatrix} \epsilon_x^0 \\ \epsilon_y^0 \\ \gamma_{xy}^0 \end{Bmatrix} = [A^{-1}] \begin{Bmatrix} N_x \\ 0 \\ 0 \end{Bmatrix} \qquad \begin{Bmatrix} M_x \\ M_y \\ M_{xy} \end{Bmatrix} = [D] \begin{Bmatrix} \kappa_x \\ 0 \\ 0 \end{Bmatrix} \tag{7.54}
$$

By following the preceding procedure, it can be seen that the effective bending stiffness for the beam is given by

$$
EI_{\mathrm{eff}} = \frac{h^3}{12 A_{11,\mathrm{web}}^{-1}} + 2 b_f \left(\frac{\xi_1^2}{A_{11,\mathrm{flange}}^{-1}} + D_{11,\mathrm{flange}} \right) \tag{7.55}
$$

The strains in the axial and transverse directions are calculated as before, using relations of Eq. (7.54). The x (axial) strain in the flange is given by Eq. (7.52), and the transverse y component is given by

$$
\epsilon_y = \epsilon_y^0 = \frac{A_{21}^{-1}}{A_{11}^{-1}} \xi \kappa_x \tag{7.56}
$$

Again, the stresses in the flange can be calculated from these strains by the procedures described before.

7.5.3 Nonsymmetric Narrow Flanges

The analysis for nonsymmetric flanges is complicated somewhat by the presence of the B matrix. However, it can still proceed as shown before, but including the B matrix. We call the inverse of the ABD matrix as the F matrix to shorten the notation, that is, let

$$
[F] \equiv \begin{bmatrix} A & B \\ B & D \end{bmatrix}^{-1}
$$

The relations for the flange can then be written as

$$
\begin{Bmatrix} \epsilon_x^0 \\ \epsilon_y^0 \\ \gamma_{xy}^0 \\ \kappa_x \\ \kappa_y \\ \kappa_{xy} \end{Bmatrix} = \begin{bmatrix} F_{11} & - & - & F_{14} & - & - \\ F_{21} & - & - & F_{24} & - & - \\ - & - & - & - & - & - \\ F_{41} & - & - & F_{44} & - & - \\ F_{51} & - & - & F_{54} & - & - \\ - & - & - & - & - & - \end{bmatrix} \begin{Bmatrix} N_x \\ 0 \\ 0 \\ M_x \\ 0 \\ 0 \end{Bmatrix} \tag{7.57}
$$

where only the terms of the inverse matrix that are needed here are shown. The first and fourth equations can be solved to get expressions for N_x and M_x as

$$
N_x = \frac{F_{44}}{\Delta} \epsilon_x^0 - \frac{F_{14}}{\Delta} \kappa_x \qquad M_x = \frac{-F_{41}}{\Delta} \epsilon_x^0 + \frac{F_{11}}{\Delta} \kappa_x \tag{7.58}
$$

$$
\Delta \equiv F_{11} F_{44} - F_{14} F_{41}
$$

From this, it is straightforward to calculate the effective beam stiffness as before to get

$$EI_{\text{eff}} = \frac{h^3}{12A^{-1}_{11,\text{web}}} + 2b_f\left[\left(\frac{F_{44}\xi_1}{\Delta} - \frac{F_{14}}{\Delta}\right)\xi_1 + \left(\frac{-F_{41}\xi_1}{\Delta} + \frac{F_{11}}{\Delta}\right)\right] \qquad (7.59)$$

where the dimensions are as defined in Figure 7.11. The transverse strain in the flange can be found from Eq. (7.57):

$$\left\{\begin{array}{c} \epsilon^0_y \\ \kappa_y \end{array}\right\} = \begin{bmatrix} F_{21} & F_{24} \\ F_{51} & F_{54} \end{bmatrix} \begin{bmatrix} \dfrac{F_{44}}{\Delta} & \dfrac{-F_{14}}{\Delta} \\ \dfrac{-F_{41}}{\Delta} & \dfrac{F_{11}}{\Delta} \end{bmatrix} \left\{\begin{array}{c} \epsilon^0_x \\ \kappa_x \end{array}\right\} \qquad (7.60)$$

The strains and then the stresses in the flange can be obtained from this expression.

7.5.4 Nonsymmetric Wide Flanges

This case assumes zero transverse curvature in the flanges, but a nonvanishing B matrix for the flange. The relations for the flange can be written as

$$\left\{\begin{array}{c} N_x \\ 0 \\ 0 \\ M_x \\ M_y \\ 0 \end{array}\right\} = \begin{bmatrix} A_{11} & A_{12} & - & B_{11} & - & - \\ - & - & - & - & - & - \\ - & - & - & - & - & - \\ B_{11} & B_{12} & - & D_{11} & - & - \\ B_{21} & B_{22} & - & D_{21} & - & - \\ - & - & - & - & - & - \end{bmatrix} \left\{\begin{array}{c} \epsilon^0_x \\ \epsilon^0_y \\ 0 \\ \kappa_x \\ 0 \\ 0 \end{array}\right\} \qquad (7.61)$$

From the preceding, it is easy to eliminate the flange transverse center-line strain ϵ^0_y, resulting in

$$N_x = \left[A_{11} - \frac{A_{12}A_{21}}{A_{22}}\right]\epsilon^0_x + \left[B_{11} - \frac{A_{12}B_{21}}{A_{22}}\right]\kappa_x = \alpha_{11}\epsilon^0_x + \alpha_{12}\kappa_x \qquad (7.62)$$

$$M_x = \left[B_{11} - \frac{B_{12}A_{21}}{A_{22}}\right]\epsilon^0_x + \left[D_{11} - \frac{B_{12}B_{21}}{A_{22}}\right]\kappa_x = \alpha_{21}\epsilon^0_x + \alpha_{22}\kappa_x \qquad (7.63)$$

From this, the effective beam stiffness can be obtained as before as

$$EI_{\text{eff}} = \frac{h^3}{12A^{-1}_{11,\text{web}}} + 2b_f[\alpha_{11}\xi_1^2 + (\alpha_{12} + \alpha_{21})\xi_1 + \alpha_{22}] \qquad (7.64)$$

As shown before, the stresses in the flange can be obtained once the beam curvature κ_x is found from the moment solution. The strains in the flange in the axial and transverse directions are calculated as shown previously, using relations of Eq. (7.61). The x or axial strain in the flange is given by Eq. (7.52), and the transverse y component is given by

$$\epsilon_y = \epsilon^0_y = -\left(\frac{A_{21}}{A_{22}}\epsilon^0_y + \frac{B_{21}}{A_{22}}\kappa_x\right) = -\left(\frac{A_{21}}{A_{22}}\xi_1 + \frac{B_{21}}{A_{22}}\right)\kappa_x \qquad (7.65)$$

As usual, these flange strains are transformed into fiber-direction strains, and the fiber-direction stresses are obtained from the lamina stress–strain equations.

EXAMPLE 7.4   Analysis of a composite I-beam

The I-beam to be considered has flanges with a layup of $[90/\pm45/0_2]_s$, and a web with a layup of $[90/\pm45]_s$, both made of AS4/3501-6 carbon/epoxy. The height of the web is 19.05 mm (0.75 in) and the width of the flange is 12.7 mm (0.5 in). The I-beam is simply supported with a length of 508 mm (20 in) and a distributed loading of 1751 N/m (10 lb/in), as shown in Figure 7.14. Find the deflection at the center of the beam, and also calculate the strain in the 0 plies in the flange. The strain in the 0 plies are used as a design criterion for the beam. Both flange and web have plies that are 0.1321 mm (0.0052 in) thick.

Solution: The effective EI for the beam is needed both for the deflection and the strain distribution in the beam. Stresses would also be calculated from the strains if they were required. The EI is calculated from Eq. (7.50) (assuming narrow flanges). The A^{-1} and D^{-1} matrix are calculated for the flange and web separately. The geometry and calculated properties are as follows:

$h = 19.05$ mm (0.75 in)

$b_f = 12.7$ mm (0.5 in)

$\xi_1 = 9.525 + 5 \times 0.13208 = 10.19$ mm $(0.375 + 5 \times 0.0052 = 0.401$ in)

Web: $A_{11}^{-1} = 4.83\text{E} - 8$ m/N $(8.46\text{E} - 6$ in/lb)

Flange: $A_{11}^{-1} = 1.140\text{E} - 8$ m/N $(1.996\text{E} - 6$ in/lb)

Flange: $D_{11}^{-1} = 0.01770$ N^{-1}-m^{-1} $(2.00\text{E} - 2$ lb^{-1}-in$^{-1})$

$EI_{\text{eff}} = 243.3$ N-m^2 (84,800 lb-in^2)

From this, the deflection is calculated to be

$$\delta = 5qL^4/384EI = 6.25 \text{ mm } (0.246 \text{ in})$$

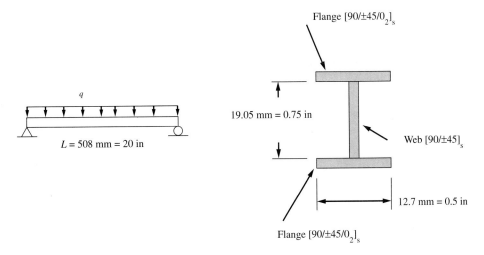

Figure 7.14   Geometry of laminated I-beam used in Example 7.4.

The moment at the center of the beam is found from $M_{\text{beam}} = qL^2/8$. Dividing this by the EI value gives the curvature at the center, and, finally, the strain at the outer 0 ply is found from $\epsilon_1 = z\kappa_x$. The distance to the outer 0 ply is given by

$$z = 9.525 + 7 \times 0.13208 = 10.45 \text{ mm} \ (0.375 + 7 \times 0.0052 = 0.4114 \text{ in})$$

giving a value for the strain as

$$\epsilon_1 = 0.243\%$$

It is interesting to note that about 4.9% of the EI was contributed by the web, less than 0.1% by the bending stiffness of the flanges about their own axis, and about 95% of the stiffness comes from the A^{-1} term for the flanges. The lack of bending stiffness of the flanges results from their relative thinness, and would occur in an isotropic beam with similar dimensions, but also because the 0 plies are clustered at the center of the flange. In cases like this, it makes little practical difference in the stiffness prediction whether the flanges are taken to be either wide or narrow, and whether symmetry exists in the flanges. The response is dominated by the A^{-1} matrix of the flange, which is independent of all of these assumptions. ∎

7.6 SHEAR-STRESS DISTRIBUTION IN BEAMS

The distribution of the transverse shear stresses can be obtained from the equilibrium procedure followed for isotropic beams. However, the resulting formulas are different because the normal stresses depend on the material properties. The procedure that is shown here for beams has also been used to calculate interlaminar stresses for plates, for example, in [7.4]. In the following, expressions for interlaminar shear stress are given for rectangular beams, and for the web and flange of an I-beam.

7.6.1 Shear Stress in a Rectangular Beam

The shear stress in the beam is established using the same principles as for isotropic beams. Figure 7.15 shows a free-body diagram that reveals the shear stress on a horizontal section. Axial equilibrium requires that shear stresses exist as shown if there is a change in the axial stresses with the axial coordinate x. Thus, if the moment changes along the length of the beam, shear stresses will exist.

A statement of axial equilibrium is given by

$$\int_{\eta}^{h/2} \left(\sigma_x + \frac{\partial \sigma_x}{\partial x} dx \right) b\, dz - \int_{\eta}^{h/2} \sigma_x b\, dz = \tau_{xz} b\, dx \tag{7.66}$$

where η is the value of z where the shear stress is to be calculated. Simplifying gives

$$\tau_{xz} b = \frac{\partial}{\partial x} \int_{\eta}^{h/2} \sigma_x b\, dz \tag{7.67}$$

The axial stress can be found from the stress–strain law for each ply group. Breaking up the integral into an integral over each ply gives

$$\tau_{xz} b = \frac{\partial}{\partial x} \left(\sum_k \int_{h_{k-1}}^{h_k} \sigma_x b\, dz \right) = \frac{\partial}{\partial x} \left[\sum_k \int_{h_{k-1}}^{h_k} (\overline{Q_{xx}^k} \epsilon_x + \overline{Q_{xy}^k} \epsilon_y) b\, dz \right] \tag{7.68}$$

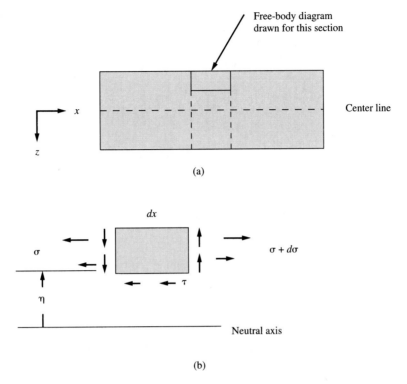

Figure 7.15   (a) Side view of beam, showing two vertical cuts and one horizontal cut, to reveal material shown in (b) the free-body diagram, showing normal and shear stresses. Axial equilibrium requires shear stress on the horizontal plane if the moment varies along the length, so that the normal stresses vary.

where the stiffness constants are those for each ply, transformed from the fiber directions into the overall x,y coordinate directions. The x-direction (axial) strain is given by

$$\epsilon_x = z\kappa_x = z\frac{M_{beam}}{EI} \tag{7.69}$$

As discussed previously, the transverse strain relationship depends on whether the beam is narrow or wide. For a narrow (symmetric) beam, and using Eq. (7.14), the transverse strain is given as follows:

Narrow beam:

$$\epsilon_y = z\kappa_y = z\frac{D_{21}^{-1}}{D_{11}^{-1}}\kappa_x = z\frac{D_{21}^{-1}}{D_{11}^{-1}}\frac{M_{beam}}{EI} \tag{7.70}$$

Wide beam: From Eq. (7.16):

$$\epsilon_y = 0 \tag{7.71}$$

The only variable in the integral is z, and using $dM/dx = V$, the expression becomes

$$\tau_{xz} = \frac{V}{\overline{EI}}\sum_{k}(\overline{Q}_{xx}^{k} + \overline{Q}_{xy}^{k}\lambda)\left(\frac{h_{k}^{2} - h_{k-1}^{2}}{2}\right) \tag{7.72}$$

where λ has the following values.

Narrow symmetric rectangular beam:

$$\lambda = \frac{D_{21}^{-1}}{D_{11}^{-1}} \tag{7.73}$$

Wide symmetric rectangular beam:

$$\lambda = 0 \tag{7.74}$$

It should be remembered that the sum is over the ply groups away from the location where the shear stress is wanted, that is, from this location to the outer surface of the beam, and that the h_{k} and h_{k-1} values are the values of z at the upper and lower surfaces of the ply groups, respectively.

EXAMPLE 7.5   Shear stresses in a rectangular beam

The laminated composite beam to be considered is made of 24 plies of AS4/3501-6 carbon/epoxy, with a $[0_4/45_4/-45_4]_s$ layup. The beam is simply supported at the ends and subject to a uniformly distributed load q, as shown in Figure 7.16. The desired answer is the shear stress at the midplane of the beam. The data for the problem are summarized as follows:

Length $L = 254$ mm (10 in)

Width $b = 50.8$ mm (2.0 in)

Thickness $t = 3.150$ mm (0.124 in)

Distributed loading $q = 3500$ N/m (20 lb/in)

Solution: The shear stress is calculated by using Eq. (7.72). The width-to-thickness aspect ratio suggests that this is "wide beam," and thus Eq. (7.74) is used with Eq. (7.72). The effective EI is calculated from Eq. (7.10). A value obtained in Example 7.1 can be corrected for the width of the present beam. Statics gives the maximum shear force as $V = qL/2$. The data are summarized as

$$V = 445 \text{ N (100 lb)}$$

$$EI = 13.83 \text{ N-m}^2 \text{ (4820 lb-in}^2)$$

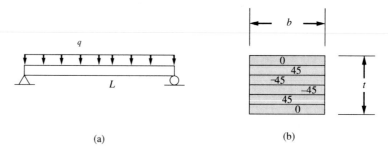

Figure 7.16   For Example 7.5, (a) laminated beam cross-section and loading (q is positive upward) and (b) cross-section showing the ply groups (not to scale).

The calculation of the elasticity constants in the Q matrix, referred to the overall x,y coordinates, is given in Eq. (2.27). The results are as follows:

Ply Group	h_k mm (in)	h_{k-1} mm (in)	Q_{xx} GPa (Msi)	Q_{xy} GPa (Msi)
-45	0.528 (0.0208)	0 (0)	42.8 (6.21)	29.7 (4.31)
45	1.057 (0.0416)	0.528 (0.0208)	42.8 (6.21)	29.7 (4.31)
0	1.585 (0.0624)	1.057 (0.0416)	127.8 (18.53)	3.11(0.451)

Substituting into Eq. (7.72) gives the interlaminar shear stress at the center line of the cross-section of the beam as

$$\tau = 3.63 \text{ Mpa (527 psi)}$$

Repeating the calculation with the narrow-beam assumption gives a value for the shear stress that is approximately 13% lower. Using the isotropic-beam formula $\tau = VQ/bI$ gives a value that is about 14% higher. The isotropic formula gives the familiar result that the shear stress at the center line is 1.5 times the average stress, that is, $\tau_{max} = 1.5\ V/A$, where A is the cross-sectional area. The comparison between the isotropic formula and the laminated-beam formula varies with the problem data, but, in general, the more dispersed the plies, the better the accuracy of the isotropic formula. A plot of the shear stress across half of the cross-section of the beam is shown in Figure 7.17, along with a plot of the isotropic-beam formula prediction for the shear stress. The results agree with intuition in that the laminated-beam formula shows a more rapid change in the shear stress across the stiffer 0 plies. As a consequence, the peak stress at the center is lower than for the isotropic beam. In an extreme case, say, of a $[0/90_{10}]_s$ laminated beam, the center portion would have a much lower modulus relative to the outside plies, and the shear stress would be essentially uniform across the beam, as in a sandwich beam with a low-modulus core. Conversely, if the stiffer plies (i.e., the 0 plies) were located toward the center, the laminated-beam shear-stress formula would predict a higher shear stress at the center line than would the isotropic-beam shear-stress formula.

To show the effect of dispersion of the plies, reconsider the preceding problem of finding the shear-stress distribution using the same data as before, but with a new layup of $[(0_2/45_2/-45_2)_2]_s$. The thickness of this beam is the same, but there are now twice the number of ply groups of half the ply group thickness. The effective value of EI changes to $EI = 11.60$ N-m^2 (4044 lb-in^2), and the shear stress at the center line is now within 7% of the isotropic-beam formula. The distribution of shear stress across half of the beam cross-section is shown in Figure 7.18. ∎

7.6.2 Shear Stress in the Web and Flange of an I-Beam

Consider the calculation of shear stresses in the web of an I-beam. Axial equilibrium requires a balance between the horizontal shear force and the rate of change of force from the axial stresses in the beam. The net axial force in the web at a location η can be expressed as

$$F_{web} = \int_{\eta}^{h/2} (1/A_{11}^{-1})\xi\kappa_x\, d\xi \qquad (7.75)$$

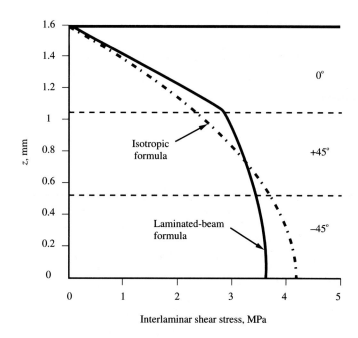

Figure 7.17 Comparison of shear stress across a half section of the beam of Example 7.5 as predicted by the laminated-beam formula and an isotropic-beam formula. The beam layup is $[0_4/45_4/-45_4]_s$.

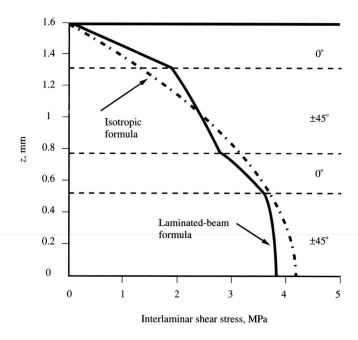

Figure 7.18 Comparison of shear stress across a half section of the beam of Example 7.5 as predicted by the laminated-beam formula and an isotropic-beam formula, using a new beam layup of $[(0_2/45_2/-45_2)_2]_s$. The more dispersed plies result is less difference between the predictions using the laminated-beam and the isotropic-beam shear stress formulas.

and the force in the flange can be taken from Eq. (7.58) as

$$F_{\text{flange}} = b_f(F_{44}\xi_1 - F_{14})\kappa_x/\Delta \tag{7.76}$$

and symmetry of the flange about its center line is not assumed. Using standard relations,

$$V = dM_{\text{beam}}/dx = EI_{\text{eff}}\,d\kappa_x/dx \tag{7.77}$$

From the preceding, the shear-stress distribution in the web is given by

$$\tau_{\text{web}} = (V/t_w\,EI_{\text{eff}})\,[(1/A_{11,\text{web}}^*)\,(h^2/4 - \eta^2)/2 + b_f(F_{44}\xi - F_{14})/\Delta] \tag{7.78}$$

The web may well have fibers placed at angles to the axial direction in order to resist the shear. For example, as mentioned previously, the layup of the web may include fibers at ±45 degrees for this purpose. It is thus of interest to be able to calculate the stresses with respect to fiber directions. This can be easily done by noting that the stress resultant N_{xy} with respect to the usual coordinates for in-plane loading of a laminate is given by

$$N_{xy} = t_{\text{web}}\tau_{\text{web}} \tag{7.79}$$

and the peak value of the shear stress in the web can be used to get an equivalent in-plane loading N_{xy} that can be applied to the layup of the web.

The shear-stress distribution between the layers in the flange, although considerably smaller than the shear in the web, also may be of interest. It can be calculated by a similar procedure using axial equilibrium. Consider the case of an I-beam with overall symmetry and with flanges that are wide and have a symmetric layup. Using axial equilibrium as before gives

$$\tau_{xz} = \frac{V}{EI}\sum_k (\overline{Q_{xx}^k} + \overline{Q_{xy}^k}\lambda)\left(\frac{h_k^2 - h_{k-1}^2}{2}\right) \tag{7.80}$$

where for wide, symmetric flanges

$$\lambda = \frac{A_{21}^{-1}}{A_{11}^{-1}}\,\xi_1 \tag{7.81}$$

where the A matrix terms pertain to the flange only, ξ_1 is as defined in Figure 7.5, and the h_k and h_{k-1} values are for the outer and inner surfaces of the ply groups that are located in the flange away from the location of interest for the interlaminar shear stress and are measured with respect to the overall beam center line.

7.7 CLOSURE

A simple theory has been presented for the analysis of laminated composite beams. For many practical laminated beams, the individual ply groups are in a state of biaxial stress and strain even with the usual one-dimensional loading of beam theory. It was shown that this can be easily taken into account by using principles of two-dimensional lamination theory. Examples were given for rectangular beams and I-beams.

REFERENCES

7.1 Rehfield, L. W., and A. R. Atilgan, "Shear Center and Elastic Axis and Their Usefulness for Composite Thin-Walled Beams," in *Proceedings of the American Society for Composites, Fourth Technical Conference* (Lancaster, Pennsylvania: Technomic Publishing, 1989), pp. 179–188.

7.2 Bank, L. C., "Modification to Beam Theory for Bending and Twisting of Open-Section Composite Beams," *Composite Struct.* 15 (1990): 93–114.

7.3 Cook, R. D., and W. C. Young, *Advanced Mechanics of Materials* (New York: Macmillan, 1985).

7.4 Pagano, N. J., "Exact Solutions for Composite Laminates in Cylindrical Bending," *J. Composite Mater.* 3 (1969): 398–411.

PROBLEMS

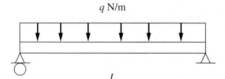

q N/m

L   **Figure 7.19**

Many of the problems refer to the simply supported beam shown in Figure 7.19.

7.1. Consider a beam with a $[0_{12}]$ layup of carbon/epoxy. Calculate *EI* according to Eq. (7.7), and compare with the usual isotropic-beam formula.

7.2. A rough approximation for calculating an effective *EI* for a beam is to use the average modulus for the laminate along with the isotropic-beam formula for *I*. Compare values for *EI* calculated this way with that from Eq. (7.7) for a $[0_{10}/90_{10}]_s$ and a $[90_{10}/0_{10}]_s$ layup of carbon/epoxy. Note that the average modulus can be obtained from the average stiffness of Eq. (3.22), or more easily from the inverse of this average stiffness.

7.3. Repeat Problem 7.2 using a $[(0/90)_{10}]_s$ and a $[(90/0)_{10}]_s$ layup of carbon/epoxy.

7.4. Repeat Problem 7.2 using the properties of a glass/epoxy material.

7.5. Repeat Problem 7.3 using the properties of a glass/epoxy material.

7.6. Consider a simply supported rectangular beam with a width equal to twice the thickness, with a layup of $[(0_{16}/\pm60_4)]_s$ carbon/epoxy and a ply thickness of 0.132 mm/ply (0.0052 in/ply), length $L = 203$ mm (8 in), and with a distributed loading of $q = 1.751$ kN/m (10 lb/in). Find the center deflection and maximum strain in the outer fiber.

7.7. Repeat Problem 7.6, but use a $[(\pm60/0_4)_4]_s$ layup.

7.8. Repeat Problem 7.6, but use a glass/epoxy prepreg layup.

7.9. Repeat Problem 7.7, but use a glass/epoxy prepreg layup.

7.10. Repeat Problem 7.6, but calculate the stress in the axial direction at the inner and outer surface of each ply, at the axial center of the beam. Plot the axial stress across the cross-section of the laminated beam, and compare with the isotropic formula $\sigma = M_y/I$. It will be seen that for layups like this, there are large differences between the stress distributions predicted by the laminated- and isotropic-beam formulas.

7.11. Compare the estimated *EI* for a beam with a layup of $[(0_{16}/\pm60_4)]_s$ carbon/epoxy, according to the wide- and narrow-beam formulas, and compute the percentage difference (using the same actual width).

7.12. Repeat Problem 10, but use the wide-beam assumption. Compare the stress distribution through the thickness with that of Problem 7.10.

7.13. Calculate the effective EI for a sandwich beam with a foam core of thickness 6.35 mm (0.25 in) and carbon/epoxy facings, each with a layup of $[0_4/\pm60]_s$ carbon/epoxy. The beam cross-section has a width of 50.8 mm (2 in).

7.14. Repeat Problem 7.6, but use the cross-section of Problem 7.13.

7.15. Repeat Problem 7.10, but use the cross-section of Problem 7.13.

7.16. Repeat Problem 7.13, but remove the sandwich core from the beam cross-section. Compare displacements with that of Problem 7.13.

7.17. Compare the stress in the outer fiber for the sandwich beam of Problem 7.14, and compare with the stress computed for the cross-section without the sandwich core.

7.18. Repeat Problem 7.13, but assume that the face sheets of the sandwich beam are thin so that bending stiffness about their own center line can be neglected. Compare the effective EI with that of Problem 7.13.

7.19. Calculate the effective EI for a sandwich beam with a foam core of thickness 6.35 mm (0.25 in) and carbon/epoxy facings. The top face sheet has a layup of $[0_4/\pm60]_s$ carbon/epoxy, and the bottom face sheet has a layup of $[(0_4/\pm60)_2]_s$ carbon/epoxy. The face sheets are cured and then secondary bonded to the foam core. Also calculate the location of the neutral axis. The beam cross-section has a width of 50.8 mm (2 in).

7.20. Find the shear stress at the center line of the cross section and the axial midplane of the beam of Problem 7.6. Also find the shear stress at the interface between the 0° and the 60° ply. Compare both values with that given by the isotropic-beam formula.

7.21. Find the shear stress at the center line of the cross-section and the axial midplane of the beam of Problem 6, but use a $[(\pm60/0_4)_4]_s$ layup. Compare this value with that given by the isotropic-beam formula.

7.22. Find the shear stress at the center line of the cross-section and the axial midplane of the beam of Problem 7.6, but use the sandwich beam cross-section of Problem 7.13. Compare this value with that given by the isotropic sandwich beam formula, $\tau = V/A$, where A is just the cross-sectional area of the foam core.

7.23. Repeat the calculation of the effective EI of the laminated I-beam of Example 7.4, but use the thin-flange assumption. Compare with the values given in Example 7.4.

7.24. Find the strain distribution throughout the cross-section of the laminated I-beam of Example 7.4.

7.25. Calculate the stress in the fibers in the flange of the laminated I-beam of Example 7.4.

7.26. Calculate the shear stress in the fibers in the flange of the laminated I-beam of Example 7.4.

7.27. Find the shear stress at the bottom surface of the 0° plies in the flange of the laminated I-beam of Example 7.4.

8

Design Examples

This chapter presents several examples of fiber-composite applications and demonstrates how the principles introduced in this book can be applied in practical applications.

8.1 DESIGN OF AN AUTOMOTIVE DRIVE SHAFT

8.1.1 Introduction

Composites have been used or considered for torque transmission shafts for a variety of applications, including cooling-tower-fan drive shafts and automotive drive shafts. The automotive case is discussed here. Composite drive shafts have been used in race car and light-truck applications for rear-wheel drive. In addition to saving weight, the composite drive shaft is potentially cheaper. Traditional steel drive shafts are usually limited in length because of vibration considerations, so that the steel drive shaft is made in two sections connected by a support structure, bearings, and U-joints. If the composite drive shaft can be made in one piece and still satisfy the vibration requirements, it can eliminate all of the assembly connecting the two-piece steel drive shaft, and thus save money as well as weight. Commercial products have utilized all carbon-fiber construction, an aluminum inner core with composite overwrap, and a hybrid construction utilizing both glass and carbon fiber. An example is shown in Figure 8.1.

In the following, a hybrid design using glass and carbon fiber is examined that is intended to be used in a rear-drive light-truck application.

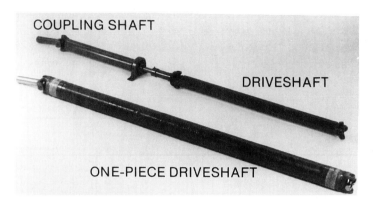

Figure 8.1 Example of a one-piece fiber-composite automotive drive shaft, and a conventional two-piece steel drive shaft. (*Source:* Alliant Techsystems.)

8.1.2 Loads and Requirements

Torsion. The primary load carried by the drive shaft is torsion, and the shaft must be designed to carry the torque without failing. The primary failure mode is fiber failure, and fibers must be oriented at ±45° from the axis of the shaft to withstand the torque. In addition, the possibility of torsional buckling must be considered, which will be shown to create different requirements on the layup.

Bending natural frequency. The second major design requirement is that the drive shaft have a bending natural frequency that is sufficiently high. If the natural frequency in bending coincides with the rotational speed (i.e., frequency) of the shaft, a condition known as "whirling" will result, with unacceptable results. As described in vibration texts, this condition results from a mass imbalance in the shaft, causing it to bow slightly as it rotates, which is greatly amplified if the bending natural frequency coincides. The rotational speed of the shaft is determined by the engine speed and gearing of the transmission, and thus can be calculated directly. The shaft design must then ensure that the bending natural frequency of the shaft is sufficiently high. The stiffness involved in the calculation of the natural frequency is the axial stiffness, and fibers in the axial direction are likely required to give the required properties. Because the bending natural frequency also decreases with increasing mass, all changes in the layup and design can influence the natural frequency. For example, increasing the amount of ±45° fibers increases the torque-carrying ability, but likely decreases the natural frequency. Thus, the overall design must be carefully balanced to fulfill all of the requirements.

8.1.3 Design and Analysis

Torsion. The torsional load can be carried most efficiently by fibers placed at ±45°. Fibers with 0° or 90° orientations carry the torsional load in matrix shear rather than in the fibers and thus offer comparatively little torsional load-carrying ability. The 0° and

90° orientations are needed for other reasons, but do not function effectively in carrying the torsion load. The analysis of the stresses in the fibers and matrix due to the torsional loads proceeds as usual by constructing the A and A^{-1} matrix for the layup, calculating equivalent in-plane loads from the applied torque, solving for the laminate strains, and then examining the stresses in each layer produced by these strains.

The A matrix is formed using Eq. (3.17):

$$A_{ij} = \sum_{k=1}^{N} (\overline{Q}_{ij})_k (h_k - h_{k-1}) \tag{3.17}$$

where the term $(h_k - h_{k-1})$ is the thickness of each layer, and the individual stress–strain matrices Q_k depend on the composite properties and the angle of orientation, as given in Eq. (2.29).

$$[\overline{Q}] = [T^{-1}][Q][R][T][R^{-1}] \tag{2.29}$$

The overall strains are then given by

$$\{\epsilon\} = A^{-1}\{N\} = A^{-1} \begin{Bmatrix} 0 \\ 0 \\ N_{xy} \end{Bmatrix} \tag{8.1}$$

and the N_{xy} term is the shear-stress resultant, which is related to torque T by

$$N_{xy} = \frac{T}{2\pi r^2} \tag{8.2}$$

The overall strains from Eq. (8.1) are then rotated into the fiber direction for each layer, and the fiber-direction stresses are calculated from

$$\begin{Bmatrix} \sigma_1 \\ \sigma_2 \\ \tau_{12} \end{Bmatrix} = [Q] \begin{Bmatrix} \epsilon_1 \\ \epsilon_2 \\ \gamma_{12} \end{Bmatrix} = [Q][R][T][R^{-1}] \begin{Bmatrix} \epsilon_x \\ \epsilon_y \\ \gamma_{xy} \end{Bmatrix} \tag{3.38}$$

The ply stresses are then used with a suitable failure criterion to determine a factor of safety for torsion loading.

For a preliminary estimate of the thickness of the ±45° layers required, it is possible to neglect all of the contribution of the 0° and 90° layers. Consider that the thickness of each of the 45° and −45° layers is called t, so that the total thickness of the two layers is $2t$. The average applied shear stress is then $\tau_{avg} = N_{xy}/2t$. This average shear stress can be transformed to ±45° coordinate directions by means of standard transformations such as Mohr's circle, and it can be seen that the normal stresses on the ±45° axes is equal to ±1 times the average shear stress. Thus, the state of stress in the fibers is equivalent to biaxial normal stresses equal to ± the average shear stress, applied to a cross-ply laminate. Finally, the normal fiber-direction stress in each layer is then equal to twice the average normal stress applied to the laminate.

As an approximation,

$$\sigma_1 \approx 2\tau_{avg} = \frac{N_{xy}}{t} \tag{8.3}$$

This expresssion gives a rough estimate of the fiber-direction stress, but the procedure described before, using the A^{-1} matrix and the usual coordinate transformations, should be used for the final calculation.

Torsional buckling.   An expression for torsional buckling of a thin-walled orthotropic tube has been given as [8.1]

$$T_c = (2\pi r^2 t)(0.272)[E_x E_h^3]^{1/4}(t/r)^{3/2} \tag{8.4}$$

where t is the overall wall thickness, r is the mean radius, and E_x and E_h are the average moduli in the axial and hoop directions, respectively. The critical torque for buckling then can be calculated if the average moduli are known. These can easily be obtained from the A matrix. From the earlier definition of the A matrix, it can be seen that the A matrix divided by the total thickness is just the average stress–strain matrix, or

$$Q_{\text{avg}} = \frac{1}{t} A \tag{8.5}$$

The inverse of this is

$$Q_{\text{avg}}^{-1} = t A^{-1} \tag{8.6}$$

The average moduli then are found easily by noting the definition of this inverse matrix:

$$Q_{\text{avg}}^{-1} = S_{\text{avg}} = \begin{bmatrix} \dfrac{1}{E_x} & \dfrac{-v_{hx}}{E_h} & 0 \\ \dfrac{-v_{xh}}{E_x} & \dfrac{1}{E_h} & 0 \\ 0 & 0 & \dfrac{1}{G_{xh}} \end{bmatrix} \tag{8.7}$$

The average moduli then can be obtained from the reciprocals of the 1,1 and 2,2 terms. The hoop-direction modulus is very important in determining the buckling strength and is likely to require that fibers be placed in the hoop direction to achieve an adequate value. The hoop fibers can be placed on the outside of the shaft to help compact the layup during manufacture.

8.1.4 Natural-Frequency Calculation

The drive shaft can be idealized as a pinned-pinned beam. The expression for the lowest natural frequency is given as [8.2]

$$f_n = \frac{\pi}{2} \sqrt{\frac{g E_x I}{W L^4}} \tag{8.8}$$

where f_n is the lowest frequency in hertz, W is the weight per unit length or W/g is the mass per unit length, E_x is the average modulus in the axial direction, I is the moment of inertia, and L is the length. The moment of inertia of the thin-walled tube is given by

$$I_x = \frac{\pi}{4}(r_o^4 - r_i^4) \approx \pi r^3 t \tag{8.9}$$

where r is a mean radius, and t is the total wall thickness. The average modulus in the axial direction is found from Eqs. (8.6) and (8.7). The natural-frequency specification is likely to be a significant design driver and is likely to require that fibers be placed in the axial direction to achieve sufficient axial stiffness. Further, as will be shown in the following example, in a hybrid design utilizing glass fibers, it is likely that carbon fibers are required in the axial direction in order to achieve the required axial stiffness combined with light weight.

8.1.5 Design of a Hybrid Fiber-Composite Drive Shaft

The required length of the drive shaft is 173 cm (68 in), and the mean radius is 50.8 mm (2 in). The loads are shown in Table 8.1. The material properties used are given in Table 8.2.

Table 8.1   Load Requirements for Drive Shaft Design

Ultimate torque:	2030 N-m (18,000 in-lb)
Peak torque for 100,000-cycle reversed fatigue:	678 N-m (6,000 in-lb)
Minimum bending natural frequency:	>90 Hz

The design then proceeds as described before considering torsional strength, torsional buckling, and minimum natural frequency.

Layup and thickness selected.   The layup selected consists of ±45° glass layers, a 0° (axial) carbon fiber, and a 90° glass-fiber hoop layer on the outside. The thicknesses selected are as follows:

±45° glass-fiber layers (total): 0.381 mm (0.015 in)

90° glass-fiber layer: 1.016 mm (0.04 in)

0° carbon-fiber layer: 0.635 mm (0.025 in)

Note that most design problems involve an initial selection of geometry, followed by analysis, and then followed by redesign in an iterative process. The previous values selected can be considered to have already been through the selection–analysis–redesign loop at least once.

Table 8.2   Material Properties of Glass- and Carbon-Fiber Composites Used in Drive Shaft Design

Material	V_f (%)	E_{11} GPa (Msi)	E_{22} GPa (Msi)	G_{12} GPa (Msi)	ν_{12}	Ultimate Strength* MPa (ksi)	Weight Density g/cc (lb/in³)
E-glass/epoxy	60	40.3 (5.84)	6.21 (0.9)	3.07 (0.3)	0.2	827 (120)	1.91 (0.069)
Carbon/epoxy	60	126.9 (18.4)	11.0 (1.6)	6.6 (0.95)	0.28	1170 (170)	1.61 (0.058)

*These are conservative values for design, based on laboratory tests of fatigue after impact. The fatigue strength after impact of E-glass at 10^5 cycles is taken as 0.25 times the tensile strength.

Torsional strength.   The design load for torsional strength involves fatigue considerations and is 678 N-m (6000 in-lb). The allowable stress in the ±45° fibers is 207 MPa (30 ksi). This allowable value incorporates an allowance for degradation due to fatigue after impact, as determined in laboratory tests.

The stress in the hybrid layup is calculated by constructing the A matrix, calculating the overall strains from the inverse of the A matrix and the applied torsional load, and then transforming the strain into the fiber directions and multiplying by the fiber-direction stress–strain properties to get the stresses. The A matrix for the present design is

$$A = \begin{bmatrix} 92.9 & 71.5 & 0 \\ 71.5 & 53.7 & 0 \\ 0 & 0 & 10.48 \end{bmatrix} \text{MPa-m} = \begin{bmatrix} 5.306\,\mathrm{E}+5 & 4.081\,\mathrm{E}+5 & 0 \\ 4.081\,\mathrm{E}+5 & 3.066\,\mathrm{E}+5 & 0 \\ 0 & 0 & 5.982\,\mathrm{E}+4 \end{bmatrix} \text{psi-in}$$

The 678-N-m (6000-in-lb) torque gives an N_{xy} loading from Eq. (8.2) of 0.0435 MPa-m (248.6 psi-in), and using Eq. (8.1) gives strains of

$$\begin{Bmatrix} \epsilon_x \\ \epsilon_h \\ \gamma_{xh} \end{Bmatrix} = \begin{Bmatrix} 0 \\ 0 \\ 0.004 \end{Bmatrix}$$

Transforming these strains into the 45° fibers and multiplying by the glass-fiber-layer stress–strain properties gives the stresses as

$$\begin{Bmatrix} \sigma_1 \\ \sigma_2 \\ \tau_{12} \end{Bmatrix} = \begin{Bmatrix} 81.6 \\ -10.38 \\ 0 \end{Bmatrix} \text{MPa} = \begin{Bmatrix} 1.183\mathrm{E}+4 \\ -1.505\mathrm{E}+3 \\ 0 \end{Bmatrix} \text{psi}$$

Using a maximum fiber-direction stress for a failure criterion, along with the reduced allowable for fatigue loading, gives a factor of safety of 2.54.

Torsional buckling.   The effective moduli in the axial and hoop directions can be found from Eq. (8.7). The values obtained are E_x = 45.3 GPa (6.57 Msi) and 26.1 GPa (E_h = 3.79 Msi). Substituting into Eq. (8.4) gives a predicted buckling torque of 2130 N-m (18,840 in-lb), which gives a factor of safety of 1.047. It can be seen that without the hoop-direction fibers, it would be difficult to get the hoop modulus up high enough to satisfy this requirement.

Natural frequency.   Using the value of average modulus in the axial direction of 45.3 GPa (6.57 Msi), using the weight per unit length as calculated from the density and area of the glass- and carbon-composite layers, and substituting into Eq. (8.8) gives a value of the natural frequency of 92.6 Hz, for a factor of safety of 1.029. It should be noted that the present natural-frequency requirement cannot be satisfied without the carbon-fiber layer in the axial direction.

The values given here satisfy the design requirements and can thus be considered to give a successful design solution. However, a number of other possibilities exist for the given load specifications, and, in addition, the design is sensitive to load specifications. The parameters are interactive in the sense that, for example, adding hoop layers to raise the buckling resistance or adding ±45° fibers to increase the torque-carrying ability lower the natural frequency, which then must be raised by adding additional 0° carbon-fiber layers. The materials cost for the design can be computed from the cost per unit weight of the glass- and carbon-fiber composites, along with the relative weights of the materials involved.

8.2 DESIGN OF A COMPRESSED NATURAL GAS TANK

8.2.1 Introduction

Compressed natural gas (CNG) is being considered for use as a motor vehicle transportation fuel, primarily for reasons of pollution control, relative economics, and availability. This entails each vehicle having a compressed-gas storage tank on board. Obviously, if CNG came in to widespread usage, there would be a large market for these tanks. A number of companies have developed designs for tanks. A typical design involves an aluminum inner liner with a fiber-composite overwrap applied by filament winding. The aluminum liner provides the gastight seal, and the composite overwrap provides increased pressure capability combined with light weight. Both glass and carbon fiber are being considered. Glass fiber has good strength properties and is significantly cheaper than carbon fiber. However, carbon fiber has higher stiffness, somewhat better strength, lighter weight, and, importantly, increased environmental resistance relative to glass fiber. Because this application involves long-term loading, the possibility of stress-corrosion failure in the glass fiber must be considered. In Canada, regulations are in place that require higher design factors of safety for glass than for carbon fiber because of this difference. Some examples of tanks are shown in Figure 8.2.

8.2.2 Design Concepts

The tank design starts with an aluminum cylinder with elliptical end closures. The composite overwrap is applied by filament winding, first by winding helical layers at an angle of $\pm\alpha$ in the cylindrical section. These helical windings are continued over the domes (the end closures) with an angle that varies with position on the dome. The helical angle in the cylindrical section is determined by the design of the dome and the diameter of the dome end fittings relative to the diameter of the cylinder. Typical values of the helical angle can vary between 10° and 35°. Equations for dome design are discussed in [8.2]. Additional hoop windings are then wound over the cylindrical section. It is typical practice to design the domes to be stronger so as to force the ultimate rupture of the tank to take place in the cylindrical section, as this simplifies the design without significant weight or material cost penalty. This is typically accomplished by requiring the helical fibers to carry a lower strain (or stress) relative to the hoop fibers in the cylindrical section. There is typically a stress concentration at the dome–cylinder junction, and the lower stress in the helical windings helps to prevent this from being a weak point. Calculation of the stresses in the dome–cylinder junction is usually carried out by numerical methods such as finite-element analysis.

Figure 8.2 Examples of filament-wound tanks for pressurized-gas applications. (*Source:* Structural Composites Industries.)

An advantage can be obtained by subjecting the tank to an initial overpressure cycle so as to cause yielding in the liner. Releasing the pressure then results in a state of residual compression in the liner and residual tension in the composite overwrap. The residual compression in the liner increases the factor of safety for subsequent yielding during the normal pressure cycles of usage and increases fatigue resistance of the liner. Additionally, the residual interface pressure between liner and overwrap ensures that no slip of the fibers takes place. This is important particularly with temperature variations, because of the different coefficients of thermal expansion.

8.2.3 Design and Analysis

Elastic analysis. Although the overall average stresses in the combined aluminum liner and composite overwrap can be related to the usual membrane equilibrium expressions, the sharing of this load between the liner and overwrap depends on the relative stiffnesses and is found by considering that the strains are equal between liner and overwrap, a thin-shell assumption. Thus, the stiffness properties of the liner and overwrap must be considered. A straightforward way of doing this is to construct an A matrix for the liner and composite overwrap, use the A matrix to relate the strains in the cylinder to the pressure loading, and then to recover the stresses in the liner and composite from these strains.

An expression for the A matrix has been given as

$$A_{ij} = \sum_{k=1}^{N} (\overline{Q}_{ij})_k (h_k - h_{k-1}) \qquad (3.17)$$

where $\overline{Q}$ is the stress–strain matrix in the overall coordinate system, and the $(h_k - h_{k-1})$ term is just the thickness of each layer. The stress–strain matrix for the isotropic liner is given by

$$\begin{Bmatrix} \sigma_x \\ \sigma_h \\ \tau_{xh} \end{Bmatrix} = [Q_l] \begin{Bmatrix} \epsilon_x \\ \epsilon_h \\ \gamma_{xh} \end{Bmatrix} \tag{8.10}$$

where the subscripts x and h stand for the axial and hoop directions, respectively, and

$$Q_l = \begin{bmatrix} \dfrac{E}{1-v^2} & \dfrac{vE}{1-v^2} & 0 \\ \dfrac{vE}{1-v^2} & \dfrac{E}{1-v^2} & 0 \\ 0 & 0 & G \end{bmatrix} \tag{8.11}$$

The properties in Eqs. (8.10) and (8.11) are those of the aluminum liner. The stress–strain matrices for the composite depend on the fiber angle, and have been given as

$$[\overline{Q}] = [T^{-1}][Q][R][T][R^{-1}] \tag{2.27}$$

where the Q matrix is given in Eqs. (2.14) and (2.16).

The loads on the entire cylinder wall can be calculated from the usual thin-walled cylinder equilibrium equations as $N_x = pr/2$, $N_h = pr$, and $N_{xh} = 0$. The strains then can be calculated from

$$\begin{Bmatrix} \epsilon_x \\ \epsilon_h \\ \gamma_{xh} \end{Bmatrix} = A^{-1} \begin{Bmatrix} pr/2 \\ pr \\ 0 \end{Bmatrix} \tag{8.12}$$

where again it is noted that the A matrix here is that for the entire cylinder wall, combining the aluminum liner and the composite overwrap. The stresses then can be recovered from the strains (which are common to the liner and composite overwrap) by use of the stress–strain laws. For the liner, the stresses are calculated from Eqs. (8.10) and (8.11). The expression for recovering the stresses in the fiber directions in the layers of the composite has been given as

$$\begin{Bmatrix} \sigma_1 \\ \sigma_2 \\ \tau_{12} \end{Bmatrix} = [Q] \begin{Bmatrix} \epsilon_1 \\ \epsilon_2 \\ \gamma_{12} \end{Bmatrix} = [Q][R][T][R^{-1}] \begin{Bmatrix} \epsilon_x \\ \epsilon_y \\ \gamma_{xy} \end{Bmatrix} \tag{3.30}$$

where the x and y directions are replaced by the x and h direction strains.

It is also of interest to calculate the interface pressure p_{if} between the liner and the composite. This can be found by noting that the stresses in the liner result from the pressure drop across the liner, which is the difference between the internal pressure p and the interface pressure p_{if}. A free-body diagram is shown in Figure 8.3. By using the equilibrium equation in the hoop direction for the liner,

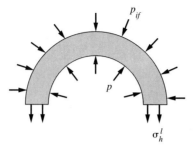

Figure 8.3 Free-body diagram relating pressure drop across the liner and the hoop stress in the liner.

$$\sigma_h^l 2t_l = (p - p_{if})2r \qquad \text{or} \qquad \frac{p_{if}}{p} = 1 - \frac{\sigma_h^l t_l}{pr} \qquad (8.13)$$

the interface pressure, as a ratio to the internal pressure, thus can be obtained from the stress calculated for the liner.

Initial yielding of liner. The pressure required to cause initial yielding of the liner can be calculated from the stresses given before by substituting in a suitable yield criterion. For example, say that the stresses are calculated for unit pressure. The pressure at initial yielding then can be found, using the usual Von Mises yield criterion, as

$$p_{yield} = \frac{\sqrt{2}\sigma_{yp}}{[(\sigma_h^l - \sigma_a^l)^2 + (\sigma_h^l)^2 + (\sigma_a^l)^2]^{1/2}} \qquad (8.14)$$

Postyield overpressure. As mentioned before, favorable residual stresses in the liner can be obtained if the pressure vessel is subjected to an initial overpressure cycle, so that the liner is subject to plastic straining. The stresses can be easily calculated if it is assumed that the liner is perfectly plastic. Thus, assuming that the stresses in the liner do not change past the initial yield, the pressure drop across the liner also does not change. Thus, the further response of the outer composite cylinder can be calculated as if it were acting alone, with an internal pressure given by the actual internal pressure minus the constant pressure drop across the liner. The stresses in the liner stay constant, and the total stresses and strains in the composite are the sum of the stresses at the initial yield of the liner plus the stresses from increasing the pressure past that causing initial yield.

The additional response of the composite to the overpressure can be calculated from

$$\begin{Bmatrix} \Delta\epsilon_x \\ \Delta\epsilon_h \\ \Delta\gamma_{xh} = 0 \end{Bmatrix} = A_c^{-1} \begin{Bmatrix} \dfrac{\Delta pr}{2} \\ \Delta pr \\ 0 \end{Bmatrix} \qquad (8.15)$$

It should be noted that the A matrix here is just that of the composite. The total strain in the composite (and the liner) is then given by the strains at yield plus the additional strains from the preceding. The term Δp is defined as the internal pressure minus the pressure at the initial yield of the liner, given in Eq. (8.14).

Pressure at failure. The rupture pressure is the value of the overpressure (past yielding of the liner) at which the composite overwrap fails. Maximum fiber-direction strain is widely used as a failure criterion for ultimate failure of pressure vessels (and elsewhere) and is believed to give an accurate prediction of rupture. The composite overwrap is designed so that the hoop layers have the highest strains and thus are most critical. Because the hoop strain is given directly in Eqs. (8.15) and (8.12), the rupture pressure can be calculated from these equations. One method of carrying out the algebra is to calculate the ratio of the additional axial- and hoop-direction strains from Eq. (8.15) as

$$\frac{\Delta \epsilon_x}{\Delta \epsilon_h} = \frac{A_{c11}^{-1} + 2A_{c21}^{-1}}{A_{c21}^{-1} + 2A_{c22}^{-1}} \equiv R_{\Delta \epsilon} \tag{8.16}$$

The rupture or failure pressure then can be given from the preceding as

$$p_{\text{ult}} = p_y + \frac{1}{r}\{(A_{c21}R_{\Delta\epsilon} + A_{c22})(\epsilon_{\text{ult}} - \epsilon_{hy})\} \tag{8.17}$$

where the subscript y denotes the initial yield condition. Again, p_y is given in Eq. (8.14) and ϵ_{hy} is calculated from Eq. (8.12), using the pressure at initial yield p_y.

The strain in the helical fibers predicted at rupture is an important part of the design, and can be calculated by finding the axial- and hoop-direction strains at the rupture pressure (with the shear strain being zero), and then transforming them into the helical fiber direction. As mentioned previously, it is reasonable to have the predicted strain in the helical fibers be on the order of 60 to 70% of the strain in the hoop fibers, to ensure that the failure takes place in the cylindrical section, and also to account for the stress concentration in the helical fibers due to the cylinder–dome junction.

The ratio of the predicted rupture pressure to the working pressure gives the factor of safety for this aspect of the design.

Residual stresses.   The stresses on unloading from the peak overpressure can be calculated from those solutions already obtained. The unloading is elastic, as illustrated in Figure 8.4. The residual state with zero internal pressure consists of a residual compression in the liner and a residual tension in the composite. An interface pressure also exists. All of the stresses and interface pressures can be calculated by superposition of elastic unloading from the state of stress at the peak overpressure.

A number of important features can be calculated without detailed calculations. For example, the residual compressive stresses in the liner must be limited to prevent either further yielding on unloading or possibly compression buckling of the liner. Assume that β is defined as the ratio of the compressive residual stresses or strains in the liner to those that cause initial yielding of the liner. The value of β may be set either as a factor of safety for yielding or by buckling considerations. It can be easily shown that the peak overpressure then must be set as

$$p_{op} = (1 + \beta)p_y \tag{8.18}$$

where the pressures p_{op} and p_y are the peak overpressure and the initial yield pressure, respectively. Further, note that the peak overpressure is also the value of pressure for which yielding is predicted on reloading. Define α as the ratio of the working pressure to this reyielding pressure, so that the factor of safety with respect to yield of the liner for subsequent reloading is given by $1/\alpha$. It is then easy to show that working pressure must be related to the initial yield pressure by

$$p_{\text{work}} \leq (\alpha + \beta)p_y \tag{8.19}$$

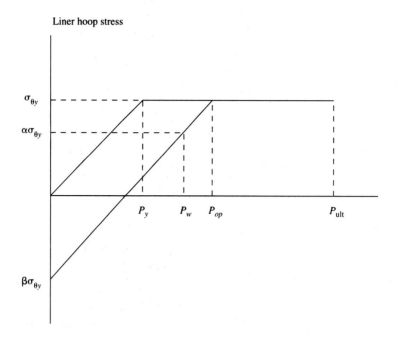

Liner hoop stress

Figure 8.4   Liner hoop stress as a function of pressure in a CNG tank with liner reinforced by a composite overwrap. The liner yields at pressure P_y and liner hoop stress $\sigma_{\theta y}$. Pressure is increased to the overpressure P_{op}. Unloading gives a liner compressive hoop stress of β times the yield stress. Reloading to working pressure P_w gives a liner stress of α times the yield stress. Rupture is predicted at P_{ult}. The design must have acceptable values of α, β, and P_{ult}/P_w.

This places an upper bound on the working pressure based on the liner conditions, in addition to the limit placed by the required factor of safety for ultimate strength.

It can be seen that the application of an overpressure cycle can significantly increase the working-pressure capability of the cylinder. The overpressure cycle uses principles that are similar to those used in autofrettage of metal thick-walled cylinders.

8.2.4 Compressed Natural Gas Tank

As a specific example, consider a CNG tank that is 305 mm (12 in) in diameter and required to have a working pressure of 20.7 MPa (3000 psi). The tank consists of an aluminum tank overwrapped with AS4 carbon/epoxy. The cylindrical section is wound with ±30° helical windings and 90° hoop windings, and the helical windings are carried out over the domes. The design of the domes is not specifically considered here, but the strains in the helical fibers are designed to be no more than 70% of those in the hoop windings, so as to make the hoop windings critical for rupture.

Other design decisions that have to be made are to have the value of $\beta = 0.6$, where this parameter is the ratio of the compressive stresses in the liner to those causing yielding on unloading. Thus, the residual compressive stress in the liner on unloading is 60% of that stress that would cause yielding. Also the ratio of working pressure to yield pressure on reloading, α, should be not greater than 0.75. Finally, it is desired that the factor of safety for ultimate rupture of the fiber overwrap should be not less than 2.0.

Material properties.   The aluminum is 6061-T6 with a modulus of $E = 68.9$ GPa (10 Msi), $\nu = 0.33$, and a yield stress of 290 MPa (42 ksi).

The AS4 carbon-fiber composite has the properties given in Table 2.1, with a fiber failure strain in tension of 1.4%.

Selected geometry.   As a starting point, select the thickness of the aluminum liner, each helical winding, and the hoop winding as follows.

$$t_{Al} = 3.18 \text{ mm } (0.125 \text{ in})$$

$$t_{30} = 1.207 \text{ mm } (0.0475 \text{ in})$$

$$t_{-30} = 1.207 \text{ mm } (0.0475 \text{ in})$$

$$t_h = 2.54 \text{ mm } (0.100 \text{ in})$$

Total thickness = 8.13 mm (0.320 in)

Calculations.   The A matrix for the overall composite is calculated as

$$A = \begin{bmatrix} 464 & 144.6 & 0 \\ 144.6 & 619 & 0 \\ 0 & 0 & 162.9 \end{bmatrix} \text{MPa-m} = \begin{bmatrix} 2.647 & 0.8258 & 0 \\ 0.8258 & 3.535 & 0 \\ 0 & 0 & 0.9301 \end{bmatrix} \text{Msi-in}$$

The overall elastic strains are then calculated for a 6890 Pa (1 psi) internal pressure loading as

$$\begin{Bmatrix} \epsilon_x \\ \epsilon_h \\ \gamma_{xh} \end{Bmatrix} = \begin{Bmatrix} 6.513 \text{ E} - 7 \\ 1.545 \text{ E} - 6 \\ 0 \end{Bmatrix}$$

A summary of the rest of the results is as follows:

Initial yield pressure: $p_y = 16.65$ MPa (2415 psi)

Peak overpressure: $p_{op} = 26.6$ MPa (3864 psi)

Closeness to liner yielding on reloading: $\alpha = 0.642$

Ultimate factor of safety: $FS_{ult} = 2.158$

Ratio of strain in helical to hoop fibers: 0.698

All of these values are acceptable, and the design is considered to be satisfactory. If a higher factor of safety for ultimate failure is required, the thicknesses of the helical and hoop layers could be increased. The relative thicknesses of the helical and hoop layers would have to be adjusted in order to keep the strains in the helicals at an acceptable level lower than in the hoop windings.

Note that the layup for this pressure vessel is not symmetric. If this layup were used in a flat plate, the plate would bend under the in-plane loadings. The cylindrical geometry prevents this bending due to the in-plane loads (not to be confused with bending at the junction of dome and cylinder). However, additional stresses must be introduced to suppress these bending deformations. These stresses are believed to be small in practical thin-walled cylinders and are typically neglected. Programs written for analysis of in-plane loads and bending in plates, such as the program supplied with this text, can be readily used to solve the preceding problem of a laminated cylinder under internal pressure loading. However, it is necessary to circumvent the extra stresses and/or deformations described here that are due to the vessel layup not being symmetric. An easy way to do this is to input the total layup as being symmetric, even though it actually is not. This forces the B matrix to be zero and uncouples the in-plane and bending responses. Thus, the in-plane loads do not produce bending deformations, in accord with the situation that actually exists in the cylinder. Although this procedure does not give an estimate of the stresses in the cylinder required to suppress the bending deformation, as stated before, they are usually considered to be small. For the present problem, the actual thicknesses of the liner and the composite layers should be cut in half and the layup then input as being symmetric to get the actual thickness.

8.3 DESIGN OF A FIBER-COMPOSITE I-BEAM

The I-beam to be considered is intended to be the main structural member of a wing spar for a model airplane. The airplane was designed for a "heavy lifting" contest. The principal design driver for the wing spar was the stiffness-to-weight ratio. Although the dimensions and load-carrying ability of the beam under consideration are small, the principles used here can be employed for other applications.

Two geometries considered for the beam were the I-beam and a box beam. Both geometries can be highly efficient in terms of stiffness and strength to weight. The box beam is much stiffer in torsion, and this may be a significant advantage. The box beam poses manufacturing considerations, relative to the I-beam. Closed shapes such as cylinders can be made by wrapping prepreg material around a metal mandrel. When cooled from the elevated cure temperature, the metal mandrel contracts as dictated by the coefficient-of-thermal-expansion (CTE) characteristic of aluminum or steel. If the composite part has fibers in the hoop direction, it will contract much less, and in the case of carbon fiber will expand because of the negative CTE in the fiber direction. It is then easy to remove the part from the mandrel. However, the flat sides of a box beam have a tendency to bend sufficiently so as to make removal from the mandrel very difficult, and ordinary solutions like mold-release agents may not suffice. Other solutions are possible, such as using foam or balsa wood mandrels that are left in place, in conjunction with lower-temperature-cure matrix materials. The I-beam shape can be fabricated easily, using square aluminum tubing as a mandrel on each side, as shown in Figure 8.5. Beams of this type have been made by students in the author's laboratory using hand layup techniques with prepreg tape. As shown, the layup for the web is carried around to form the under side of the flange. Additional plies are then added to the flange, which can be primarily 0's to produce the required axial stiffness for bending resistance. The total layup of the flange may or may not be symmetric. If it is made nonsymmetric, thermal cooldown from cure will make the flanges distort in the

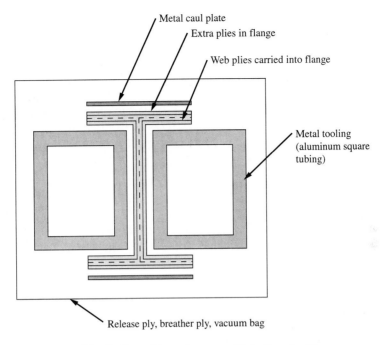

Figure 8.5   Tooling and layup for prepreg fabrication of an I-beam.

sideways direction away from the web. However, this distortion may be tolerable and the nonsymmetric flange can have a more efficient layup.

8.3.1 Loads and Geometry

The wing spar is brought through the fuselage as a continuous I-beam and is analyzed as two cantilever beams. The load is taken as being uniformly distributed. The layup of the web is $[\pm45/90]_s$, with the ±45 plies carried into the flange. The flange has four additional plies of 0 (axial) and another set of ±45 plies to give it a symmetric layup. The loads and dimensions of each cantilever beam are as follows:

Length: 1143 mm (45 in)
Distributed load, with $qL = 222$ N (50 lb)
Web height: 25.4 mm (1.00 in)
Flange width: 19.05 mm (0.75 in)
Material: AS4/3501-6 carbon/epoxy prepreg
Web layup: $[\pm45/90]_s$
Web thickness: 0.792 mm (0.0312 in)
Flange layup: $[\pm45/0_2]_s$
Flange thickness: 1.057 mm (0.0416 in)

Analysis.   As discussed in Chapter 7, the first task is to find the equivalent *EI* for the beam using the *A* and *D* matrices and their inverses for the web and flange, which are computed individually. The case of an I-beam with wide flanges is taken from Eq. (7.55) as

$$EI_{\text{eff}} = \frac{h^3}{12 A_{11,\text{web}}^{-1}} + 2b_f\left(\frac{\xi_1^2}{A_{11,\text{flange}}^{-1}} + D_{11,\text{flange}}\right) \qquad (7.55)$$

Using the values of $h = 25.4$ mm (1 in), $b_f = 19.05$ mm (0.75 in), $A_{11,\text{web}}^{-1} = 4.83\ N^{-1}$-m (8.45 E $-$ 6 in-lb^{-1}), $A_{11,\text{flange}}^{-1} = 1.257$ E $-$ 8 N^{-1}-m (2.20 E $-$ 6 in-lb^{-1}), and $D_{11,\text{flange}} = 5.25$ N-m (46.5 lb-in) gives the value

$$EI_{\text{eff}} = 559\ \text{N-m}^2\ (194{,}700\ \text{lb-in}^2)$$

The calculation of the beam stiffness and deflection, the strain in the axial fibers in the beam under load and the strains in the web under the shear load are shown in the following.

Beam deflection.   The deflection is calculated by means of the usual beam formula for deflection under a distributed load, with *EI* replaced by the effective *EI* given before. Thus,

$$\delta = \frac{qL^4}{8EI} = 74.2\ \text{mm} = 2.92\ \text{in}$$

Flange strain.   The maximum moment, curvature, and fiber strain in the flange are

$$M_{\text{max}} = qL^2/2 = 127.1\ \text{N-m}\ (1125\ \text{in-lb})$$
$$\kappa = M_{\text{max}}/EI_{\text{eff}} = 0.228\ \text{m}^{-1}\ (0.00578\ \text{in}^{-1})$$
$$\epsilon_1 = \xi\kappa = 0.00307 = 0.307\%$$

Because the critical strains in the flange are in the 0° (axial) fibers, no coordinate transformations are necessary.

Shear in the web.   The shear force is carried primarily by the web in a beam with thin flanges, as is also the case in an isotropic beam. Dividing the shear force by the height of the web gives an estimate of N_{xy} that then can be applied to the web layup. The resulting strains and stresses are then converted to the ±45 plies. The calculations are summarized as follows:

$$V = qL = 222\ \text{N}\ (50\ \text{lb})$$
$$N_{xy} = V/h = 8760\ \text{N-m}^{-1}\ (50\ \text{lb-in}^{-1})$$

$$\{\epsilon\} = A_{\text{web}}^{-1}\begin{Bmatrix} 0 \\ 0 \\ N_{xy} \end{Bmatrix} = \begin{Bmatrix} 0 \\ 0 \\ 4.55\ \text{E} - 4 \end{Bmatrix}$$

Calculating ply stresses from these strains then gives a stress in the ±45 plies of the web as $\sigma_1 = \pm 28.4$ MPa (±4110 psi).

Comments.   The parameters calculated here are all reasonable values, and the design was considered successful. The resulting structure is extremely light in weight. The stiffness of the beam was verified experimentally to be within a few percent of that calculated here. Additional 0 plies could be added to the flange to increase the stiffness if desired. Also, a stiffness increase with no weight penalty could be obtained by replacing the outer ±45 plies in the flange with 0 plies, thus making the flanges unsymmetric. The resulting stiffness of the beam would increase by 31% and would have been desirable in this case. Also it was noted that although Chapter 7 developed formulas for beams with nonsymmetric flanges, just ignoring the nonsymmetry and using Eq. (7.55) changed the resulting stiffness by less than 1% for the nonsymmetric case.

Although the stresses/strains in the critical plies of the web and flange are well within the allowable values for AS4/3501-6, the maximum load of the beam, when tested alone, was limited by buckling of the flanges and not by the fiber or matrix allowables. In actual usage, this flange buckling was mitigated by foam bonded to the beam.

The torsional stiffness of an open thin-walled structure such as the I-beam is quite low. In the present design, the torsional stiffness was increased significantly by the additional foam bonded to the beam. An estimate of the stiffness can be made by using the strength-of-materials formula for the angle of twist in a thin rectangular beam given as [8.4]

$$\phi = \frac{3TL}{ab^3G}$$

where ϕ is the angle of twist, T is the torque, L is the length, a and b are the dimensions of the cross-section with b being the thin dimension, and G is the shear modulus. For bodies made up of a number of thin rectangular sections, such as the I-beam that is made up of two flanges and the web, the angle of twist is considered constant and the torques additive. Thus, the relationship between the total torque and angle of twist for the I-beam is given by

$$T_{total} = \frac{\phi}{L}\left[\frac{2}{3}(ab^3G)_{flange} + \frac{1}{3}(ab^3G)_{web}\right]$$

The effective shear modulus for the flange or the web is obtained from either the A^{-1} or for a balanced layup, from the A matrix.

$$G_{eff} = \frac{1}{tA_{6,6}^{-1}} = \frac{A_{66}}{t}$$

As mentioned previously, the torsional stiffness of this open section is quite low.

REFERENCES

8.1 Column Research Committee of Japan, ed., *Handbook of Structural Stability* (Tokyo: Corona Publishing, 1971).

8.2 Thomson, W. T., *Theory of Vibration with Applications*, 2d ed. (Englewood Cliffs, NJ: Prentice Hall, 1981).

8.3 Hojjati, et al., "Design of Domes for Polymeric Composite Pressure Vessels," *Composites Eng.* 5 (1995): 51–59.

8.4 Cook, R. D., and W. C. Young, *Advanced Mechanics of Materials* (New York: Macmillan, 1985).

PROBLEMS

8.1. Redesign the automotive drive shaft of Section 8.1 to provide a factor of safety for torsional buckling of 2.0 while still satisfying the other requirements.

8.2. Redesign the automotive drive shaft of Section 8.1 to have a length of 203 cm (80 in) while still satisfying the load and natural-frequency requirements.

8.3. Compare the weight of an all-carbon-fiber drive shaft with the hybrid glass- and carbon-fiber construction of Section 8.1, with similar ability to meet the load and frequency requirements.

8.4. Consider the design of an aluminum-tube-core hybrid drive shaft, with load and frequency requirements as given in Section 8.1.

8.5. Redo the design of the pressure vessel of Section 8.2 using a fiber helical angle of 18° instead of the 30° used in the example.

8.6. Design the cylindrical section of a pressure vessel with an aluminum liner that is one-half the thickness of the liner used in Section 8.2.

8.7. Redo the design of the pressure vessel of Section 8.2 using glass fiber, and compare the weight per unit length of the cylindrical section with that of the carbon-fiber vessel with similar factors of safety.

8.8. Redo the design of the pressure vessel of Section 8.2 using a factor of safety of 3.0 for ultimate rupture.

8.9. Determine the number of 0° plies that must be added to each flange of the I-beam of Section 8.3 in order to reduce the deflection by 50%.

8.10. Compute the deflection that would result if glass-fiber laminates were substituted for the carbon-fiber laminates in the I-beam of Section 8.3, using the same dimensions, layup, and loading.

8.11. Compute the interlaminar shear stress between the innermost ±45° plies and the 0° plies in the flange of the I-beam of Section 8.3.

Appendix: Computer Programs

Several computer programs are available on the web for use with this text. One format for these programs is MATLAB .m files. These files are in text form and can be run on any personal computer that has the MATLAB program available. This format makes it easy to edit these programs to customize them for personal use. A second format is compiled programs in both DOS and Macintosh. Detailed instructions are given in README files available for both PC and Macintosh.

The programs provide the following functions for analysis of fiber-composite laminates. They calculate the A, B, and D matrices for laminates using the layups input by the user. They use either standard material properties for various fiber composites or else material properties input by the user. The programs also invert these matrices and ask for loads (mechanical and thermal) input. Finally, if so directed, the programs will estimate matrix cracking and ultimate failure loads.

To access the software directly from the web, connect to http://www.prenhall.com. Click on "custom catalog," and search for either the author or the title of this book; click on the proper response; scroll down to the end of the page; click on "download library." From there one should be able to download the software. To access the software directly from the ftp site, go to ftp.prenhall.com, change the directory to pub/esm/mechanical_engineering.s-048/swanson/intro_adv_composite_materials, and download the software.

Index